With Affectionate Regards
P. C. Walsh
London 7.10.96

RECONCEPTUALISING THE SCIENCES
AND THE HUMANITIES

By the same author:

1. *Stone Age Industries of the Bombay and Satara Districts*
2. *Indian Civilisation: The Formative Period* (A Study of Archaeology as Anthropology)
3. *Understanding Indian Civilisation : A Framework of Enquiry*
4. *Indian Civilisation : The First Phase* (Problems of a Source book) — Ed.
5. *Dissent, Protest and Reform Movements in Indian Civilisation* — Ed.
6. *Indian Movements: Some Aspects of Dissent, Protest and Reform* — Ed.
7. *Determinants of Social Status in India* — Ed.
8. *Management and Organisation of Indian Universities* — Ed.
9. *Modern Civilisation: A Crisis of Fragmentation*
10. *Art : The Integral Vision* — co-Ed.
11. *Intercultural Dialogue and the Human Image — Maurice Friedman at the IGNCA* — co-Ed.

RECONCEPTUALISING THE SCIENCES AND THE HUMANITIES
An Integral Approach

S.C. MALIK

Issued under the auspices of
Nehru Memorial Museum & Library, New Delhi

MANOHAR
1995

First Published 1995
ISBN 81-7304-113-X

Published by Ajay Kumar Jain, Manohar Publishers & Distributors,
2/6 Ansari Road, Daryaganj, New Delhi – 110 002
Laser typeset by Pradeep Kumar Goel for Aditya Prakashan,
F-14/65, Model Town II, Delhi – 110 009 and
printed at Rajkamal Electric Press, G.T. Karnal Road, Delhi – 110 033

To
GABRIELE and ADITYA
RUKSHER and SUSHANT
and
RENUKA

Contents

Acknowledgments

This book is the result of the work carried out during my tenure of 1988-1994 as a U.G.C. Professorial Research Scientist in Anthropology, affiliated to the Centre for Contemporary Studies, Nehru Memorial Museum and Library, New Delhi. My thanks are due to the U.G.C. and to Prof. Ravinder Kumar, Director, NMML, for providing various facilities and for undertaking the publication of this book.

My gratefulness to Drs. Kapila Vatsyayan and B.N. Saraswati of the Indira Gandhi National Centre for the Arts, New Delhi, for inviting me to some of their seminars to present papers and the stimulating discussions which followed. Some of the chapters in this book are based on these papers.

For supporting me in many ways my thanks are also due to Usha, Keshav, Aditya and especially Anjali.

Finally it is the due to the cooperation of Shri Ramesh Jain of Manohar Publishers that the publication was expedited; my gratefulness to him.

4th September   S.C. Malik
New Delhi

PROLOGUE

"A human being is a part of this whole, called by us 'Universe', a part limited in time and space. He experiences himself, his thoughts and feelings as something separated from the rest — a kind of optical delusion of consciousness. This delusion is a kind of prison for us, restricting us to our personal desires and to apportion for a few persons nearest to us. Our task must be to free ourselves from this prison by widening our circle of compassion to embrace all living creatures and the whole of nature in its beauty."

Albert Einstein

For some time after the second World War, humankind basked in a great deal of assurance, for the practical dimensions of the notion of 'progress' on a global scale equated with high technology. That confidence is missing today, for progress has led also to unprecedented inhumanities everywhere. The reason for this change is that applied science and technology continue to be governed by an intellectual comprehension of the material world as being composed of separate objects or particles. It is evident that humankind is in the throes of a deep crisis not only externally but psychologically. The predicament of the modern world lies in the many unexamined assumptions that continue to govern its way of life. These issues will be taken up later. There are, however, several others in the social and cultural life of twentieth-century civilisation that are uppermost in one's mind, as follows:

i. The issue of humanity's survival, in the face of the threat of nuclear, ecological, population and other disasters that face the entire planet.

ii. Reassessing notions of tradition, development, modernity and post-modernity; the values inherent in these words having arisen due to the impact of science and technology.

iii. The need to ameliorate the substandard existence of fellow human beings, since the values of egalitarianism, social justice and so on have widespread acceptance — and hence cannot be ignored.

iv. The specific problem of Indian cultural variation, its socio-cultural and psychic maintenance — problems which are perhaps common to most of the developing world.

The intent of this Prologue is to highlight the areas under discussion rather than take up them in any detail. This is done in the subsequent chapters. The stress here is on the fact that cultural transformation may become possible not in any revivalistic sense but within the context of the growth of contemporary scientific knowledge which has drastically altered the philosophical assumptions that governed it for the last three or more centuries. Just as earlier the approach to the study of human behaviour was an offshoot of developments in science, the new vision of scientific knowledge needs to be taken into account in the study of human and social sciences. Clearly, the New Age science is converging towards certain perennial philosophical wisdom.

The old paradigms and the consequent biases, however, continue to dominate the world. For example, what is considered universal today usually implies an overarching Western world view — howsoever one defines it; and in the name of universalism all other categories have to be subsumed within it. In this one may include the idea of linear time, progress towards a certain state, and so on. These approaches are not, however, open-ended systems, and are less flexible compared, for example, with those world views in cultures which see evolutionary developments in terms of cosmic — holistic — cycles wherein human events, including catastrophes, are encompassed within a universal context.

Modern science and technology — Scientific Revolution — emerged within a specific historical-philosophical climate of Western Europe during the sixteenth-seventeenth centuries. It is worth our while to recapitulate certain of these philosophical presuppositions that are essentially western, which dominate contemporary times in general. The background against which science arose, historically, is as follows:—

The tensions between the Church and science in the western culture around the seventeenth century formed the basis of the new ontological and epistemological assumptions that underlie modern science. By the eighteenth century it had adopted an ontological assumption of separateness: observer from the observed, man from nature, mind from matter, science from religion, fundamental particles differing from each other, a mechanical differentiation of the various parts of an organism, specialisation within scientific disciplines; and, finally, the psychological fallout — competition among scientists. In short, humankind could pursue its objectives with no need to take the earth and its creatures into account, exclusively for its own benefit. Many of these reductionist postulates, which social sciences and humanities borrowed wholesale, led to the ethos of competition. The emphasis was on the localisation of causes, to the exclusion of action at a distance, since the sole epistemological assumption was one of empirical evidence, i.e. data arising from our physical senses. By the middle of this century these two metaphysical assumptions, of separateness and empiricism, became intrinsic to science.

Much of this is well known. It is also known that the ethos and postulates of western science differ radically from presuppositions available in non-western traditions. Within the western millieu itself, many a poet and mystic has felt at odds with the cultural implications of modern science and technology. The recent advances in science also are beyond these early assumptions, especially in physics. Beyond that, however, there has been no serious challenge to these assumptions. Thus unchallenged, their hegemony has widely spread like a surgical transplant, even to India, subverting all that lies deep in the indigenous and is inherent to Indian traditions.

At the root of modern science is the notion of the earth as a complex system within which organisms interact, and undergo geophysical and chemical processes, all in a predictable manner. This notion is the deep undercurrent of all western and westernised cultures. It permeates the whole spectrum, beginning with elementary textbooks. The interrelatedness is entirely in terms of a mechanical interpretation, a one-to-one cause-effect relationship. For instance, earthquakes have geophysical causes; this we deduce since we know that the earth is made up of inert matter, explainable locally and regionally. It does not call for an explanation in any global systemic terms. Nor does it entertain the notion of an independent variable — say a god in heaven.

A consequence of the belief that the earth is made up of inert components has been the passive exploitation of the resources. Contrast this with the attitude of the Navajo, who treat the earth as mother and as sacred. They would consider coal mining analogous to digging into a mother's body — a heinous crime; or other non-western civilisational groups who apologise to the tree before cutting it. Within the boundaries of their world views, both - the eastern and the western — are equally compelling truths. At the same time, long-term sustainable development cannot but be based on the holistic view; for the exploitation of maximum resources for development and progress is a short-sighted approach even in historical-evolutionary terms.

Clearly, no longer can one describe earth and life in terms of mere laws of physics and chemistry; that life just happened on earth by chance. The shifting world views within the western tradition are reflected not only in the developments in physics, chemistry and biology but also in the Gaia hypothesis — the world view, that is both holistic and multicentred, and is congruent with many eastern world views, that developed from within the scientific tradition of the West, in the framework of evolutionary biology (Lovelock 1979,1988). If such convergencies between eastern world views and the new developments in western science are possible, these approaches become crucial for the survival of humankind, provided that the idea of interrelatedness within the framework of Consciousness is taken seriously.

All over the world the prevailing world view of modern man in terms of humanistic psychology contrasts with the traditional world views; i.e. nature is unfriendly, confrontational and therefore the need for control. The consequent feeling of alienation and separation in turn gives rise to the necessity to provide orderliness, protection and predictability for members of that civilisational group through structure, property rights, laws, enforcement agencies, a central hierarchy of authority, and so on. The transformational world view, which the new science and ancient insights suggest, is of a friendly universe, to be accepted, experienced and celebrated. Space and time are relative — infinitesimally small units, or infinitesimally large. Nature is an evolving eco-system of which you and me, the human species, are a part. In enhancing nature we enhance ourselves. Life is a matter of contributing, through myself and others, to the universe. The purpose of human society is to maximise the service of its members to other human beings and to themselves. This is possible only when every human being realises the full potential of body, mind, and spirit. It requires an environment that supports and encourages self-actualisation and self-responsibility. In this world view, each be-ing is both unique — particular — and universal at the same time, one with humanity, nature, the planet and the cosmic order. This quest for a unified field — scientific or otherwise — begins with one's self, with personal yearning. It is with this creative urge that throughout history, in every endeavour, humankind has searched for connections, for ways to make a harmonious whole out of par s.

This exploration of integrative answers cannot escape c n-flict since the social system one lives in is based on separation, fragmentation and dualities. Most humanities, and even science in many parts of the world, with their stress on technology and scientism founded on notions and generalisations of the nineteenth century, feel threatened by such a fundamental challenge. Not all of the current state of science perhaps accepts the notion of an ocean of Intelligence, a unified energy field, an attributeless, nameless and formless energy, Universal Consciousness.

The time has come to speak of alternate blueprints — world views — which believe in living within open-ended systems, as human beings and not merely as good scholars. For example, for molecular biologists to think that the entire nature of life may be comprehended in terms of molecular biology, is to think mechanistically that this is what science is about and that is all that matters (Mayr 1991). Often, the open-mindedness of science is limited within established ideas or paradigms. (One might say the same about many religions — theologies — which operate within closed systems, or social scientists who think that the framework or content one is examining is the whole thing itself). Although the rational approach has been very useful in many productive — material — ways, it has seriously ignored, at its own peril, psychological areas especially at the level of Consciousness. Even today this area of knowledge is considered a fruitless activity, a waste of time, fit only for non - academic religious persons. In the work of the scientist, in the act of creativity, while intuition is recognised, it is little understood. But is it not part of the process of knowledge within the crucial aspect of knowing one's self before knowing the univer se? The present narrow vision of science, its extreme specialisation — while at the same time claiming open-endedness — has resulted in the neurotic state of humanity at large. This is exemplified amply by the destructive consequences that are very much upon us.

The philosophy of science has largely rested on empirical methodology; it involves formulating a hypothesis, then subjecting it to experimental procedures via carefully collected data that verify or falsify it. The tentative conclusions thus drawn may then form a theoretical base for new discoveries, or perhaps in formulating mathematical equations that have the force of law. Science is thus concerned both with concrete details and abstract reasoning, between inductive and deductive ways. Its structure is very sophisticated indeed, but its vision of reality will remain narrow unless the subject of study at hand, is studied for itself and goes beyond itself. Unless this is so, science loses meaning and becomes dogmatic and destructive in the long run. This is the fate of science and technology when these turn into scientism and empiricism. Scientific details acquire meaning only when they glow with another, meta-scientific, reality. The collective information from sense data is not a mere collection, since it depicts, not describes, reality within symbolic structures. This is not unlike music, art and poetry which do not represent a single reality but the multifaceted grandeur and beauty of the universe which may be experienced at multiple levels. Among scientists, it is only a handful, like Einstein and Heisenberg, who have acknowledged these ideas publicly. Feeling and experiencing this oneness is, if it must be defined, mysticism. Science, originating from philosophical searches, also arises from the idea of wonder and awe; this is why there is clearly both an ethical and aesthetic side to it. Perhaps, science after all is trying to explain the mystery of existence, of being, while mysticism experiences it; one is limited, the other unbounded. Nevertheless, both seek unity, a unified field of existence which forms the link, the substratum. What is this, and how is it tied to the existence of the scientist-scholar itself? It is possible that now one is speaking of a realm that is beyond language, schema-symbols too feeble to translate that ineffable domain, of Silence. It is knowable, communicable none the less even if whatever one says about it, it becomes an untruth. As in physics, there can only be approximations of the statements one makes.

The point of the above discussion is to highlight certain new directions of holistic science, of oneness — Consciousness — as the new foundations and metaphysics, which then allow whole new vistas to open before us. Many anomalies, paranormal phenomena, may begin to fit into this framework, that does not insist on fitting everything into a reductionistic science; or conclude that we humans are here solely through random causes, in a meaningless universe; or that our Consciousness is merely the chemical and physical processes of the brain, an epiphenomenon.

Few scientists are prepared to question the philosophical issues underlying their work; that they are part of the underlying definition of science — say the objectivist, positivistic, determinist, and reductionist assumptions of logical empiricism. These have served science and technological development all right. But when the social scientists have aped these approaches the results have been disastrous.

Most scientists would assert that science has moved away from all this for over half a century. But it is not clear, towards what; and Consciousness has not come into the picture yet even though a host of paradoxes are facing science today, namely:

1. The fundamental nature of things does not appear to be convergent. As more and more of fundamental particles are appearing, reductionism is in fact pointing to a wholeness; in their separation these are connected.

2. The fundamental organising force in living systems, from the largest to the smallest, is unexplained by physical principles (homeostasis; intricate flower patterns, butterfly wings, etc.; healing, regeneration, ontogenesis, etc.).

3. The problem of action at a distance, or non-local causality, appearing in the far reaches of quantum physics; meaningful coincidences or connections, or Jungian

Synchronicity — called paranormal, telepathic, clairvoyant communication; a host of others.

4. The knowledge of the universe is incomplete since there is no place in science for the consciousness of the observer, as if he is not in it, i.e. the notion of free will, volition and other characteristics of consciousness. The idea of going from the physio-chemical to consciousness is not working; it is the movement from the higher, subtle, to the lower or gross which may take many of these aspects into account.

5. The notion of the self; the concept is not clear and not taken into account even though it is involved in the act of observation.

6. What are the altered states of consciousness, which mystics and others know of ? These, sought after by one and all — in aesthetic experience and so on — are indicated in ordinary mundane lives also. If atom splitting causes the release of unforeseen energy, the splitting of the ego releases another dimension of consciousness little known in everyday 'normal' living.

Given these puzzles, researchers are moving into new areas to understand matter and consciousness, unthinkable a couple of decades ago. It requires a restructuring of the approach towards a oneness picture, a holistic science as some would like to call it. This is to say, one experiences the world from inside as Consciousness, which is the whole also since the outside experienced by the senses is its external manifestation. In this context evolution is the manifestation of Consciousness, not just a single track of separate evolution from times immemorial. Consciousness thus becomes an agency, in the relevant data which we desire to create for our images and pictures of reality.

＊　＊　＊　＊　＊　＊

As hinted above, recent developments in physics, and science in general (for example the Complementarity principle), especially the epistemological basis of quantum mechanics, throw a new light on the notion of scientific explanation itself. These new trends have an important bearing on the current cultural and spiritual crisis facing humankind. It is also known that these developments have a striking resemblance to certain Upanishadic sayings or even the Shunyavad of Buddhism, and so on.

The point here is not that it has all been said in ancient Indian philosophical systems. If it were, the reaction of the reader may be, as it was with the earlier book (Malik 1989), that it is yet another statement critical of the Cartesian-Newtonian approach, but will all this make a difference to those who are living in the urban areas, and even those to whom we attribute the so-called holistic world view, such as in India? The issue is that it is for the intellectuals to be aware of the new trends since it is the haves who control resources and decide policies. But this minority continues to be swayed by the old approaches, especially those disciplines that deal with human behaviour at many levels. It is worth remembering that even in scientific research there exist prevailing fashions and trends governed by the socio-cultural set up within which the collectivity and the individual function.

As in any area of life, a researcher and teacher, whether in science — social-science — humanities, becomes an 'expert' once he has crossed thirty years of age. But the problem with being an expert — and one can be an expert if only there is social support and approval of the agreement within the community — scientific or otherwise — is that the current style of one's discipline becomes dominant. Consequently, experts become uneasy and fearful of asking questions which clash with prevailing accepted theories and standpoints, even though they may tend to agree in principle that raising such issues is also of

extreme significance in any scientific enquiry. An expert, therefore, tends to live off the work done in earlier days which makes
him an authority; and to maintain the status position within the
discipline in terms of the so-called expertise. The status will be
threatened if someone comes along and starts to question certain fundamental assumptions, albeit ideally this ought not to be
the case. But this way of thinking is built into the social system
based on a hierarchically arranged structure, at home or outside
in the profession.

The sciences are equally value-laden by notions other than
those which govern their basic propositions of the 'search for
truth'. How much true of this must be those who claim to study
human societies, like sociologists, psychologists, anthropologists, and the like! And also of religious studies, which is the
search for the truth in the inner movement. But institutionally
religion is also governed by the establishment, the prevailing
socio-cultural environment. This is not to say that the approval
or agreement with the community is not important. But when
this factor becomes dominant at the expense of free enquiry, the
search for truth, it becomes unacceptable. It is easily forgotten
that it is the search and learning itself which is the goal; not any
end product, or a final statement. Such forgetfulness is dangerous for the society at large, not for scientists alone. The
endeavour for truth is itself a value, embodying a creative mind,
nature or being; it reflects not only that learning is part of the
process of biological well-being, but that in the dynamic universe of perpetual motion, a moment from one state to another
in a sense is a totality of NOWs, whichever way it may be
defined. This enquiry and search is not to be subsumed in terms
of a linear-time, linear-mind framework, and not even in the
liberal cyclical time-framework — the expectation that the
search will lead one, in time, to the truth when it will all be
revealed once and for all!

This is how it is assumed in the social set-up by every generation that the experts have finally arrived. An expert is one

who either hangs on to the discovery or whatever, and tries to repeat it; hoping thereby to maintain an equilibrium in a straight line, status-quo-wise, so to speak. One does so in normal life too, when one speaks of any experience which one wants repeated and continued. In scientific explanation also one tends to feel as if the answer has been reached; and the 'I know' state of mind holds sway with social approval, whereby it assumes a psychological dimension of the personal self. This process is, however, seldom seen clearly since it is governed by one's socio-cultural behaviour and response; one is conditioned by a stimulus-response, reaction-reaction pattern — erroneously considered to be action.

At the moment of discovery the ego, the personality which is made by societal needs of approval and attention, feels satisfied and elated. But after that moment has gone, the ego takes over and subjectivity tries to be objective, impartial, to attain a detached scientific-observer state. In the process of discovery, there is no ego, just as in any experiencing or a creative moment like an aesthetic one (This is true no matter how it is labelled in mathematics, science, or religion and art, music and so on, where the discovery and the experience are simultaneous). But the subsequent operation of putting the experience into words, to communicate it even to one's self, as a manifest expression of that experience in terms of any language or image or symbol, is entrapped in the socio-cultural millieu. Even more is this true where it is the psychological entity of the 'me' which is seeking explanations or giving a commentary on the experience of discovery (say of Eureka); all this movement is of time, thought, the me and the ego, whichever pronoun one may use. The continuous one process is thus split up, fragmented, since language and symbols inherently as abstractions must do so.

Creation implies change, movement, process. Even in nature there is adaptability and dynamism which biologists commonly speak of today; it is not static as a finished product. There is constant movement, a rhythm which is dynamic. This dynamism is inherent; this flux, or the specific order or chaos is in science infact a search for a new order of level of stability. Similar is the case with the inner state of the mind, which requires a continuous process of search and learning. There is only the travel, and no destination to reach in the sense of linear time.

Of the constant experimentation in nature man is an intrinsic part. He has the inherent need to be creative, to be new moment to moment; to feel fresh in all ways. Thought tends to make this creativity in man linear, inhibiting the experiential moments of freshness. This problem, which indeed imperils mankind, has been ignored in the modern world. The human organism cannot do without creativity; but this the current stress on individualism thwarts, leading to the contemporary widespread feeling of alienation and neurosis. Every child is born with this creativity; but in the growth process the conditioning of socialisation kills the innocence of enjoying the here and now, of the ability to say 'I do not know'. The child explores the universe in the freshness of a first-time experience, in constant wonder and delight. But the grown-up is always emphasising the 'I know' psychological state. Thus while one part of the organism wants to be in touch with this creativity of beingness, the lesser me, the lazy part wants repetition as a subjectivity of the linear-time framework within the 'one day' philosophy of 'arriving'. The same paradigm governs the search for truth, which one will arrive at one day, like the peace and harmony one has heard being stated for millennia. The claims of being 'open-minded' and allowing for a multiplicity opinions and questions therefore is mere rhetoric.

This saying one thing and doing another is the split-brain symptom of the current crisis. The package singularity of the 'one day' implies that the ego, as the commentator, believes, not lives, in knowing and searching, in sincerity, love and action — all of which it shall achieve soon like the donkey chasing after the carrot dangling before it. Then, it says, all strife will be over and peace will reign supreme.

Despite the turmoil it engenders in the brain, this pretence is really a lazy way out and putting the wrong foot first, especially as one is not even aware of this double-speak. Obviously, not everything will be all right, not every goal will be reached. In saying what it ought to be like (whatever the context be of this 'it'), one has reached certain conclusions — even if relative — one is posing to be an expert. But this conclusion (to conclude) only projects the known past into the future, which therefore is the same as the past. The past is thus perpetuated, more often as an unconscious socio-cultural conditioning. But this assertion itself, has it not been made over and over again? Of course it has. After all, the same framework which subsumes even this statement within its model of the linear-time framework, of chasing a mirage even if it be of eliminating itself. The only alternative to this split between perception and action, is simply to not say what one intends not to do; at least lessen the double-think moments in which one is so caught up. The unity of the timeless and time-bound must be seen not as any concept but as an awareness of waking up to what is. In that flash of eternity, at any time that we want it consciously, the portals open up to give us a glimpse of the vastness available to us. The game of splitting reality is then over. This change of perception itself is action.

'The search for truth.' In this statement, what is crucial is the search part, and not the finding of 'truth', as some object discovered. The search in the present — NOW — is the important dimension. There are milestones on the road but no end in sight, no ultimate destination. Whatever destination one sets is an arbitrary one, created for the game. Milestones of course are there but not fit for worship. They are merely indicators on the way, and not signs of having arrived. In the metaphor of Being, there is no arriving anywhere, as there is no end in fact. Thought and time in the linear mind believes in this movement towards a set goal — Becoming — of going from here to there physically and psychologically. It is true that in the relative sense, for the time being, one creates goals and ends through playing various roles, but it is a game being played within the larger game. To see this game of one's self and of the universe without trying to vanish it, is to awaken from the somnambulism of the split-brain fragmentation confronting humankind.

For the linear mind, which is the me — ego — the question will arise: is this not another goal, to move beyond the duality by evolving yet another high-sounding philosophy of detachment, of being an observer, and suggesting that one ought to be some kind of yogi? And if one agrees with all this, how does one achieve this state of awakening; what are the methods, and how, when, where does one know of it, etc.? The split linear mind, which asks these questions, has to realise its limitation. If there is any such state to be achieved, it is beyond the intellect. The awakening is of a larger context that sees the duality as a manifestation, a dialogue, an indicator of the nondual. The linear dual aspect must be seen to be the shadow of the non-dual. It is as one sees one's own body's shadow and, thereby knows of the existence of the body which one cannot otherwise perceive physically as a whole as one sees another — the other being also a reflection of one's self in another sense.

The shadow must realise that it cannot possibly become the substance, which it is struggling to become in its unconscious conditioning of *maya*, within which each of us is caught over and over again, in this and in other lives. The shadow perpetuates the illusion by asking questions of how, when and where along with why; all this seeking — which appears very significant — creates the illusion of hard work, of a destination to be reached and taking one's self very seriously. This is the nature of the finite self; these several selves seek unity with false notions which only accentuate and reinforce the earlier states and conclusions of the finite self. The psychological process is the same as that of an expert who asserts his authority, whether within the dialogue that most of the time is running in his head or outside. This commentary on the actual and the experiential acts as a thought 'censor' in the context of a socially conditioned personality, which has become hardened with years, at the cost of the given genetic and mental potentialities — *sanskaras*.

In functioning as the authority that is constantly attempting to dominate both within and without, the personality, this expert, is basically lazy. Also, being an incomplete structure, it is inevitably dissatisfied. It is all the time wanting and desiring to have more functions without actually completing any. At the same time, it deludes itself on being complete. The personality is like a bucket with a hole trying to measure the ocean. All these games are basic to its existence, even its own denial, since all this splitting and duality perpetuates its self and is not merely seen as a manifestation of the ONE. The split is from here to there, from the self to the other, of saying one thing and doing another, and separating perception from action. How else would it perpetuate itself?

It is this primary nature of the 'ego' that is reflected in the social world, giving experts meant 'naturally' to govern, to 'tell' others what to do in science, religion, politics, economics, the arts and so on. The phenomenon has continued in tandem with claims of bringing into existence, for the last two thousand years, open-mindedness and equality not only between humans but also between human and non-human life. The 'me' is framed within the dominant and subordinate paradigms, hierarchy, and so on. Therefore the entire debate hinges on knowing the 'I', me or the ego, this unit, this subjectivity; what is it? It is not a question of me becoming the we or the universe. For the latter itself is an extension of the ego which subsumes the so-called altruistic role. In the search for truth, it is almost inevitably forgotten that it is the seeker that is sought, like the person forgetting to count himself when enumerating the persons in his group.

May be this has been said before, and often enough. But it does not imply that the idea of knowing the self, or self-knowledge also becomes another abstraction, an idea that has to be pursued intensely, another 'becoming', a goal. This 'objective' is once again subsumed by thought within the same linear framework which the ego takes over for its operations. In another sense, the problem is not that there is nothing new in this statement; because in this abstract sense there is nothing new under the sun — everything is as old as breathing, eating, sex and so on. But at the existential-experiential level everything is always new and unique, and that is the charm of it all. At every moment one must breathe afresh, the cells must renew themselves if one is to stay alive. This dynamic nature is part of the universe, where a particle at the same time becomes a wave in terms of the context. The energy does not function in a limited split manner, unlike human thought which functions within the binary confrontational dualities. All that needs to be done is to drop the glasses, or for the split mind to clear up by simply being aware of the split, without having to do anything about it. That is to say, one needs to realise the limited role which the 'who I think I am' plays, and instead be aware — be with it — of 'who I am'. Most of the modern man follows the former, whereas one's Be-ingness lies in the latter.

This split-level paradigm operates all the time, since this paradigm itself becomes who one is, at all of the inner and outer existences. Immediately the question is asked is: then what is one to do? This question itself is inappropriate and misleading even though the intention may sound very pious. It is a trap which once again leads one into the linear framework.

The above intellectual statements are meant as indicators for one to notice — the finger that points to the moon is not to be mistaken for the moon — to observe choicelessly. It is this witnessing that may create a sense of authenticity, sincerity, and creativity; whether one is designated as a scientist, politician or a religious person. The awareness, the awakening itself is the action — perception itself is action. When the split-eyeglasses are removed, metaphorically speaking, everything becomes clear and transparent. This once again is nothing to be reached for, because the first step is the last step, and an important one albeit not because one will know what the next step will be. At the operational level, amazing possibilities open up for one since the neurotic split is dropped. The impact is tremendous as the old paradigm diminishes its hold. Now, to put it simply, everything, you and me, are okay. One is Here and Now, for the sake of the search, for joy, in whatever one is doing, or not doing. Miracles may begin to happen.

In this light, in general for the humanities and the sciences, and especially those who claim to study the whole man, even in the context of the holistic approach of Indian tradition in general, research orientations will have to change direction by 180 degrees. The old split-brain approach is not only redundant but out of date as the disastrous consequences clearly show, and do not lead to a true understanding of the nature of society and culture. Its incorrect generalisations, incorporated into decision-making for millions all around, have led to barbaric results.

II

Civilisational Studies and Knowledge:
A Holistic Approach

"From the direction of falseness
I am closer to truth."

The search for holistic multidisciplinary approaches to the study of civilisations, especially the Indian one, is certainly not new. Most such research studies ultimately aim to produce an integral picture. Why then do these attempts seldom succeed in breaking away from the earlier fragmentary conceptual models/ frameworks to evolve a holistic methodology, that goes beyond prescriptive statements, to exemplify the actual through the study of socio-cultural phenomena? Could it be because the underlying assumptions of research endeavours are seldom questioned, such as the notion of 'wholeness, excellence, understanding, knowledge, perception' and so on? Could it be that every new idea-image continues to be interpreted within the general socio-cultural context within which each scholar functions? Is not the scholar constrained and dependent upon both the wider social context and the long historical evolution of the professional discipline? In short, is it not the perceptual, conceptual and metaphysical context within which each of us functions that governs research endeavours? To illustrate, the various studies of Indian civilisation are framed within concepts which reflect the views of an urban-oriented colonial heritage closely linked to socio-politico-economic ideologies. Pure objectivity may be a myth, but one can at least be consciously aware of one's biases and prejudices. Such awareness may possibly allow for various correctives to be available from time to time. This level of detached self-consciousness might, for the time being, at least minimise one's prejudices and value judgments, enabling one to invoke a more rigorous methodology than one would otherwise do.

Subjectivity, of course, will remain an integral part of one's research. Since academic work arises out of the collective socio-psychological structure — and this means it is influenced by cultural values and is governed by social groups — it also has the power and potential to change social and cultural structures, in turn. In this way questioning fundamental assumptions becomes both a source of radical change and, therefore, a threat to the existing social order. It is well to remember in this context that it is the old unexamined assumptions that continue to govern 'modern' times, and have provided the ground from which all attempts — both individual and collective — to create a whole are made. All such good intentions are bound to miss their mark since the outdated paradigm continues to form the ground on which one stands. The error is in the first step itself — broken eye-glasses will always give a broken view of the universe, so to speak.

It is well known, for example, that attempts at cross-cultural life style studies in anthropology arise from a concern for studying the broad human problems which face modern man — a concern with universal problems beyond narrow specialisation and chauvinistic boundaries of any sort, including that of a nation. But is this possible unless scholars are able to transcend their own socio-cultural conditioning by becoming conscious of the covert assumptions which govern both their personal boundaries and those of the discipline? This is the crucial first step for moving towards holistic studies, i.e. it is necessary to raise questions about the way we know what we know — the source, origin of ideas and such other epistemological issues.

This chapter is an attempt to raise these various issues, ask some basic questions especially within the framework of the structure of knowledge, and the dynamics of Indian civilisation. Some examples for alternative futures that are available within the tradition are highlighted. Perhaps, in this way one may move away from the fragmentary approach that has caused so much havoc and agony in the twentieth century, to a holistic one. But first let us briefly look at the history of the study of civilisations, especially the Indian one.

2.1. *Civilisational Studies: Brief Background*

Civilisations have been studied for many generations and answers to the questions raised have been given in many ways. For instance, under the immediate impact of Darwinism, human societies were classified in terms of the biological principle of natural selection. This resulted in a quest for locating and studying such non-European societies as would exemplify various 'natural' stages in the history of societies; it also led to the investigation of Greek, Egyptian and Chinese civilisations. For instance, the approaches of Gibbon, Spengler and Toynbee (1947) presumed that civilisations have a definite life course and death similar to that of an individual organism. In fact, this idea has its roots in the thirteenth century, and even earlier universal histories. In short, the history of such studies is a long one, and we need not go into their details here. Some of the relevant conceptual assumptions of such studies may be summarised as follows:

2.1.1. *Evolutionist and Progress Assumptions*

These stress predominantly the technological criteria of material progress, as formulated by Lewis H. Morgan in 1877, Engels in 1884, and following in their footsteps Childe (1954) who, from archaeological and other evidence of ethnography, characterised civilisation by the presence of cities, large monuments, agricultural surpluses, writing, etc.

2.1.2. *Organic View Points*

These consider civilisations in terms of life cycle, of youth, manhood, old age, and death — especially as enunciated by Gibbon, Spengler and Toynbee, among others.

2.1.3. *Non-Evolutionist Definitions*

These include such viewpoints as the consideration of truth, beauty, adventure, art and peace as chief characteristics — qualities — of a civilised society. We may here also include views which characterise India by its spirituality, or other moral judgments.

2.1.4. *Levels of Integration*

a. Sorokin (1962) and Cowell (1952) have viewed various cultural systems at high levels of integration in such fields as science, philosophy and art. Sorokin divides cultural systems into sensate, ideational, and idealistic, depending upon the respective viewpoints of ultimate reality. But he does not consider a total civilisation as integrated since for him subsystems, even clashing ones, alongside may be integrated.

b. Redfield (1956,1961) considers civilisation in terms of the integration of folk and urban cultures, and the interaction of high and low traditions.

c. Kroeber (1963a,b) views civilisations as a 'superstyle' or a 'way of life'. For example, in considering the climax or culmination of a civilisation in terms of art and intellectual activities, he indicates two such periods for India; from the Upanishadic period to the development of Buddhist and other heretical religions around 500 B.C., and the Gupta period (traditional Golden period) from A.D. 400 to 600. The delimitation of culture and civilisation corresponds closely to periodisation, and for him history is an end product of learning and of judgment by conscious choice, whereby we organise endless continuum of culture and past happenings.

2.1.5. *Literate Civilisational Studies*

In studying societies and cultures as a whole, either in terms of social and cultural integration, or in some other form of abstraction, it was thought that in literate civilisations, as contrasted with non-literate societies, there is a possibility of greater abstraction because of the presence of historical or philosophical sources. Literate civilisations are those which accumulate a wealth of written documents of all sorts, having a rich intellectual tradition - religious, historical, legal, scientific and the like. The word civilisation has been chosen because in contrast to society and culture, it implies an extra increment of scope and elaborations (Hsu 1969).

To illustrate, in summary, questions which may be asked for Indian civilisation could be, by and large, as follows:

A) i. If a civilisation is viewed as a system, in terms of levels of integration, is not a basic assumption of conflict equally valid for our analysis?

ii. What are the fundamental aspects of discontinuity and change in a system, and the most fruitful ones of analysing them?

iii. What criteria do we use to identify and define cultural stages, phases, periods, beyond mere chronology? How do we work out a time-scale to judge the rates of socio-cultural and techno-economic changes?

B) i. Can one speak meaningfully of a finite number of prerequisites for a civilisation, and in their absence, of its decline and death ?

ii. Are certain crucial socio-cultural institutions more necessary for the maintenance of a system than others, and if so, what?

C) i. What are the units of our study, both for contemporary and historic times? The units may be ethnographic, historical (*janapada*), ecological, cultural or even a sampling of statistical units.

  ii. How do different-similar environments lead to similar-different technological and cultural levels? Has a detailed correlation of techno-economic levels to socio-cultural levels been worked out?

  iii. Do social and cultural spheres and values produce economic needs? Or, do needs, physiological or ideological, create the potential for socio-cultural and technological changes? If, however, there are multiple interacting variables involved, how is this multivariate process to be identified and analysed?

  iv. What multivariate models will explain the interrelationships of technology and economics to culture, or even the role of technology and economics in social systems? What models, and evidence, do we have for seeing land use, trade pattern, population density, social relations, property rights, etc.?

  v. Is pre-industrial — traditional — society inherently conservative, especially the village one? If so, what is the context and empirical evidence for it? Supposing it is not, will we not need to look at historical evidence afresh? Are some variables have more prone to change than others; technology, arts and crafts, economics, social life, or ideology?

D) i. Under what conditions and who in a socio-cultural group migrates? Does migration always lead to replacement and no acculturation?

  ii. When do ideas alone spread, or do ideas and trait-complexes diffuse together with techno-economics and subsistence levels?

  iii. What is the role of convergent and parallel evolution in processes of diffusion and migration?

iv. When do cultures borrow, replace or adopt alien technology, culture, economic systems, ideology and so forth?

v. How do we see inner differentiation and change within a given cultural unit (boundary system), instead of invoking external cultural factors as a cause for change, i.e. do we not have to take certain inner compulsions as indigenous (local and regional) needs of a society?

2.2. *History of Anthropological Studies*

Beginning with the nineteenth century, theories were propounded in the West on society, which attempted to examine 'society' like a biologist under a microscope, from outside. Thus, anthropology, until recently, mainly investigated out-of-the-way non-European 'small' societies. It was thought that such micro-examination would enable one to understand the larger problems of the whole as well as that of cultural evolution. In the subcontinent Indians inherited the British system, which began with physical anthropology (racial types, blood groups, etc.) and descriptive cultural studies/ethnology, into recordings of the so-called institutional arrangements so that the sum total of these specific practices would typify these 'cultures'. This disinterested classificatory research was primarily an encyclopaedic account for the consumption of administrators, to acquaint the British with the people they were governing. Later, the impact of the American school was to influence Indian anthropologists, which studied not only isolated tribes, but also caste groups, village structure, urban communities, etc.

There were two other main reasons for such studies. It was expected that through such studies, (a) the non-industrial 'tribal' societies would disclose the stages through which the advanced industrial society must have passed, and (b) one could identify motivations which kept these societies 'stagnant' and replacement of which would take them forward along the lines followed by the advanced societies. A later derived reason was to assert the congenital character of backwardness and these societies' opposition to any effort at the introduction of modern institutions.

In the post-independence era, there was a general dissatisfaction amongst Indian scholars with the application of western methodology to study non-white communities, and scholars have been in search of grounding their quest in 'Indianness'. At the same time, scholars have accepted the linear stratification (such as food-gatherers, hunters, cultivators, nomads, economically backward, literate, illiterate, etc.) as the basic premise from which to explore the functioning of society.

Anthropologists have also felt that plural societies may be studied through elaborate techniques of field investigation in a manner similar to studying traditional small societies, i.e. one may arrive at a totality by aggregating or multiplying a single dimension. But this also gives a fragmented picture, and has seldom provided a total picture of a society, culture or civilisation. In other words, these attempts have often resulted in a patchwork of elements without any apparent overall pattern. There are, of course, those who argue that it is seldom possible to comprehend the totality, and that each culture or society, even civilisation may be highlighted by basing its emphasis on one or the other of the following: (a) investigation of a single aspect, e.g. art, mythology; (b) examination of a single village or a community; and (c) a psychological approach, based on broad personality generalisations or on other underlying characteristics. The first approach concerns itself with politics, art and literature, and economics. The second group deals with what people of a local community think and do, ignoring traditional literature. The third group emphasises shared patterns between the written literature, fiction, myths, folktales, sacred books, and traditional philosophies; and the values, feelings and preoccupations of the common people as expressed through their activities, problems and utterances, or national character studies (Hsu 1969).

In India, in the early years, anthropological research was closely interlinked to historical research The main trends, in summary, until the end of the first World War were:

a. a humanist tradition which emphasised the relationships between textual study and static models of contemporary Indian society;
b. Indian society was seen as a collection of different entities the traditions of which could be classified and studied separately, such as of caste, rituals, village, arts and crafts;
c. Economic study of villages with some interrelationship shown with social structure; and
d. Tribal studies.

By the end of the second World War, the entire orientation of anthropology, its methods, theories and even subject-matter were transformed, through a conscious effort throughout the world. The beginnings of this transformation may be seen during the 1930s and 1940s, especially in the works of Rivers and Radcliffe-Brown (Dube 1971).

Beginning from 1906 until 1952, the bulk of anthropological research in India consisted of descriptive anthropology and speculative ethnology. There were, however, many exceptions to this trend. After 1952, conceptually and methodologically sound models as evolved by Redfield, Kroeber, and Levi-Strauss were utilised. By 1955, attempts were made to rectify earlier views, through systematic field work and empirical studies all over the country. No one now takes the basic social units of family, caste and village as structural or cultural isolates. Rather, they are seen as networks of various kinds, and even the caste system has been related to the great traditional structures, as represented in *dharma-shastras* and other historical texts. The structural-functional relationship of religion and politics to social structure, and of economics and language to social structure have also been examined. Social change as an organisation of structural and cultural traditions, as well as the concept of social mobility in terms of social hierarchy, ritual purity, pollution, etc. have been accepted and made use of in various studies now. But many anthropologists continue to use equilibrium-adjustment models, considering these as adequate explanations of various processes; while others, since they see linear transformations as not possible, use such concepts as universalisation and parochilisation (Marriot 1963). Nevertheless, emphasis on 'conflict-tension' models, or the structuralist approach, in terms of function-dysfunction, is in relatively less use today (Mathur 1972).

Anthropologists have also realised that examination of such subsystems as village, caste, etc. is a necessity, since these may then be correlated into the wider setting of a civilisation; i.e. micro-studies are useful as points of reference against which different aspects of a 'total' society and culture may be examined. But historians have yet to investigate structural relationships of sub-societies and subcultures (subsystems), both spatially and temporally. These methodological standpoints may enable the sequence of facts and events, from historical to the modern, to be examined in a comparative manner by seeking out the repetitive social and cultural processes that have existed through time and space.

Thus, modern anthropology has gone beyond descriptive analysis to develop explicit techniques and systematic theories. Of course, it continues to use such descriptive accounts as are available in historical documents, evidence from archaeological field work, ethnographic details, and so on. This vast information today is analysed to explain processes, and to focus attention on various dimensions of research methodology and theoretical problems.

2.3.1. *Brief Background of Indian Studies*
a. *Historical Studies*

Indian society has been studied by people and travellers for a long time, since at least the third century B.C. by the Greeks, Romans, Byzantine Jews, and the Chinese, such as recorded in the accounts by Megasthenes. These accounts increased rapidly from A.D. 1000 onwards with the coming of the Arabs, Turks, Afghans and Persians. The accounts of Megasthenes, who had the advantage of observing Indian society directly, were mainly of urban political centres. Arab accounts also followed the classical view of mentioning seven classes of Indian society. Roman accounts were mainly geographic in nature, while the later seventeenth century accounts tend to give the Mughal court version of political and commercial matters, such as by Al-Biruni.

Eighteenth-century Europeans saw Indian society much the same as European society, i.e. living on agriculture, craft production on a large scale, legal systems based on written law, kinship systems, taxation based on regular assessment, and so on. In short, a multiple cultural and religious system based on sacred texts, ritual specialists, scholars and so on (Singer and Cohn 1968, Cohn 1971, Malik 1971). With British rule began large scale land movements and land became marketable as a result of British revenue arrangements. As land was acquired, expanded and resettled, social and cultural mobility increased, obviously with changing economic and technological developments. This differentiation historically between the pre-industrial, industrial and post-industrial periods needs to be borne in mind.

The British allowed the basic socio-cultural fabric to stay, while they took over the top of this structure. The European view of Indian civilisation was based on a theoretical textual model of the four *varnas*, kinship and other social categories followed in the village. There were, however, different images and emphasis laid on the study of this civilisation. Three major traditions of study may be noted — (a) administrative, (b) oriental, and (c) missionary. All three felt the need to reform and modernise it in their own way. For example, William Jones and trained scholars wanted to maintain the status quo view of the stability of Indian society; the missionaries, particularly baptists from the lower order of British society, committed themselves to reform both Indian and their own society.

The orientalist had uncritically accepted the textual view of Indian society, which was considered to be timeless and static; the statements from the texts of the third century were as good for the eighteenth century. In this view, there was no regional variation so that no questions were asked about the relationships between prescriptive normative statements derived from the texts and the actual behaviour of individuals and groups. This stereotype, that every Hindu follows the textual rules, seems to continue to haunt not only the academic but also the lay man. The missionary view was at polar ends to the orientalist's; it condemned Hindu society outright in order to destroy the social basis of Hinduism. Though, indirectly, it contributed a great deal to the initiation of empirical studies of Indian society, the missionary view firmly believed that Indian society had always been corrupt, degraded and filled with absurdities.

In all these efforts, the increase in empirical knowledge was linked to the collection of taxes, to support administration for military and commercial activities. There was, of course, an attempt to understand the theory and practice of land revenue and associated socio-philosophical notions, and anthropological observations such as interviews, population figures, social hierarchy in terms of caste entities, and so on. But knowledge was collected not for India's welfare, but to support the administration and collect land revenue for military and commercial activities of the East India Company, and the British Raj. At any rate, there was an attempt to understand the theory and practice of land revenue, to clear conceptions or misconceptions regarding the functioning of philosophical and social notions prevalent at least in Bengal, and later on other social structures. There was curiosity too; and observations of the earliest techniques of anthropological investigations meant observations, interviews and noting crops, population figures, social hierarchy, etc. Most early solutions of administrative officials and their viewpoints also changed, as more of India was annexed. In the publications of the district gazette and historical manuals there was always the official view of caste entity as a concrete, measurable, endogamous category with commensality rules, fixed occupations, common ritual framework of practices and so on. All this was done by sending assistants to collect data, a practice still followed in the Indian Administrative Service (IAS).

The basic desideratum of gazettes of early times, caste categories, labour divisions, occupations, tribes, linguistic identities, sectarian groups, etc. is still followed, in terms of Risley's classification. All this was reflected in the anthropological theory of 1870-1910; *Notes and Queries* is a book still prescribed — validly in some ways — for anthropology students. All these notions affected later Indian society; thus, when groups converged into urban areas, they called themselves brahmins, kayasthas, etc. In the early twentieth century because of the gazetteers, linguistic and other identities were created due to political exigencies, where none existed before.

There was then the 'official' view of Indian society, which was based on the administrator's collected information on caste, family, village, etc., i.e., India was a land of village republics (Baden-Powell 1892,1953), self-sufficient and corporately organised, as mentioned in the Minutes of Metcalf on the villages of Delhi c. 1830. Later, the emblem of village as the traditional economy and polity became a watchword of Indian patriotism, and revivalism, which saw India as being well off and democratically governed prior to the coming of the British. This was no different to the orientalist's view.

Some modern sociologists speak of certain common changing components of a village community, as a body of owners of land and its produces, which includes everyone. But in fact it is only landholding groups that make major decisions in the village and control social and economic structures. This is so in north India, whereas in south India, it is the headman who represents a group or the panchayat. At any rate, villagers were seen as self-sufficient in produce, services, crafts, etc. and relatively unconnected through taxes. The notion of dislocated communities has given way, as also that of the unchanging villages; but traditional India continues to live in its villages, it is felt even today. Marx and Maine accepted these basic assumptions and ideas of a village community, incorporating them into social and economic theory; and, Baden-Powell worked out a massive study of social structure of rural India and of the nature of Indian village community in relation to states, and to landholdings, etc. In short, Victorian students of Indian villages were interested in the village as a type from which they could infer evolutionary stages that could be compared to other parts of the world. These theoretical and conceptual notions suited administrative or political motivations. The intent was not to see the actual, to see what was happening to wealth, its distribution, nature of social relations in these contexts both within and without. It was all done for the riches of the British Empire and its associates on the Indian scene. As a result, with a lot of deliberate policy, mismanagement, famines took place and rural economy was neglected.

By the nineteenth century Indians had acquired a new outlook and new consciousness about themselves — which transcended the limited outlook of the British — and about the identity and image of the motherland. With the nationalist viewpoint emerged a new political awareness, accompanied by complementary economic processes. These developments formed the base for the search of an identity, which was sought by an interpretation of Indian heritage which amounted to an idealisation of the past. In many ways, this nostalgia preserved in the new intelligentsia the old feudalistic attitudes, and boosted the vested interest rather than help highlight the general misery of the masses. Of course, the view of a reformed future did exist among the new western-educated intellectual class, who also welcomed European science and technology. But they continued to hold a mystical faith in India's past and a 'spiritual' future for the nation. One reason why the early writings by Indians in the nineteenth century idealised India's past is that these reconstructions almost entirely relied on textual sources. This partial view, representing only certain sections of society in some ways continues to have a hold on our goals even today.

In any case, the nineteenth century viewpoint which evolved with the emergence of Indian nationalism, gave the discipline of 'Indology' a place of pride in academic research. It was not until the end of the nineteenth century and the beginning of the twentieth century that professional historians, properly trained, began to emerge. By and large, the history of the study of the Indian village had developed for checking landholdings and their structure until the 1940s. The approach of socio-cultural anthropology was based on implicit assumptions of the past 200 years. Has that disappeared today or does it remain as the commonly underlying assumption among the controlling elite and bureaucrats? Perhaps the zero benchmark remains the same; caste is central to rural India, and a village is the major focus — the romantic view of the orientalist's India. Of course, anthropological studies have changed these viewpoints, somewhat, only after 1955. The colonial viewpoint has been replaced by the urban-elite view, and it would be interesting to note the village view of urban India!

2.3.2. *Archaeological Studies*

Very briefly, similar developments took place within the above context, during the course of Indian archaeological studies. These were related to the study of history, with the main objective to collect material evidence for filling in missing links which historians were formulating in the study of the past. Part of this sequential examination was revealing especially Harappan protohistoric sites, their origin and disintegration;

then the problem of the second urban revolution, and so on was taken up. Most scholars, following European footsteps, were scholars of Sanskrit, and historians who were seeking material remains to supplement the textual evidence. Even prehistoric studies, until recently, were part of Ancient History, Culture and Archaeology departments. Ethno-archaeology, and archaeology as a social science has as yet to take roots as a separate discipline. Be that as it may, the goals continue to be determined by nineteenth century models of filling in evolutionary gaps in the succession of events in a linear fashion, dominated by techno-economic frameworks. The use of elaborate techniques of scientific developments does not distract us from this fact, in our attempt to understand man in the past in order to know ourselves in the present. For example, the concept of the Three Age System developed by C.J. Thomsen is based on the technological framework, followed by the techno-economic models. Without going into the historical records of archaeological studies, it is clear that modernistic (as enumerated above) world views dominated a study of the past — including socio-cultural stages. The evidence was thus looked into from these viewpoints. Later on, there is the ecological-cultural approach of normative archaeology; followed by new archaeology, symbolic and semiotic approaches to the study of the past. The range is wide — normative, analytical, anthropological, social, behavioural, processual, postprocessual, structuralist, ideographic and what have you. All this research is related to the same basic paradigm of the modern or post-modern era, linked to the fragmentary approach of studying the past in order to project the future — such as to the rewriting of history for political purposes which is taking place all over the world. The important point is that the basic paradigm of anthropocentrism, competition — 'success in trade'— continues to govern research goals. The holistic paradigm has as yet to have any impact on historical and social sciences since one continues to believe that the Newtonian-Cartesian approach has served us very well. But as stated above the consequences have been disastrous at the local, regional, national and international levels.

2.4. *Indian Civilisation: Structure and Dynamics*

The complexities involved in studying a civilisation such as the Indian one are self-evident, not only because of the diversity of ecological zones but also the multitude of topics that cover the enormous time-span of many hundreds of years. No single dominant theme or life style unitary label would suffice or be accurate (Malik 1971). The perennial question has been, how do we describe the almost infinite cultural variety, and yet communicate the essential features or common interrelated elements which would make these typical of that civilisation? Bernard Cohn (1968,1971) has summed up four basic directions towards which researchers have approached its examination; namely;

- i. Cataloguing,
- ii. Cultural Essence,
- iii. Cultural Communication, and
- iv. Indian Civilisation as type based on world wide structural, and cultural processes that illustrate culture-historical or sociological principles.

The first two approaches are simple to understand; one deals with description and the latter with content. The third seeks out basic systems of communication and structural integration. The fourth states that alongside distinct values, life styles and aspects of social structuring that are unique, these have to be put within the framework of some organising conceptual principle if a coherent picture is to emerge with regard to continuity and change. Perhaps, one may see it in terms of a hierarchy of different evaluations and levels of integration rather than any unitarily integrated networks. Again, lifestyles may be defined within the framework of general systems theory, in order to seek recurrent patterns within the dynamic interaction of ecological, cultural, political, economic, social, religious and other subsystems.

Our very attempt to seek cross-cultural patterns is the result of a self-consciousness, a reflection of changing concepts in general knowledge and specifically in the social sciences, especially about national identity. At the same time, the dynamics of historical knowledge is also linked, to this interwoven tapestry of the past, present and the future, within an existential framework. Thus whatever the Indian heritage may be, it cannot be taken for granted. It is best that one clearly states this new consciousness time and again within systematically worked out conceptual frameworks, so that enduring traditions are discovered in historic depth (Singer 1959, 1968). For instance, the growth of this civilisation is interlinked now with contemporary objectives of social transformations. This implies that radical changes are taking place in traditional structures, even if chaotically. But if we are to avoid aping 'modernisms', and not consider the mere use of science and technology as indicators of modernisation, it becomes imperative to clearly state this new consciousness, bearing in mind native categories of thought and world views, which shall be elucidated later on (Saraswati 1973, 1977).

In the process of model building, seeking regularities, often a uniformity is sought overlooking inconvenient aspects. But which tradition to keep and which to discard may only be decided if the dynamic nature is kept in mind. While there are ideas, symbols and images in each socio-cultural system that contribute to the maintenance of its self-identity and self-image, imbalances and disharmonies are also created from time to time along with corrective mechanisms that are set in motion (Malik 1977, 1978, 1986, 1989a). No society can claim to be static and not changing, for it would be hard to provide empirical evidence for such a mere tradition-directed society. Even normative premises are unevenly distributed in terms of understanding and interpretation of beliefs in different segments of the population. This dynamic nature holds true equally for the rural, 'tribal' segments with which Indian civilisation is so closely tied in its rich heritage, not only culturally but also politically.

Social sciences, however, are not very clear always as to how to assess all these mechanisms, e.g. often some techno-economic subsystems may persist apparently while their symbolic meanings change; and, on the other hand, while social systems persist in parts, the system of meaning implicit in them undergoes perceptible changes. Then there is the rational orientation of man, and at the ideational level, when 'non-conformist' individuals change society through art and creativity — areas where a certain logic does not work as these may be autonomous of the other systems, including the environment; it is well known that socio-economic changes have not brought about the required political changes as envisaged, and so on.

In the ultimate analysis, models are ideal type referents against which individual cases may be compared. Any model, infact, represents a structured set of systems of concepts and ideas. This does not necessarily mean that human social systems may be compared with and expected to behave as natural systems of inorganic or organic matter (Malik 1972). Nevertheless, concepts and models are not merely heuristic devices which help to put into order our complex data and observations; these also have a self-fulfilling prophetic value, through the building up of various images to possibly realise the vision of a new society.

2.5. *Modern Civilisation — A Crisis of Fragmentation*

Modern civilisation, since the sixteenth-seventeenth centuries, has persistently subscribed to propositions which have logically led to the atomisation of the whole fabric of human existence, experience and being. Analytic dismemberment has certainly produced enormous material wealth, but with it immense suffering, both physical and spiritual. The hegemony of material and intellectual vested interests seems to preclude a basic reappraisal of this suicidal specialisation, this mechanical model of thought which has long outlived its usefulness. The old paradigm continues to merely reinforce dormancy on a major part of the brain. It is time to end the stranglehold grip of linear, causal, mechanical orientation over the intellectual culture of our times. Any attempt to overcome this conditioning essentially requires, primarily, a serious engagement with one's self.

It will be useful at this point to give a few examples of the seminal concepts which have dominated our times. These have endured for so long that they appear as self-evident axioms. They include the various Cartesian binary opposites, say, that of spirit versus matter, individual versus society, subjectivity versus objectivity, sacred versus secular, you versus me, and so on. There are, then, the notion of linear time which has given rise to the idea of development and progress, within the framework of a broad evolutionary pattern, and the initiative of science which gave importance to techno-economic models. But the basic fragmentary and mechanistic approach continues to prevail in the study of humankind and nature. It was a great hope that the Industrial Revolution, along with science and technology, would usher in an era of plenty, followed by peace and happiness — a transformed quality of life for most of humankind.

We know today that these dreams and prophecies are true for only a few in the material sense, and have not actually manifested the utopian dream in any real sense for most of humankind, not to speak of the unprecedented barbarism we see all around. To top it all, many researchers do not even consider it fit to question the underlying assumptions of modern society. It is crucial especially for intellectuals to scrutinise closely this kind of 'unthinking thinking', since that is where the cure for the contemporary malaise may be discovered. Unfortunately, those who control power, wealth and knowledge — whether in the East or the West — are not willing to give up the outdated formulations since, generally speaking, vested interests are seldom known to give up power to others. The pity is that those non-Euro-American civilisations which do have alternate world views and life styles available — such as cyclical time, a different notion of knowledge — are losing touch with their indigenous cultural psyche. The 'modernised' elite groups within these civilisations are equally responsible for ignoring contemporary scientific developments which in many ways indicate a convergence towards ancient speculative thought.

It is not that the causes and cures of the contemporary crisis of humankind prevail solely in the external world of everyday life. It is abundantly clear, as we might learn a lesson or two from the psychological crisis (of loneliness and alienation) facing developed nations, that the fragmentary approach is built into the very psyche of modern man, and he therefore has lost the ability to be in touch with the existential-experiential ontological states of human existence. This is why human beings everywhere feel lonely and alienated in the modern world. The issue of fragmentation is in fact a psychological problem: it is the crossing of wires in the brain which is at the root of the issues which one faces all around — academically or otherwise. The deep-rooted conditioning has resulted in the contradiction and conflict not only in the external situations but in the brain itself. Meaning thereby, the brain-mind complex is being pulled in two directions, not knowing which way to go; that there is a dominance of the rational analytical half of the brain which is governed by language and semantics, which of necessity must create this kind of confrontational conflicting dualities. In other words, while symbols and images are necessary for the universe of discourse in an intellectual sense, this is only half the story This analytical approach is not sufficient to get one into the experiential right-brain way of intuitive or holistic knowing — another kind of knowledge — and it certainly does not by itself lead to any experiential states of 'happiness', of any states of feeling like an integral being. This is what was envisaged earlier on, and has led to great disappointments. But the intellect by itself cannot create a common universe, any unified coherent theory, as science is attempting to do, and the hope of a psychic unity and a utopian dream of the prevalence of a humanistic system of values, will certainly not manifest itself.

Undoubtedly, while these contemporary notions have deep historical roots, thought at the mere languaging level — while claiming to become whole — can only perpetuate separation and fragmentation; fragmentation is built into it. The basic paradigm shift towards fragmentation, as is well known, begins with the seventeenth century in Europe (Cartesian dualism and consequently the emphasis on various physicalisms which also used to describe mental phenomena; and the anti aesthetic — Satanic, as William Blake had long ago predicted — assumptions of Bacon, Locke and Newton which preferred quantity — empirical reality — to qualitative values in nature, and so on). The fragmentation paradigm has of course outlived its utility, since it has led humankind to this deep end, even at the end of the twentieth century. Intellectually, we continue to ignore currently available alternatives, viz., systems theory, cybernetics, holistic medicine, ecology, Gestalt psychology and other revolutionary ideas in science. Almost all modern institutions are based on obsolete notions, which in turn perpetuate distrust, vulgarity, exploitation of resources, victimisation, commercialism and so on, which is a fallout of the binary opposites stated above — the prescriptions and subscriptions relate only to a 'success' and 'trade' philosophy in all walks of life. In such a set up is it really expected of 'centres of excellence' to produce an integral, holistic, 'vision' of a good and peaceful society?

Since, despite the urgency, intellectuals themselves do not examine and 'rethink' these fundamental assumptions, no wonder most policy-makers, bureaucrats — those who are on governing bodies holding financial strings — do not even consider it fit to discuss conceptual-theoretical issues. In the absence of rethinking, the obsolete and unthought premises become the source of contemporary anti-intellectual preferences; and, there is little attempt to search for truth. There is an in-built fear, generally, that in the very act of looking into fundamental suppositions we might lose coherence, clarity, compatibility and even sanity, and mainly the old conditioning to which one is hanging on so desperately, even though one realises that it is no longer working, it has outlived its utility and is not producing the results expected!

Obsolescence has a reference to the contrast between two components. If in a cultural system one part lags behind, we know that another part must have evolved too fast (Bateson 1984). This would be true for any system. Even in natural processes, in terms of the analogy of biological evolution, the rapid progress of technological development, acting as external selection process, has excluded development in other areas. Technology here includes mechanical thought processes at the survival level, which also is matter — stored as memory, language and symbols, in the brain. These abstract representations of reality have become the main focus of modern man, thereby ignoring the growth of other areas in the brain or its manifestations in the external world, such as creativity, intuition and other non-verbal forms of expression and communication. For example, traditional civilisations not only in India but everywhere provided continuity through oral methods of communication of knowledge, which the new technology has neglected. At the social level too, many of the administrative and legal systems are far behind our understanding of the changing contemporary scene in science and philosophy. Clearly, the inner psychological dimension, in lagging behind, not being in tune with the enormous external adaptations, control and exploitation of the environment and other phenomena, of which we are such experts and specialists today. This is obsolescence (Malik 1989a).

The problem of dualism, dichotomy, has been part of philosophical cogitation throughout history. These abstract dualist relationships, which are necessary components in the varied processes of stability and change, occur under many familiar labels; for example, pattern/quantity, form/function, letter/spirit, rigour/imagination, homology/analogy, calibration/feedback, and so on. Individual persons may favour one or the other component of this dualism — and in turn will be labelled as conservative/radical and so on. These labels divide and define the poles of contrast in terms of dialectical necessities of the living world reflecting deeper epistemological truths (Bateson 1984). There cannot be day without night nor form without function; but the divisions in the modern world are somehow placed in opposition to each other, rather than as complementarities whereby an appropriate practical combination may be achieved. This kind of complementarity does indeed occur in many Chinese and Indian world views, where these contrasting abstractions are interlinked within the totality — say *Yin-Yang*. In Christianity, the viewpoint of St. Thomas of Aquinas suggests totality and oneness, almost like the Vedantic view. Here he is one with contemporary scientific notions, which support ancient speculative thought. But during the last few centuries modern man has somehow lost touch with this holistic approach, maybe due to an obsession with 'materialism'.

To sum up this section, there are three interrelated factors which may be especially considered to be of significance, as follows:

a. The value placed on specialisation and segmentation. This begins at the thought level and is then extended outwardly, whereby we categorise forms, organise knowledge and institutionalise social systems (Kuhn 1970). We do not seem to have moved beyond this stage, since it has helped vested interests to further secure their form of narrow vision and control. Conservatism flourishes on not rethinking fundamentals, not sustaining the endeavour for a search for truth. Dominance is maintained through operations which reinforce and support compartmentalisation. This has only led humankind and the environment at large, into jeopardy.

b. There has been, as a consequence, the systematic obliteration of any alternatives that may be available, since exploitation of technologically less advanced peoples has spread globally. Technological growth has no territorial limits to its ambitions. Bureaucratic structures continue to support models that lead to the obliteration of alternatives. A hangover of colonial times, these models are imposed on interior village societies in India, labelling them as 'poorly developed'. In the process even the cultural differences are being wiped out, especially because of the media or in the name of 'national integration'. The spontaneous and natural response of societies to the environment and psychic well-being is thus compromised.

c. The belief, which is erroneous, that development of science is the only sign of progress, the only means to the comprehension of nature. But if the development of science is at the expense of indigenous ways of understanding reality — which Indians feel proud to 'export' — is it worth the affluence and rationality? It may be noted that this limited approach to science is being counteracted in the West itself.

2.6. Cognition — How Do We Know What We Know?

Our lives are mostly governed by unconscious implicit assumptions received from the socialisation process which we take for granted. These premises allow us to know what we know, but not how we know it. To understand the 'how' of knowledge requires of us to have an encounter that delves deep into some epistemological-ontological issues. Here, one can deal with it only briefly, less in terms of academic philosophy and more as a personal encounter, a serious engagement with one's self, within the context of 'experiencing', as has been said above. Yet this brief exploration is important, since it takes us into what and how we communicate, feel, think, experience and so on in everyday life.

Knowing, and therefore communication, may be seen as occurring and functioning at three levels, seen as interrelated spheres, namely:

i. Concepts, symbols, images, thought — abstractions.
ii. Experiencing, feeling, emotions, and so on.
iii. The overarching Be-ingness.

In a holistic functioning, the three categories are totally interrelated as one, in the full functioning of the mind. In normal — social — functioning, including the academic mode of analysis, operations are limited within the first category, which is governed by a linear-hierarchical model. It is also dominated by causal concepts, of cause and effect logic, from which emerges the notion of progress, development and so on (Malik 1989a). The second level also operates covertly and implicitly, within the first sphere. Feelings and sensations are triggered off by thought, words, semantic categories, even though initially it appears as if this sphere is quite distinct from the first. The reverse is also likely, i.e. it is emotions and stimulus-response functions which, stored as memory, create thought statements — symbols and images which are considered crucial for 'survival' of the individual and the collectivity. The linear model of course emphasises the need for achievement, in order to reach a goal in the future — there is the domination of becoming, over be-ing. In this mode, however, there is recurrence of repeatedly similar problems that are recreated in new garbs — new structures, forms and content that are rearranged every now and then. Because of this repetitive activity, basically nothing new, such as holistic ideas about peace and harmony, is allowed to manifest itself. This sphere of linearity and hierarchy only gives us the false assurance that we are making contributions towards harmony.

As long as thinking is confined within old concepts and

paradigms, it is an illusion to believe that transformations are taking place, giving the false notion of 'progress'. Since all ideas of change and transformation are confined within the old paradigm of 'survival', thinking of newer paradigms remains confined to the old box. Nothing new is possible, in the paradigm which runs one's life. It is like living in a prison, and imagining one is creating freedom by only painting pictures within the prison, without leaving it.

How does one do away with this conditioning? The first step is to be aware of this primary problem. Once we understand this dilemma, the limitations of the box, this paradigm, we shall be enabled to step outside its limits. It is in the awareness alone that the box may disappear, by alerting us not to get lost in the operationally created limits of the self and society. It implies being open to uncertainty; it is the wisdom of insecurity which helps create the possibility of the impossible. In fact, the new and limitless cannot be understood intellectually. It becomes possible only when we drop the old which functions by re-cognition, and not creativity as cognition. In re-cognition, all knowing of the new once again becomes the old. Here, thingness is equated to thinking which, as stored symbols, is an object, a thing. To be open is to be beyond boundaries, to accept the idea of no-thingness. The old way is to be comfortable in the knowledge of the known. It is this moving from something to something — from the known to the known — that is limiting; whereas moving from something to nothing — from the known to the unknown — is to be living. This dying from moment to moment, to all of yesterdays, is to be open to psychological uncertainty. Hence it is a movement towards peace, harmony and true creativity.

Certainty is not creativity. Certainty only reflects security and survival, domination versus subordination. In the very effort to go beyond this paradigm it creates more of the same, albeit it is shifted every time to another, 'higher', level. It takes one away from the Source, the Be-ing, the Universal Oneness which allows one to share, to be equally related to all of Creation (Bohm and Krishnamurti 1985). In 'becoming', one needs to defend a position, to be in the safe box, believing one is secure there. This kind of living is mere conceptual living, since the ego is all of these concepts, abstractions, reactions. These are limitations, which take one for from one's Be-ing, and therefore cause incessant insecurity. The more one dodges insecurity, and exerts oneself to be secure, the more is insecurity buttressed. One might as well remember that there is no such thing as security psychologically, just as there is no certainty in other areas. In short, thinking about life is not living it. Thoughts have to be seen as subsets — material manifestation of beingness — of the larger overarching category of Be-ing, and not the set.

Thoughts are about the past and future reconstructions. They are about the becoming, which assures us that we are alive. It is this becoming, this movement of thought — the mind of Zen — which causes restlessness. Thoughts are an incessant seeking of what one has not got — away from 'what is' — with their wanting, desiring, searching for certainty. For *per se* abstractions and concepts are residues of incompletely experienced experience, or 'inexperienced experience'. This is why for example, we more easily recall painful and unpleasant experiences - thoughts about them — rather than the good and beautiful times. The latter are complete experiences by themselves and have little residue as thought (merely stored as information, and not as a recall system). By this inherent logic, that concepts are about some thing, these therefore trigger off feelings and emotions — linguistic memory is a kind of experiencing which becomes a secondary feature, not a primary or original experience. For example, at the mention of the word 'anger', emotions concomitant to it are triggered off. Thought then wishes, for example, to do away with anger in the future — 'tomorrow and tomorrow we will make it better, more and more....'. This is the becoming game of thought in which one is caught up; this indeed is the ever-receding mirage, *maya*. This is what causes insecurity, the need to chase after new ideas, concepts, opinions, viewpoints, power, goods, position, status — me versus them — and on, and on. This is what governs the behaviour of modern man, to seek psycho-socially conceived goals that are perpetually about yesterdays and tomorrows and seldom about any experiential-existential states of the present or 'now'. The result of this goal-seeking is that society is made up of insecure individuals who champion the concept of a society in need of transformation. But can insecure individuals making up a society create a secure, peaceful and harmonious society?

Such insecure thinking has only led humankind to go through all kinds of motions to bring about goodness, charity, peace and harmony and the like. But this unconscious way of 'thinking' — reactions — has only enhanced disorder and chaos. After the initial feelings of satisfaction, of achievement, soon the old problems return. Having reached the moon, so to speak, humanity continues to wrestle with the same old problems.

It has been said above that thoughts have to be seen as the material manifestation of beingness. But what, one may ask, is Be-ingness? Be-ingness is not a thing, it is manifested in things. It may not be known conceptually, but experientially-existentially by a Self which transcends the boundaries of the limited person, a shadow of the Be-ing. How do we know of it? It is like electricity, or light which is known through its effects, functions, use and behaviour. These, like Consciousness, are not known or seen empirically, directly, as an object. Be-ingness is the Witnessing Consciousness, Self; it allows one to be aware, to 'know' choicelessly while at the same allowing one to participate in the world. Each one of us knows it, as it is in the universe of experience of all of us. The reference here is to primordial reality, experiencing *per se,* which does not arise out of any persona; it is an impersonal experiencing that transcends both the experiencer and the experienced. The latter are peripheral and arise secondarily as shadows of the former, like commentaries afterwards about the unspeakable, the action. It is like listening to the commentary on a tennis or cricket match and believing mistakenly it to be the game itself where the real action is taking place. The commentary is what one speaks about where the action is, yet taken to be the experiencing. Discrimination is required to be able to distinguish between these two distinct spheres, not to confuse one for the other. The proof of Consciousness is that one is aware, and that it is symbolically known through the effects, the concepts, notions and ideas stored as memory.

It is in this confusion of the different spheres that the error is further compounded, when out of the long range of memories, the thoughts of a particular set become the thinker; and this commentary is what says that there is a thinker separate from thought, unmindful that the experiencer is memory itself — the thinker is thought itself. The problem is really of knowing who one is, not who one thinks one is — an identity problem. In this false identity, he/she seeks an experience, and identifies with psycho-biological reaction, arising out of previous knowledge only. These reactions are the 'me' and its extensions, which incessantly move for endless goals, arising out of past experience. Normal actions are thus only reactions, though they create the illusion of action. In fact, this 'acting' is inaction. True action lies in a kind of choiceless awareness. It implies the total functioning of all the three spheres, to be in the 'here and now' with no purpose other than to be aware, to be conscious, to be 'awake', to be 'alive'. This perception itself is action, this itself is the transformation which arises out of the eternal 'now'. This 'action', which is beyond the normal taken-for-granted notions of space, time and knowledge, is part of the 'Indian' heritage, but also universal, its experience having been noted in many other cultures.

2.7. *Space, Time and Knowledge*

The focus in this section is, briefly, on the interrelatedness of time, space and knowledge as is related to the understanding

Indian civilisation, especially its past, mainly to exemplify the approach stated in the introduction. This is definitely not in terms of academic philosophical discourse, for which specialised books are available. Space, time and knowledge are familiar words in common parlance. For example, space has been seen as a continuous extension, as an emptiness, as a container of things — be it galaxies or dust particles. Time is normally considered a passage from past to future, or a medium within which events point in that direction so that one speaks of a flux of time, through time. Knowledge usually implies accumulation of experience, information which may be helpful in theoretical and practical matters albeit the distinction between the two is not easily discernible. In short, the usage of these words and their meaning is vague and confused if one looks at the statements with any depth of understanding. What is common to all the above definitions is that these are thing-oriented, properties which seem to be the fabric of the universe as objectivities, abstractions, secondary qualities of discrete entities independent of their properties (Tulku 1977).

2.7.1. *Space*

Until not long ago space was considered to be absolute, involving a hierarchy of positions with the earth, with man at the centre of the universe. After a time, earth ceased to be the centre, man continued to be so — with devastating consequences. The idea of absolute space continued with Newton, who proposed that space was a substance with independent existence, and it was through this sort of space that material bodies and radiation moved. Newtonian ideas of space and time were dealt a severe blow with the Einsteinian Special Theory of Relativity which explicitly denies the existence of any fixed point of any absolute space. Moving far from Euclidean geometry, modern science views space along with matter as constituted of many structural levels. It has the properties of continuity, dimensionality, connectedness, and orientability, known as topological features. There is almost no limit to our ability to construct mathematical spaces with properties different from those which we believe 'real' space has. Many scientists now think that space is curved and that its surface may be spherical (positive curvature) or saddle-like (negative curvature).

ii. *Time*

A similar fate befell notions of time in modern science. If space was assumed to be at rest, time was pictured as an ever rushing forward stream, linked indissolubly with 'things that happen', or points, instants or events. The substantiability of time was articulated by Newton when he introduced time as a parameter into the laws of physics and was forced to emphasise its uniformity and universality, and to work out the precision of its forward flow. It implied the simultaneity of two events, as an absolute property. But today we know that in simultaneity, time and space are relative. A corollary of the notion of time as an onward rushing stream was the assumption of a moving present moment, quickly absolutised into a 'now', which was steadily transported from the past to the future. The meaning of 'past' and 'future', however, is determined not merely at the surface (psychological) level but also, more significantly, at a deeper (ontological) level. In between the 'no more' and the 'not yet', lies the eternally present and equally eternally absent 'time zone' called 'now'. Both levels of psychological and ontological are excluded from the mathematician's and physicist's description of space, time, and space-time. The mathematician's description of time is very similar to that of space; space and time are but aspects of a single structure called 'space-time'. In the physicist's description of the universe the moving universal 'now' is not only totally absent, but there is no provision made for a flowing time and, by implication, for a moving 'now'.

2.7.3. *Knowledge*

Laudable as the recent developments in science may be,

these are still at the surface of the deep ocean, since not only are the ideas of mind, experience and intelligence hard concepts for the sciences, but the idea itself of taking into account the subject of these studies which is deeply embedded in the very structure of the universe one is describing. Restricting studies to pure facts of knowledge and ignoring these other areas of understanding, which are referred to in some way or the other, only creates more myths and even superstition. Unfortunately, the notions and theories about mind, experience, spirit and their various synonyms are equally riddled with loopholes; there is the dualism of mind and body, and reductive monism with its subdivisions of reductive materialism and panpsychism — their outstanding weakness being that they come up with answers even before the questions are asked.

Similarly, there is the ambiguity of the word 'experience', interpreted as objective subjectivity or objectivity depending upon whether one is a reductive naturalist or a deductive idealist. One forgets that experience antedates either the subject or the object, the interior or the exterior — in fact it is neither a thing nor thought. These views thus are myopic visions of absoluteness which was also attributed to space and time. Experience which defies any reductionism and therefore cannot be equated with a transcendental epistemological source (the ego of transcendental philosophies) or with a metaphysical ground (the soul-substance assumption of metaphysics), is nevertheless the source of interpretative notions among which 'space' and 'time' turn out to be 'horizon forms' of experience itself. Here 'space' is orientability with no fixed centre, and 'time' a retentional-potential structure with the 'now' its unifying operation. The distinguishing qualities of 'the presence of a subject' and 'the presence of an object' are results of later, thematic, construction. Although the experience is pervasively present as 'horizon forms' which are playfully imposed boundaries, experience, as continuous source, never exhausts itself.

Experience carries with it the connotation of knowledge

which is basic to, if not synonymous with all life, as we know it. Experience is also the manner in which knowledge manifests, that is, spatialises and temporalises itself. In being a process, rather than a static entity, knowledge is always in danger of becoming divided against itself by taking its intentional operations concretely, setting up a counterfeit image of itself which actually is the source of any duality. This counterfeit image still is knowledge, but it is neither commanding insight nor Knowledge as stated within Indian tradition. This counterfeit knowledge varies with the mood of the time, like fashion, and therefore its time is limited, as is the space it sets up for itself. This lower form of knowledge is fragmented, pieces, things that are attempted to be put together. Within the outdated paradigm, this knowledge is unstable since any new knowledge and information within it disrupts all attempts at unification (Tulku 1977).

2.7.4. *Space, Time and Knowledge Interrelated*

One is able to see the limitations of space, time and knowledge, provided one is in touch with Knowledge of another order, Consciousness. Because Consciousness is not a thing it can see the myopic nature of the modern approach to space, time and knowledge. Opposed to the latter notions is the idea that the infinite encompasses the finite. The transition from higher to lower knowledge does not entail a new theory about knowledge and its manifestations, as is common in academic studies. In our case, it is Being itself — as Knowledge — which is knowledge, space and time. Being is ever there but never as a thing. Neither does this transition constitute a new epistemological model. It is the restoration of an original — already there — vision which neither denies nor absolutises. The emphasis is on the insight dimension, when the three — time, space and knowledge — are interlocked circularly rather than being associated linearly. There are many levels involved, from the particular to the universal, like the recurring surfaces of a crystal that in the presentation may seem repetitive but in terms of a comprehensive outlook form meaningful parts of the whole. To see the whole is possible only in terms of some form of meditative exploration and experience — without it, one cannot do full justice to and appreciate the wholeness of all the statements made here. While the echoes of this are to be found in other theories and modern disciplines, there is perhaps, more quality of this in poetry (and the other arts) in its presentation, even if it is elusive about many other points, because in poetry the stress is on an integral approach to natural intelligence which is not split into reason, emotions, sensations, and intuition. This intelligence is one's greatest treasure. The exploration of the realm of experience with such an intelligence is bound to be an inspiring undertaking that might begin to transform our lives.

Lacking an understanding of such knowledge on some of the basics of our lives on many different levels, the unknowing mind perpetuates the various divisions, say, between our private lives and public stances. The divisiveness and separation exists everywhere, leading to lives that are blinkered both at the personal and at the social and environmental levels. It is urgent, therefore, to point out to the limitless possibilities of fulfilment and satisfaction in our lives and in our relationships with one another, through the Being which is itself a dynamic expression of the meaning and value of being human. Once this intrinsic freedom becomes a lived reality, all other freedoms naturally follow. This calls for an awareness of the unproductive and frustrating cycles — the conditioned lives — in which we are all caught up. Awareness will be followed up by clarity and comprehensive knowledge in terms of what has been stated above, for truly constructive action. One needs to first 'free' one's self for an understanding which opens this natural intelligence; one needs to be open to the various perspectives and one's senses in a holistic way. To begin with, one needs to be aware that the ideas of space, time and knowledge, with the restricting parameters associated with their respective backgrounds, are supporting mediums only. This perspective allows one to go beyond dualities and dichotomies, to a knowledge which is all-pervasive. It is perennial, is knowable, and is comparable universally because it arises out of the timeless, spaceless dimension. Here, one may see the dynamic play of space, time and knowledge — an inherent beauty unfolding itself, with dynamism and freedom. This is what allows us to discover what it is to be truly human.

2.7.5. *Notions about the Mind*

With the emerging new view of reality, it becomes clear how untrue it is to believe that linear connections and causes account for the causation of any particular existence or event. The source of experience is not the self, the mind, some psycho-physiological apparatus, or any other item within the ordinary world view. The self is no longer an independent knower that has experiences, for it has until now only obscured the 'space' which actually accommodates experienced activity and state of affairs. The tendency of the self or ego is to freeze its position, its viewpoint as an absolutely stable or motionless platform from which the changes and affairs of the world can be viewed. But 'space' in this Knowledge or Being refers to a dimension of reality the openness of which is both a requisite and a concomitant feature of all experienced happening. A discovery of this kind of space is related to the nonlinear, 'no source' view of experience, which is a challenge to the basic presupposition that the mind or some other psycho-physical structure is the source of thoughts. Such presuppositions need to be 'opened up' or rendered 'translucent'.

There are two common orientations which we need to confront and transcend. One is the self-referential perspective, which considers the mind to be the generative source of thoughts and in some ways distinct from them. But when the mind tries to discover itself as the source, it cannot; instead, it finds only mental events. Then there is the mind-body identity theory, which is actually a cluster of orientations. This theory holds that for establishing the true causal connections of a given event — even a mental event — it is appropriate to replace our familiar mentalistic vocabulary with a physical vocabulary ranging over neuro-physical and electrochemical events. In this view, all causes and effective sources are fundamentally of a 'physical' nature; the 'mind' is just an imputed source. It is, in fact, some physical interaction that produces or actually constitutes the psychic experience of the 'investigating self', 'thoughts', and 'a mind having thoughts'. This physical source exists; but because of the nature of its relationship to the apparent 'experiencer', it cannot be directly experienced. At the same time, it is not a prior cause, nor is it spatially elsewhere. Both these conventional perspectives of the 'mind' take the validity of recourse to immediate experience in searching for the 'mind'. Each postulates a source that stands 'outside' or 'behind' experience in some non-spatial sense; each involves presuppositions that are actualised on our normal level of experience. These perspectives are reasonable syntheses of both common and technical observations which tend to depend on or presuppose the points of view they express. He who functions with the tools and orientations of the ordinary realm is likely to see things this way. He sees his task as one of wrestling, again in terms of reconciling with his experience, with the mind-body relation inherited from the juxtaposition of these two quite plausible views (Tulku 1977).

But it is a cramped way of seeing space — as tied to things, events, places or situations — as if the source is outside or non-existent. It assumes and expects to encounter linear causal connections, sources, 'places from', and so on. It is to deceive one's ordinary 'knowing' capacity by the apparent interactions of these events and reactions; so one judges that fundamental comings and goings, causes and effects, can be perceived within this stream of events. For physical interactions this deception is almost total; and is usually in effect true for mental events as well.

At the ordinary level, if one tries to counteract this deception and observe a little more closely, one may come to accept that the mind is the source or causative agency which produces and orders thoughts in meaningful relations and sequences. But further introspection reveals that one can never exactly see 'the mind', but only thoughts. So one either abandons the notion of 'mind' in favour of a problematic reduction to the physical level, or accept that it has the inherent limitation of not being able to see itself directly, but only things or thoughts of a different level.

A perceptive higher awareness is necessary, an insight to clear this confusion. This would show that events and thoughts, which we may see as a continuous surface stream, do not actually have the dynamic connections that one commonly assumes and attributes to them. There is no need to keep books and accounts, to prove any thing, since more 'subtle knowing' capacities may emerge which are not indexed into any self. They are not 'our' capacities, but neither are they isolated from one and one's experience. This 'knowing' capacity, however, does not involve self-reference — something taking itself as its object. This 'knowing' does not 'take objects' at all but only provides a broad and encompassing base for apprehending factors or elements of experience which one usually cannot see. Even the facet of experience which ordinarily stands as the self, the investigator or noticer, and which directs attention outward and away from itself, can be embraced by this special knowing.

The idea of 'coming from' may be related to a generative source, and therefore to the mind and subject pole of experience. Similarly, the idea of 'going to' may be applied to the intent of thoughts, their meaning or content, and to the object pole of experience. Thoughts may be seen to involve a kind of persuasive efficacy — they range over the world of meaningful things, selecting out and manipulating items, doing things, carrying conviction. Their apparent movement owes much to their dynamic character as meaning-bearers. Given this persuasive dimension, there is also the aspect of movement or passage of thoughts that derives from one's being caught up in their meaning: one conceives of thoughts as being located in the present time somewhat like objects which, passing through space, are temporarily close at hand before they move past. By challenging the motion and directedness of thoughts, one opens up to the emergence of a knowing which discerns that thoughts are going nowhere, getting nowhere, pointing nothing out.

In this enhanced awareness, one is no longer deceived by the apparent causal continuity between mind and thoughts and the apparent connection of thoughts to things. It may now be possible to discover a kind of gap or space between thoughts. The transition between one thought and the next is very rapid, and subtle. But very sensitively one may notice the space in-between thoughts which has a quality of openness, free from the usual discursive and discriminative thinking. If one sees this in-between as another event and another thought, then it is not the silent interval after all. The new knowing cannot be appropriated by the self again, if it becomes an event and is given meaning. The usual subject-object polarisation must be absent; if not, it will become another special mental event with its concomitant limitations. When this knowing happens, in this space there are no thoughts, no consciousness, no perceptions. The experience is completely silent, a space experience. And despite its peaceful quality, it may have a tremendous liberating impact. This dimension reveals an all-inclusive unity that, rather paradoxically, is not spread out over any region; it is an infinite form or totality but without ordinary spatial extension. It is not a thing which is infinite (Tulku 1977).

Ordinarily, one considers that there is a mind, and so there are thoughts, presuppositions, and changes of mind. But if we suggest there is no mind, what does that mean? Perhaps, there is neither a mind nor its commonly experienced concomitants — these exist together and are transcended together. The mind, even when seen in the ordinary way as an agent, a producer of thoughts, does not actually do anything. In the wake of this no-mind insight, thoughts and changes in orientation are no longer problematic elements; even the appearance of mind and thought simply supports the realisation of no mind, no thought. What this insight means is rather hard to say, since it is not an ordinary proposition regarding the existence or non existence of some 'thing'. Nevertheless, the significance of 'no mind' is precisely as 'no mind as generative source'. Thus mind, like space, has no foundation. This in fact is what accounts for its capacity to accommodate appearances. It is like the viewing aperture of a camera. It is not a solid or palpable thing, except in so far as we take in feelings, tones and other mental events. It is a focus on 'Akash', Space, being open to the latter in various ways and degrees, like particular focal settings of the camera aperture. It is not surprising that this mind is hard to find when one searches for it; for how can we locate a 'setting'?

The fully open focal setting is one that reveals one fully to Consciousness, Self, Space 'allowing'. This is sufficient to accommodate ordinary things, as they are, as being 'O.K.'. It does not stand in a two-term relation to its manifestations. The mind, as ordinarily conceived, stands in such a relation to 'its thoughts'. The mind-as-focal-setting is, in a sense, midway between these — it is other thoughts, yet not locatable elsewhere as a different but still ordinary-level item; also it can be modified considerably by working directly with the thoughts. As long as one clings to an independent 'self' and subject pole, the observed contrast between mind and thought persists. The resulting pattern is frustrating, because the 'mind' itself then thwarts one's sensitivity to the available fulfilment of Being-ness. By relating to the mind as a doer and effector of change or improvement, one continues to maintain or even tighten its narrow, restrictive focus.

People courting divine intercession have long understood that they must open themselves to divine messages and purposes, as in the case of prayer and oracles. All these various orientations emphasise the importance of surrendering the self.

The real issue is to transcend the observed isolation of a self. A humble 'self', or surrender of the 'self', may constitute an opening of the focal setting to some small degree. But as long as one continues to operate within a limited 'lower space' perspective which perceives a 'self' set apart from an 'other', one's experience will remain a self-perpetuating cycle of anxiety, frustration, pain, and despair. One needs to transcend the 'isolated self' perspective altogether if one is to deal directly with the root of ones emotional and psychological problems and to fully experience the Being of a human being. In addition, one may deflate even the idea that the 'self' has ever 'come out'! This insight, when fully balanced, leads to the understanding of 'no mind', of Consciousness being the real ground and nature of appearance, of there being no linear and causal connections between items and events. This dimension is always available to one, and it provides the field for a kind of wide-angled lens to be used, rather than the narrow-angled lens corresponding to the presence of a 'knowing' and 'doing' mind-self. This mind-self lacks a sufficiently wide perspective to take itself into account; in fact, and its status as an apparently independent and potent entity depends on that very limitation. It is necessary to experience the insight that the mind is not a rigid and continuous thing, but only an arbitrary setting (Tulku 1977).

To attain an integrated understanding of the new vision, one needs to understand what it means to be a 'person'. But for an actual transcendence of the body-mind-thought closed circuit, one needs to first become more free of the tendency to structure appearance in terms of both static objects and the inner-outer dichotomy. One also needs to challenge the presupposition of a highly ordered world as the independent and containing background for all things, meanings, and observations. The 'mind' can be challenged philosophically without great difficulty, and it has become possible for each one of us to ground that challenge experientially. But when one begins to challenge the 'body', one must be prepared to abandon all half-measures, and must include the 'world-order', the fundamental touchstone of reality, in one's deliberations. It means the rejection of linear causal connections that tie appearance to something 'elsewhere', 'behind', or prior to it. The spatial 'here' and the temporal 'now' are examples. The 'subject', as opposed to the 'object', is another example. A microcosm of cells, molecules, atoms, etc. within our bodies, as contrasted with the macrocosm outside, could also be taken as a 'by-stander', and so could the body itself. 'Outside-standers' would then be anything outside one spatially, temporally, and so on, including whatever one perceives as being 'higher' in a hierarchy of power or worth. 'Outside-standers' include things which one can interact with, but which are also independent of one and more fundamental to one's reality than to any 'particular observing selves'.

Thinking and observing in terms of cause-effect sequences is so characteristic of the modern era that one assumes even the realm itself to be a thing which must have had an originating cause. The results of this assumption, however, are much less secure and comforting than one might like. Unless one takes the 'no source from' thesis, one seems to be bound to one of two options which result from the emphasis on causes and sequences. It seems that one can either decide that a particular event of a physical kind was the cause of our realm, or that there was no first cause, only a beginningless sequence. The first option is difficult to conceptualise, because a physical event or cause which itself has no cause would be impossible in any ordinary context. The second option is too diffuse, and gets 'too far afield'. It explains our world at the cost of losing it — rather than locating it — in an unbounded causal nexus.

A very attractive way out of this dilemma is to pick a first cause which, unlike ordinary ones, is not subject to the axiom that anything that is a cause must itself be located in a wider casual nexus. A metaphysical entity or divinity is something elected to resolve this difficulty, though this may be an oversimplification or distortion of the significance of such religious terms. The temporally ordered cause-and-effect scheme works well enough as an interpretive device for ordinary purposes. But it is less satisfactory when used to map out the ultimate or fundamental borders of our realm, and to understand what that realm might be. Recourse to a divinity as a cause or point of origin is not a solution or an explanation so much as a reflection of our lower-space predilections. This is not to say that there are no infinite and profound, even 'divine' dimensions that are fundamental to understanding reality.

The cause-and-sequence orientation of many scientific models of the world and its origin often reinforce one's tendency to conceptually locate oneself in a spatially and temporally extended environment. This type of picture prevents one from fully appreciating the immediacy of Consciousness. Religious and mythic accounts sometimes preserve this same tendency, thereby postulating causes in their models of creation that seem empirically unfounded to the physical scientist, and are unacceptable from this perspective as well. Although contemplation of the discoveries of the physical sciences from a conventional religious vantage point — and in support of a conventional religious perspectives — may seem illicit to many scientists, these 'religious' and 'secular' enterprises need not be seen as irreconcilable. Both can be accommodated under the larger, unifying perspectives of this Consciousness orientation. Scientific discoveries can, however, serve as guiding insights, just like the religious ones, which assist in opening the focal setting and thus indirectly complement the religious endeavour. Scientific observations need not merely reinforce the ordinary world view and preoccupation with causal connections between particular items. Religious insights are valuable in that they set forth codes and principles that encourage one to overcome one's strong tendency toward a restrictive self-orientation.

Because a relaxation or transcending of the presuppositions and structures of our realms can lead to a disorientation or a failure to cope, it is ordinarily discouraged. But this psychological disorientation is not due to the relaxation of the presuppositions *per se*, but to a failure to let go of the particular strong conceptions that the 'world' is 'out there' — an accomplished fact once and for all — and that the self is basic. When such concepts are not 'opened up', whatever other 'opening' is done is unbalanced and incomplete. It is still tied to the world and done by the self, and these 'clingings' tend to conflict in a disorienting way with new visions.

This integral vision provides a supportive environment for opening beyond the focal setting that is in force. It helps to guide the process by encouraging one both to transcend the world and to surrender the 'knowing self' to God, at least to the extent possible within the scope of the realm of Consciousness, the Self, and its suppositions (Tulku 1977).

2.7.6. *The Concept of Time in the Study of the Past*
2.7.6.1. *General notions*
The 'normal' way, whereby individuals and society perceive the universe, thus appears as a continuous process, within the framework of time-space coordinates. Events are located and expressed within this framework in the specific culture-historical context. Whether the framework is one of a linear arrow of time, or a cyclical time within which linear time is included, the past, the present, and the future are always taken as given, as actualities. These are the recorded memories, orally or otherwise, that form the tradition of events and situations. The distinction between personal and social memories is only in terms of operational categories since these arise out of each other in a feedback mechanism. At any rate, it all appears real, as if there actually is a time framework within which all of this did take place.

It is obvious that all such memories are really interpretations and reinterpretations of events and situations within the contemporary context. But this simple fact is seldom realised in everyday living. It is noticed even more rarely that these records and memories are what constitutes time — that time is not a separate dimension. In any case, this is how societies and cultures place events — as history or mythology — origins, ancestry and so on within a conceptual chronological order. Similarly, if one notices, one places one's personal history within the time-framework of bodily existence, e.g. "When I was a child, an adolescent, young, middle aged, etc. etc. this and that happened". It all appears psychologically as if it is happening in time.

From these notions of the past — in terms of the dreams, desires, wants or in terms of the supposedly 'true' evidence of previous memories, of 'pain/pleasure' notions — contemporary problems are examined and future projections made. The basis of all action-activity — actually mere reactivity — is this movement of the location of events in a past-present-future framework, at both the socio- and physio-psychological level. The movement of time is generally considered external, outside the body-brain mechanism; or internal as a narrative dialogue within the mind-brain set-up. But the internal-external movements are not only closely related but in fact one movement of socially conditioned individuals and cultures, in symbolic-semiotic-languaging terms that make up the space-time conceptual framework. Elsewhere, one has discussed this dual movement of time as thought, this subject-object dichotomy, its advantages and disadvantages, within the mechanical fragmentary view of the universe which has dominated modern life (Malik 1989a). Not only are academic programmes subsumed under these notions, the researcher himself as a social entity, as a product of his collective background, functions psychologically as a fragmentary being, not holistically. History, anthropology, archaeology and other social sciences dealing with society and culture are governed by this 'colonial' heritage tied to contemporary 'ideologies' of the decision-makers who also function without examining unconscious assumptions that govern one's life. The history of social sciences illustrates this well, as briefly discussed earlier on, with reference to India.

The intellectuals, studying tradition and culture in this context reflect the elite-urban sophisticated groups with certain self-images that arise out of long standing personal and professional histories. The shift required, therefore, is towards the holistic framework; an awareness of the falseness of the self as a separate entity is its first step. The question to be asked is whether this person (persona — meaning a mask), an integrated shadow put together, can form the totality of the world. This is a matter of introspection, to which we shall return later since it concerns Indian civilisation as a whole. Anthropology studies the entire man, or claims to do so, and therefore cannot exclude any dimension, such as Be-ingness (Consciousness) from its purview.

In recent years, the dynamic nature of the universe, the interrelatedness of phenomena as a total system — including man as a subsystem — has been realised more and more. There is the oft-heard talk of ecosystems, human ecology, etc. all of which refutes the mechanical, subject-object dichotomous framework. These perspectives have not, however, penetrated seriously into the academic or socio-psychological systems since the old thoughtways continue to dominate communication and behaviour. There is a greater acceptance of the holistic approach intellectually but it has not trickled down to living it at the experiential level. New ideas are quickly swallowed by old thought-ways expressed in old habits, within the fixed pathways of linear time.

To illustrate: this integral — holistic — idea is instantly converted into an ideal, a goal, something to be achieved in the future. After all, have not many world views since times immemorial stated the same approach, and if so, why has it not been fulfilled? It is because it is once again something to be captured, another utopia to be gained. Like all else, holistic approaches become another ism, a belief system, another bandwagon whereby societies may be transformed (deriving now from current scientific theories and not necessarily from the mystics of yore). It is in this context that intellectuals discuss the matter of integral life, unrelated to one's life at the personal-relational level, i.e., one's psychological behaviour with others. Holism becomes another goal to be achieved, since the mechanical way of life has proved disastrous. A fresh blueprint, a new plan of action for the future becomes an imperative, in the light of scientific discoveries. A new model of change, of a dynamic universe, is prepared for new schools, for a new generation. All these goals will be achieved 'one day' — hopefully of changing attitudes, new organisations and structures, a new dynamism, and so on.

Once again, in other words, renewed activity in the context of an integral way of behaviour and action is subsumed in a linear time framework. This thought pervades, in a different way, even in the context of cyclical time, such as a dynamic change within cyclical karmic influences; i.e. a movement from one state to another — disorder-order-disorder or imbalance-balance-imbalance, etc. While these transformations are understood well in the non-human phenomena as simultaneity, contemporaneity and so on, at the level of socio-psycho-physico existences (as if all this is outside the pale of the universe, as if man is outside the painting), the laws of human functioning have remained closely tied to the old linear ways of thought. Thus, while philosophically and intellectually the dynamic and holistic way of life is accepted in principle, even logically in terms of scientific verifiability, for all practical purposes in everyday life, in the socio-economic and political set-up, it is considered far removed, and irrelevant.

Nevertheless, its intellectual acceptance by a few puts pressure on others to work towards it by asking such questions as 'how' and why' about holism; viz., "While I understand it intellectually, what is the practical way of doing it, going about it, and what is the discipline or path to tread whereby I may live this integral life so as to contribute to society, to go beyond personal-selfish goals?", and so on. These apparently serious rhetorical questions seem justifiable, yet these are framed within the old ways. To the holistic way of life there is no philosophy or ism attached; there is no new renaissance 'out there' — another 'heaven on earth' — to be achieved. The movement of thought from 'here' to 'there', which these question signify, is in linear time. In such questioning the old conditioning functions very subtly, by means of a deceptive 'logic and rationality'. After all, the paradigm of 'survival' requires the preservation of the old psychological security, of moving from the known (past) to the known (future): It is not really unknown since it is a projection from the past and is re-cognisable as what it ought to be like; and one is comfortable in these expectations that have a strong hold both at the personal and social levels. The known to which one moves may be modified in order to be 'understood' and may appear as new.

But have we ever questioned, in the light of recent advances in the sciences and the mystical insights, that this movement, this becoming, is always a repetition of the old, both psychologically and socially? The old perspective is deadly. Unless this false security is questioned, and confronted in terms of one's personal-existential-experiential lives — by being here and now — no breakthrough is possible from the momentous crisis which faces humankind today.

2.7.6.2. *A Study of the Past*

A study of the past is an attempt to record and interpret events in an evolutionary-chronological sequence, within some accepted canons of knowledge, like its counterpart science. Acceptance is by consensus of a group of people in terms of contemporary times or the existential present. This tracing of the past is, however, conceptual in nature as the knowledge on which it is based is itself partial. There are thus limitations on the historical method, and on historical knowledge itself. In

spite of these limitations, this narrow vision of the past permeates contemporary educational system, and our civilisation, to
their detriment. Since knowledge is governed by one's perceptual, conceptual and metaphysical notions, one needs to delve
deep into the epistemological background of one's research.
Today, science itself has narrowed the gap between the subjective and the objective, stating that the viewer and the viewed are
inextricably tied to each other.

This being so, the view of the past — all phenomena in fact
— will change in terms of the overall growth of contemporary
knowledge. Thus no writing of human events is possible, objectively. History is, in fact, a kind of contemporary 'mythology'. This
may be why interpretations of the past are frequently used by
social groups to enforce their demands and justifications. There is
no single history for any community or nation, the latter itself
being a concept. This is true even for any single linguistic group
which is not homogeneous, for different sections of it incorporate
and interpret the same events in different ways. Thus divergent
histories are maintained by different castes. No historian may,
therefore, claim to make any objective, comprehensive history
of a group, except from a specific viewpoint. Methodologies
also change. Even more basically, the past event that is created
permeates the notions of the present itself. Human perception
and human action, within the framework of Consciousness and
within the framework of NOW, are inseparable. A unified sense
of knowledge of the past (or the future) begins in the present,
moment to moment.

Broadly, the aim of historical research is to enlarge human
experience, of which recorded history is a minuscule fragment
known to us. Even if we take the unrecorded event as revealed
by the many sophisticated means available to us, the knowledge
about man, who appeared at least a million years ago, is fragmentary. The evidence has to be sifted by means of the conceptual frameworks available to us, which have expanded considerably along with the scientific means.

To illustrate: it is widely assumed that the linear cultural evolutionary sequential model is a close approximation of reality. This viewpoint, of European origin, placed various non-European societies in this hierarchy according to their techno-economic stages. It may be noted that in the European logic, the techno-economic stages of a society reflect its socio-cultural and metaphysical levels as well (Malik 1968b, 1969, 1971, 1975a, 1977, 1978, 1986). Similar is the division of history and prehistory along the dividing line of writing. This criterion of division, which gives secondary importance to the oral tradition, detracts for example, from the importance oral tradition had in the maintenance of Indian civilisation (Singer; 1959). Ignoring oral traditions is to ignore Indian notions of historicity and to describe Indian society as ahistorical. Again, cyclical notions of the universe, based on rhythms and processes that overlap one another like intersecting circles or a spiral mobile, are ignored — because they are not easily comprehended — in the linear view that is so ingrained in modern man.

Many non-European cultures have a different world view that understands the occurrence of 'historical' events within the framework of cyclical cosmic time, wherein a human life-span is not the focal point. Time and history is inclusive in this rotating wheel in which the past, present and the future concur. The simultaneity idea forms the background of this world view, where time is not sequential and is not based on the idea of cause-and-effect. The idea of a moral order is also thus based on what is a continuous presence of the NOW. On the other hand, linear time suggests a continuous change along the irreversible arrow of time in which the major concern is always with the past or the future, so that the least substantial part is the present which then becomes impossible to grasp. It ignores the reality that any understanding of human phenomena requires an understanding of multi-dimensional interrelatedness, the mutual influence of simultaneous processes and patterns on a particular event.

The notion of an unbroken linear sequence, when used to explain our individual and social existences implies fixed points that are interconnected as cause and effect. This fundamental notion of unbroken causation, that certain events exist because of certain previous events, is another misconception that intrudes into not only constructing the past but also in the perspective of reality in general. It is an oversimplification for understanding human history, and an imposition by us of a limited pattern on the universe. All explanatory systems and concepts are therefore approximates, probability statements, and do not reflect reality. This awareness has to be acknowledged.

In sum, the past is extremely difficult to reconstruct except in terms of probability statements from the present. One's own personal history is similarly governed existentially, making one believe that such and such event occurred. All future projections also arise from this kind of explanations, since thought continually flits between notions of the past and the future, little realising that both in fact are the same. In fact, the present itself is only a modification of the structural abstract notions arising out of various psychological anxieties.

The old philosophical traditions clearly state that there is no separation between the observer and the observed; modern physics supports this view. But historical knowledge continues to follow the old approaches, and fondly believes that a quantitative leap in information knowledge will somehow automatically broaden our horizons. Physics now speaks of rhythmic processes, cyclical notions and patterns. For example, cyclical time is composed of rhythmic patterns like the seasons, the phases of the moon, the tides, day and night. Time and history is inclusive in this cyclic notion, with its idea of simultaneity. In this rotating wheel, these interacting circles, the spiral mobile, the past, present and the future concur.

This is why a study of past has to move beyond notions of sequential time, to inquire into evidence in the context of multi-dimensional interrelatedness, of the mutual influence of simultaneous events on a particular object or process. For example, a hand-axe is many things — a tool, an object of social exchange, a ritual weapon, an aesthetic object and so on. It is many things at the same time depending on the context, which is governed by the interaction of:

1. physical properties;
2. intention or design which is related to functional requirement; and,
3. the transmission of tradition which has to be viewed within the set of technical and morphological patterns that are functionally adequate and socially acceptable.

Again, functional variability may be seen in terms of:

1. vegetable foods;
2. the importance of hunting-fishing activities;
3. environmental variations and seasonal migration of animals on which palaeolithic groups depended;
4. the intended function of artifacts and the probable use of perishable material; and,
5. establishing relative chronology on the basis of these industries.

In the study of history as in all other matters, we need to remembered that whatever we perceive is governed by our unexamined hidden perceptions that control and govern our investigations (Malik 1968). Accepting subjectivity is to accept the responsibility for what one does, since it brings with it rigour in our imagination while presenting the evidence. A study of the past will always remain partial, modified by our present notions and the distorted projections of our state of mind. This realisation, rather than lead us into pessimism and despair, should direct us towards greater responsibility in terms of what little we know. Accepting limitations is one of the first steps to move beyond limitations, for other dimensions of explanations, beyond one's limited framework into many view-points. This is the kind of humility which allows us to learn.

2.8. *Psychological Aspects of Cultural Symbols*

All concepts, however subtle and sophisticated, are socially accepted — agreed upon — values, which include self-con-scious or unconscious notions of one's identity. It is this 'me', the ego, which is then projected on to local, regional and na-tional identities and even larger networks. This identity arising out of socio-cultural and political realms is crucial, since it en-tails a psycho-biological identity and all that is implied by men-tal and emotional states. Personality categories are therefore culture specific, whereby the subject-object dichotomy is made, for the functioning of society. One lives in this system of shared values evaluations, and judgments about everything in the phe-nomenal world. This manner of socialisation creates a sense of security, by giving a sense of belonging, a place under the sun. The security comes from the datum line it allows, from which to make comparisons in order to cherish and preserve certain ideas. At all the levels, the ultimate objective is the survival of the self, the personal or the social, both being the same es-sentially. The ego extends from the social microcosm to ever increasing social extensions, say from the nuclear, to the joint family and to the other kin groups, subcastes, *jatis*, and so on. Involved in all these extensions is the continuity of the process of maintaining values. All this is well known and needs no rep-etition. The emphasis is on the identity of the 'I' under various labels and forms within the binary polarities of 'you' versus 'me', 'us' versus 'them'. All this is crucial within the framework of language, symbols and images — all these creations in the cul-tural context are caught up in the web of their own making (Malik 1989b).

In other words, concepts linguistically manifested as thoughts are tangibly very powerful, as these are materially lo-cated in the brain and are not intangible as one commonly may tend to believe. These trigger off tremendous energy, since the symbolic code is the working of the mind, its manner of giving self-expression to itself in imagery, thereby creating the external world. While language, the vehicle of thought, is the medium it has become the message — the image now governs the self, society and the mind. In turn, since it is governed by a limited set of structures in the socio-cultural world, this feedback mechanism limits the creative potential of the symbolic expression. While both these realms — of concept and image — act as autonomous, neither is really so since they are interacting and are interdependent.

Since, however, some of these basic assumptions are not examined, there is little awareness of in what specific sphere one ought to create change. As a consequence, attempts at transformation are superficial. Radical revolutions seldom take place; instead we have only reactive measures and a kind of old re-creations in new garbs. Real creative activity is rare; innovation, adaptation and superficial change is the norm rather than any radical transformation or mutation. More commonly, it is a replay of the past processes in different garbs, at many levels. It is thus that there appears to be a process set up for ever enlarging, ever expanding the socio-cultural inheritance of the past. Tradition continues in a symbolic manner, and language becomes a carrier of heritage like a geological rock, within which the history of the cultural group concerned may be discerned, just as we learn about earth's history from any geological specimen. The continuity of socio-cultural groups embodied in this manner thus becomes the creation of the technology of thought-forms, that carry within the archetypes of various levels, specially the cultural history. There is a feedback mechanism involved, but today it is thought — as the dominant mode of transformation and communication — which has transformed its creator, as it has its own rules and regulations. It is much the same way that the automobile, created by man, is governing his behaviour.

Cultural games, played within these intersecting circles or wheels within wheels, keep rotating like a mobile spiral through space and time. These symbolic ways, or thought-forms, are actualities which create space and time — the latter not being independent entities. All comprehension of reality is, however, limited by the agreed upon definitions, delimited by a set of cultural values and goals — be it academics or otherwise. Whether in the cities, towns or villages, it is the powers that be whose voice is heard because it is status via power or money that matters. The longer this agreed upon comprehension of reality persists, the stronger form it takes as a truth statement — that it is intrinsically true. The longer any of these values persist, the deeper the motives go into the unconscious structures. This is how all research is also motivated by hidden variables, arising out of the old heritage.

It is important to be aware of these processes, so that there is a rethinking and re-evaluation from time to time, of the symbolic linguistic structures that govern our lives. This can be done only by being conscious of the basic problems, so that issues are tackled explicitly, and clearly restated. Where such an awareness is absent, the old 'colonial' research goals are perpetuated. For example, in the social sciences and for political and economic goals too, the urban notions are dominating the scene. One has to question: why are 'we' (what social category is that?) concentrating on life style ethnographic studies, villages and the fast disappearing heritage? Do they not involve some level of vested interests, including an extension of the 'me', not involved with all its wider implications mentioned above? To illustrate, let us briefly examine some examples of this approach in the Indian context.

2.9. *Some Examples*
2.9.1. *The Village Context*
The heritage of the villager — his tradition, language, festivals, fairs, etc. — is, despite his being illiterate, as sophisticated

as of the urbanite. His style of life is linked to the totality of Indian civilisation, this Indianness, howsoever we may approach it. He has needs, fears, anxieties, dreams and conflicts that are universal to all human beings. His wisdom and knowledge is passed on by the reflective few in his community, through the pandits who interpret and expatiate upon the meaning of life, and have a form of analysis that is no less throughgoing than that of any other intellectual and academic.

There is also close interaction between the village and the town or city, since both the village and the urban areas take each other into account in their universe, equally. Yet the urban elite think that they are the carriers of what is India — more so the professionals who consider themselves especially qualified for the task! Are we really 'better' qualified, less conditioned and more aware of it all than the villager? Every statement, every definition that we make, every bit of data that we adduce and every thought that we think reflect our conditioning, our unexamined background. It is this one has to be aware of, for any radical change to come about; to make the box disappear, for another paradigm to appear. Above all, to be aware that it is all more of the same, is true transformation!

It is in this light that we may see the symbolic relationship of the rural-urban network, especially in relation to oral traditions. This is where religion is part of what anthropologists call the cultural realm, in the sense of sacred activity that governs all life. This is not merely a 'Hindu' view but a general view of the notion of the oneness of man and his universe which cannot be separated except conceptually. The latter mode separates beingness from becoming; and becoming is given emphasis in the modern world at its own peril.

2.9.2. *Indian View of Civilisation*

(a) Civilisation as a western notion forms the basis of most academic studies, primarily reflecting a culture of cities, of the so-called urban sophistication. The equivalent in the Indian context is *sabhyata*, a word derived from *sabha*, which earlier meant 'shining together' and later 'an assembly of men in harmony'. The harmony of mind, action and speech is an oft-repeated theme of Vedic prayers. Everything emanates from the centre in the same way as *rta* (cosmic order) emanates from *satya* (eternal truth). The concept of *sabhyata* is not so much refinement, as it is an attempt to re-seek the rhythm of existence. This concept of perfect internal harmony — the centre holding the circle and vice verse — pervades not only the idea of the Vedic village (*grama*) but also music, art, aesthetics and even sciences, astronomy and civil engineering (Misra 1971).

A civilised person thus is one who may appear crude yet is endowed with an understanding of the inherent harmony in things, both sentient and non-sentient. This way of understanding civilisation subsumes urbanites within higher values of cultural growth rather than at the peak of growth. It stresses the coexistence of many worlds rather than any unique or absolute world. This fundamental way of life, this dynamic rhythm, of the intertwined and seemingly incongruent and divergent manifestations of nature and man are depicted as an integral vision in the apparently repetitious aspect of Indian art, Sanskrit poetry, and so on.

Linear time is not the driving force behind the creative process; creation did not — and does not — take place within the concept of time. Time and space are, however, real in the modern context, and man's achievements are landmarks in terms of the arrow of time, evolution as the apex of the universe with the rest of existence subservient to him. The Indian view does not reject history; it transcends it, since life and reality are not acts of an irreducible human destiny. Human existence is simultaneously temporal and atemporal, as exemplified by exponents of Indian aesthetics. It implies an innate tolerance towards other viewpoints and a ready acceptance. In the Indian view, *itihas* — history — means 'so it has been', and not 'so it was', which is the case with western notions. This interpretation makes one both tradition-bound and free, acknowledging one's obligation to the cosmic being and to the ancestors. With the gods intervening in the world dynamic rhythm, there is mutual complementarity; both universal being (*narayan*) and man (*nara*) depend on each other in a two-way movement. All contradictions and apparent divergences are reflected in this movement, which reflects the same Brahman.

This basic two-way process, this interaction is what allows for the dynamic coexistence and interchange, e.g., between Sanskrit, Dravidian and Munda languages; between textual and non-textual traditions; Between the *margi* and *desi* trends in art and music; and between the socio-religious levels of *itihas* and *puranas,*. Similarly, philosophy as *darshan* — insight within, without and beyond — governs all laws, physical and mental, that come under the Supreme or Truth. This requires sacrifice — to make sacred — self-surrender, which is a continuous process of self-expansion. Through self-surrender man breaks through his egoistic shell to glide into the ocean of infinitude. It is a ceaseless process of give and take. Art, literature, science and technology are products of this self-expansion, as expressions of truth that is beautiful, that is bliss (Bhattacharya 1971). In short, the Indian worldview reflects a universe which is curvilinear, multi-layered and multi-directional, going back and forth.

(b) The phenomenological world was tackled rationally in the Indian understanding. The physical world and human phenomena were explained in terms that did not take recourse to divine explanations. Certain universal cosmic principles were evolved during the Vedic times — and even during the Harappan times, as reflected in their material remains — about the cosmos (natural laws or *rta*) within which even the gods had to function. Later on basic elements of matter with their properties were also expounded. The enquiry in the *Upanishads* into the intelligible reality of the physical world reflects this. The early evidence of astronomy, mathematics and life sciences is a clear indication of this rational way of looking at natural phenomena. Somewhere along the line this rational attitude was lost, but that requires another study.

Most research, until recently, highlighted the elitist or other-worldly nature of Indian civilisation within an equilibrium model, ignoring the dynamics of change. One can no longer ignore the set of values as reflected in its literature, arts, scientific manuscripts, etc. which are as detailed and voluminous as its religious and philosophical sources. The modern confrontational viewpoint, with its singular or monolithic interpretation such as that of only metaphysical and normative texts, will not allow one to provide a realistic view of the life style of this civilisation.

(c) Social systems in non-European societies used to be seen within some generalised western notions. But Marriot and Inden (1963, 1974) illustrated that within indigenous thought cognitive terms are already available as explanatory models of culture. In the indigenous thought the social system is seen within a structure of a continuous flow or movement which has a certain enduring non-duality. There is no clear separation in this system between the natural and the moral order of things. The code of conduct for living persons is not regarded as transcendent over bodily substance; the former is maintained within the latter. Thus, a person's moral qualities are influenced by the kind of food he eats, and the other activities and ceremonies which he undergoes at the social level. Similarly, the moral code and action taken upon it transform the substance in which they are embodied. There is, thus, a universal axiom of cognitive non-duality, of 'action' and 'substance'. In recognition of this reality, authors now do not see authoritative texts merely as prescriptive or descriptive but as cognitive statements of categories and their relationships, which they use as analytical-sociological models.

The term caste is inappropriate in such models, since its definition of rank, heritage, and endogamous occupational groups assumes a foreign conception. There is no indigenous word or idea to express the caste system. The word *jati* is prob-ably more appropriate, as it covers a whole range of popula-tions in terms of families, kin groups, gender, occupational cat-egories, language speakers and regional communities, along with their categories of gods and demons. In the Indian view there is no linear order or exclusive differentiation, branching or taxonomic patterns, as is done in genetic evolution, for instance. Instead, these categories typically intersect and interbreed, in many complex ways.

There is no opposition in the Indian system between matter and spirit; the idea of nature and the idea of morality and law. *Jati* or occupational caste groups are at the same time natural and moral units of society. This perhaps is because of the plurality and diversification of animal, man and other forms the origin of all of which is from a single all-powerful and perfect undistinguished substance (*Purusha?*). Not only are fully coded words or thought-forms embodied in sound, shape, matter and force; even one's gross body and ethereal or subtle forms are embodied within these codes with their own properties or *gunas*. There is never a form of living substance that lacks in-herent morality.

Every living being, in this context of immanent codes of conduct, shares from the moment of its generation, its defining qualities or *gunas*, powers or *shakti*, and actions or *karma*. This code of conduct, *dharma*, when realised through actual appro-priate conduct *(achara)* nourishes and sustains *jiva* or body. Codes are inherent in all generic categories, such as *varna*, *dharma* and *jati-dharma*. In the individual person, too, is em-bodied the moral code for this world, *swadharma*. In him also exists an enduring subtle body *(sukshma sharir)* with the as-cending hierarchy of *jiva, atma* and *purusha*.

Unlike the genetic codes of the West these Indian codes of conduct are not necessarily fixed modes of conduct. If a person, or a group, clings to a certain code, it is because that code is appropriate to that person or group; it is a congenial way that produces the maximum good. Unlike the character of a race in the western sense, it is not absolutely limiting or determinative of the conduct of *jati* or *dharma*; and it may be modified by action at any given moment of time. In other words, the sacred-profane dichotomy, every kind of dualism, are more typical of the Judeo-Christian world views than of the Indian.

The Indian view, however, does not negate the existence of particular elements or units in the socio-cultural system in which action takes place. In a sense, the genera and the persons are highly particularised (a) because they are peculiar and unique parts of a highly differentiated order of interacting categories; and (b) they are thought of as being constituted of coded particles, *pindas* or substances. It may appear, from this conception of the larger order within which there are these coded particles, that individuals are not primarily valued in Indian society. It may indeed be so from the western viewpoint. But in terms of the indigenous value system, within this framework each person is unique in his own right even though he is composed, in various proportions, of diverse, subtle-gross substances that are common to the rest of the natural and cosmic order as well, since ultimately everything is derived from one Source. In a sense, having these properties in common makes the individual unit unique since it is at the same time universal in nature and thus becomes equally effective in the centre. Since there is no fixed centre in such spherical and cyclical notions, this perception of spiritual orderliness in the social dimension within the framework of non-dualistic ordering is very much like the orders conceived by modern linguistics or physicists, by which we may systematise moral or social complexity.

These positive sub-individual particulars or 'particles' or flow are transferred from various sources and are disposed of by persons and genera continuously. They are heterogeneous, ever flowing and changing substances which are made to flow by means of right action exchanges, right eating, right marriage and so on. In other words, the *sanskaras* not only determine but also allow one to sort out and select from, or add to, the mixture of particles present at the gross and subtle level. This allows one to seek to improve one's social and moral standing naturally and appropriately in the hierarchy of genera.

Previous western characterisations of India's thought have largely considered it to be static, with closed compartments, allowing little variability for individual *jatis* to create movements for their own betterment. Perhaps, this came about due to the over-emphasis given to the notions of avoidance and purity-pollution, even though these may be seen as dimensions of life processes which are valued and used as major means of improvement. Of course, there is an elaborate systematisation in everyday life in terms of exchanges between various groups, especially social interdining rules and regulations since one is likely to become what one eats. One becomes equally involved in what one feeds to others. Therefore, there exist elaborate bodily and nutritive rules for substances that must be especially managed (Marriot 1963, 1974).

2.9.3. *The Awareness Context of Sanskrit*

Sanskrit literally means that which has been adorned, decorated or transformed. It is translated to mean perfected, the perfect language of the gods. In turn, the devnagari script is called the dwelling place of the gods. Like many other ancient languages, Sanskrit has a logical mathematical structure. Every word is divisible into component parts, most of which can in turn be traced to one of about 800 roots. These roots, the foundation of the language, are monosyllabic sounds representing general qualities of action. They are also said to constitute, as also represent, the basic energies of the universe. For example, the root 'ram' means: 'to be calm', 'to rest', 'to delight in', or 'cause delight to', 'to make', 'to join', 'to make happy', 'to play', 'to be peaceful', and also 'to stand still', or 'to stop'. (Lannoy et al. 1978)

An analysis of a Sanskrit word or idea draws us from the

expressed world of multiplicity to a more elemental and causal level, the field of the root. The concrete world of thought and action is seen to stem directly from a more abstract one. Sanskrit is a mediator between this causal area of potential action and the world of a particular name, form and function.

The world view which shaped Sanskrit was a holistic one, and the language reflects this breadth of vision. Objects are defined in terms of their function; actors and actions are seen as interrelated parts of a greater whole. Thus the word *mushika* comes from the root 'mush', meaning 'to steal', in this case a mouse. And, taking it a step further, the word *mushikarati*, a compound of *mushika* and *rati* (from the root word 'ram'), means literally 'that which delights in, or stops the mouse'— in other words, a cat! (Lannoy et al. 1978).

At a less domestic level, *mushika* is used to symbolise the Self, the unattached pure consciousness. For the Self, in assuming an identity in the world of particulars, 'steals' that which does not really belong to it. And hence *mushikarati* symbolises the realised man, one who 'enjoys the Self'.

In this way one sees manifestation as the play of polarities, and this dual nature of life is reflected in certain abstract nouns which contain both the meaning of their root and its opposite. For example, the concepts of *advaita* (unity), *aditi* (unboundedness) and *amrita* (immortality), which are central to the philosophy of *dvaita* (duality), *dita* (the bound) and *mrit* (death). Both aspects of life are seen to be inextricably linked and we are reminded that the Infinite contains within it the finite. (Lannoy et al. ibid)

Although stable historically, Sanskrit is very fluid in usage. The same word may have several different meanings and can sometimes take opposite meaning according to the context. Nouns and adjectives are interchangeable, verbs are often omitted as understood. Philosophical Sanskrit is extremely aphoristic; one word in the original usually needs several English words to render it correctly — sometimes even a para-graph. In addition, this tradition often analyses words sym-bolically, rather grammatically. Each syllabic sound is thought to have its own meaning, and thus the interpretation of a word when taken as a combination of symbolic syllables may be quite different from its etymological meaning.

This unique versatility makes Sanskrit ideally suited to sug-gesting subtle nuances and multiple associations, and to con-veying different levels of meaning. Thus the same text could be understood as a mythological story, a psychological treatise, a spiritual discourse, or a teaching on the Absolute — or all of these simultaneously. The *Upanishads* should be contemplated rather than just read; coming from an oral tradition, it is the power of the sound that is important, hence the need for proper chanting and incantation.

The *Vedas,* and the *Upanishads* have generally remained unfathomed by western scholars, for two reasons. First, the *Vedas,* for instance, are cognitions of sound and this fundamen-tal value is inevitably lost in any translation. Secondly, they are cognised from an enlightened state of consciousness and need to be seen in this light. They are the records of perceptions not available to normal consciousness. Many of the sections which have been interpreted as mythology and ritual may also refer to subjective experiences of changes within the seer's own ner-vous system.

The *Upanishads* are a distillation of the Vedic teaching. Whereas the *Vedas* deal more with the mechanics of the innu-merable levels of existence, and man's connection and commu-nication with higher beings in the different strata of creation, the *Upanishads* are primarily concerned with the Absolute from which all existence has come.

The *Vedas* are the oldest records of human thought. The word *veda* means 'knowledge', and the *Vedas* are said to be direct cognitions of the mechanics and structure of the universe. These cognitions came to the ancient seers in the language of nature and are held to contain the seed form of the various levels of manifestation. They are the DNA of the Universe.

The whole structure of creation is based on the same set of laws, time after time, cycle after cycle, and the codification of these eternal laws are the *Vedas*. Hence the *Vedas* are eternal. The emphasis of the *Upanishads* is on experiencing the Absolute rather than learning about it intellectually. The texts stress that there are two levels of knowledge: a lower and a higher. The lower covers the whole are of priestly expertise, which includes 'sciences of pronunciation, ritual, grammar, etymology, metre and astronomy', whereas the higher is that through which the Eternal is directly perceived through meditation. The *Upanishads* are a celebration of a state which lies beyond thought and the workings of the intellect. And as this transcendental realm is beyond words, any attempt to describe it must at best be a 'near approach'— an *upanishad*.

Throughout the history of human thought there have been those who have taught that we are usually aware of only the surface of life, the world of variety, but that there is also a deeper, all-pervading level which unifies this diversity. All the changing relative world is but an expression of this unchanging absolute level. To take either the Absolute or the relative on its own is to take a partial view of life; the wholeness of life comes from living the two together. The relative world is the manifest aspect of Brahman, the Absolute in its unmanifest aspect. Everything has this unmanifest aspect within it. As our own essential nature is also unmanifest Brahman, there lies within us the possibility of experiencing it. This essential nature is Consciousness itself. It is pure Consciousness, which as it vibrates becomes the substance of our thoughts and experiences. On this unbounded underlying substratum of Consciousness all thinking and experience, including that of an individual self or ego, takes place. Pure Consciousness is not the content of the mind, just as a beam of light is not the object it illuminates (Lannoy et al. 1978).

Awareness of the pure Self in meditation is known as

samadhi — still mind. Enlightenment is the state in which *samadhi* is maintained along with all activity. The surface levels of creation become translucent and one appreciates the Self in everything, and everything as the Self. The relative and the absolute aspects of Brahman are both experienced in their completeness yet are simultaneously appreciated as one wholeness. Returning to activity and infusing pure Consciousness into everyday life is as important as meditation itself. Fulfilment comes from living both sides of life — a full material existence along with a full spiritual one.

Samadhi comes not through forcibly restraining the mind, but through allowing it to 'enjoy the inner', as the *Isha Upanishad* says, during meditation, thereby spontaneously withdrawing from the world of change. In the Vedic literature the number 100 is often used to symbolise this state; it does not refer merely to long life. The two zeros symbolise the fulnesses of the Absolute and the relative, the one their unity.

In this tradition sound is of primary importance. Sound is *shakti*, the creative energy, of the Absolute, and through the power of sound, *vach*, the universe is created. The unstruck sound, the primordial vibration from which the rest of manifest creation emerges, is OM. Om creates and sustains the universe, and at the end of each cosmic cycle the universe returns to OM. Complete knowledge of an object requires complete knowledge of the subject, the knower. Thus the words 'knowledge' and 'knowing' (*vidya*) have special meaning in the *Upanishads*. *Vidya* comes from the root 'vid', which contains not just the sense of knowing intellectually or being acquainted with, but knowing fully, from the depths of one's being. 'Knowledge' is that state in which the infinite in the perceiver resonates with the infinite in the perceived. 'Knowledge' is enlightenment. To 'know' Brahman is to live Brahman. Brahman is *sat-chit-ananda*. It is *sat*, eternal and unchanging. It is *chit*, pure Consciousness, the Self. It is also *ananda*, bliss. Bliss is the nature of Brahman, and the experience of Brahman is blissful. The expansion of bliss is the purpose of creation.

This world of the *Vedas* was a sacred one in which every action was understood as part of the cosmic. The ancient sages saw the universe as an eternal ritual of sacrifice. It is the self-sacrifice of the Absolute which gives birth to the relative and the very nature of life is one of transformation of energies. Every aspect of creation, divine or human, reflects this transformation. One cannot live without taking part in this cosmic ritual, both as instrument and as victim, and it is through one's conscious participation in the sacrificial ritual that cosmic order is maintained. The seers taught that the universe is maintained by a hierarchy of energies knows as *devas* — literally the shining ones. These are the causal energies from which the subtle and gross worlds evolve, and are personified as the numerous divine beings of Vedic mythology. The *devas*, although diverse and often of opposing natures, are just the different aspects and subdivisions of the one absolute causal energy. The whole of manifestation is a chain of subtle correspondences, and it is through ritual, correctly performed, that these subtle correspondences can be enlivened and the human linked with the divine (Lannoy et al. 1978).

2.10. *The Role of Intellectuals and Tradition*

Intellectuals are conventionally taken to be rebels and critics, political or otherwise opponents of the established order. But they are something other than iconoclasts or heretics; they are also important as the creators and carriers of traditions. This idea has generally not been accepted, since there has been an implicit and explicit denial of the all-too-facile distinction between intellectuals in a pre-modern or 'traditional' society and those who exist in a so-called 'modern' society (Eisenstadt; 1973). Every tradition — every interpretation of social reality — posits certain questions and provides certain answers, thereby effectively excluding the possibility of other questions and answers. Tension is inherent in intellectual life, precisely because every intellectual construction of reality is challenged. If a construct of 'rational society' is developed by one group of intellectuals this provides an incentive for another group of intellectuals to view the matter in another way. Every tradition has both symbolic and structural organisational dimensions. But traditions are not the creation of intellectuals alone; they are also creations of men of power (politicians and bureaucrats), who are often in conflict with the former. The struggle is not simply between intellectuals who deal mostly with symbols and political men who deal mostly with organisations. Each group creates both, and, in fact, they are mutual by interdependent. Authorities, religious or secular (king or brahmin), seek to be legitimised by intellectuals. Authority then derives legitimacy largely from recognition by the elite of a society. But the intellectuals and their organisations also require the protection of political institutions for survival. Both seek to maintain maximum autonomy while trying to achieve the maximum control over each other.

The term intellectual is a coinage less than one hundred years old. Before, men were satisfied to call themselves writers, poets, dramatists, philosophers and the like. Be that as it may, the fundamental aim of all intellectual effort is the belief that one's concern is with important, even ultimate things. But in doing so an intellectual also comes into association with other powerful individuals. He becomes himself a participant in a social category of powerful individuals, economically and politically. The contacts are sometimes positive, often hostile, but more often the powerful beguile the intellectuals. In fact, unconsciously following old concepts, he/she often follows suit, to support the powers that be. The rebellious change appears transitory, and it soon becomes a conformist one. It supports the same paradigm, in which the parameters of change are the old formulations about human understanding of itself, of nature and of the universe (Eisenstadt 1973).

The outcome of the conflict between the power groups and

intellectuals depends, to a great extent, on the intellectuals' attitude to their own products. The latter, in turn, is closely related to a certain conception of tradition. This conception has strong roots in the history of modern sociological analysis, the central concern of which was the distinctiveness of the modern social order. At the beginning of this century sociological thought was a confrontation between modern societies, which were supposedly open, and non-modern or pre-modern or traditional societies, which were considered as closed societies. Anthropologists typified the latter in terms of 'great', 'little', 'primitive', 'folk', 'tribal', etc. These typologies have dominated our thinking for many years. So we have come to believe, for example, that traditional societies are static, with little differentiation of specialisation, low levels of urbanisation and of literacy (the two latter terms being evaluative); and that 'modern' society has a high level of differentiation or urbanisation, with literacy and exposure to the mass media being commonplace. In the political realm, it has been believed that while traditional elite rule by virtue of some mandate, modern elite are based on a wide participation of broader strata of the population who do not accept the traditional legitimisation of the rulers and who hold the rulers accountable in terms of values and efficiency. Above all, traditional society was conceived as a society bound by the cultural horizons set by its tradition, while post-traditional society was conceived as a society of cultural dynamics, oriented towards change and innovation. This dichotomy between the two was discovered to be false later on, and it was realised that variety and changeability do exist in traditional societies and also that a great deal of traditionalism — conservatism — exists in modern society. Thus, tradition is not an obstacle to change; it is in fact an essential framework for creativity. Every tradition has enduring elements that underlie its continual changing symbolic forms and structural expression. Tradition is the reservoir of the most central social and cultural experience prevalent at the level of the collective social and cultural reconstruction of reality. The reservoir is not an undifferentiated one; it has a structure of its own (Eisenstadt 1973).

Intellectuals are themselves linked to their traditions through time — to the beliefs, symbols, conceptions of form, sense of verbal and symbolic usages, rules of procedure and so on incarnate in those traditions. This triad of tradition/development/modernity is not clear. For example, great religions in ancient times touched a great many people, and they continue to influence intellectuals even today.

In India, for example, the transmission of cultural tradition may be seen within native categories of thought in terms of: (a) in the context of material arts of life, (b) the processes by which it cultivates excellence in social and religious life, such as among certain potter groups. Importance is given in the Indian system to kinsmen, and to castemen in the production of caste occupation. Consider, for example, the potter's relations with his clientele within the *jajmani* system. Not only affluent peasants but also poor peasants, artisans and service castes come within the ambit of this system, which often functions by a simple exchange of goods and/or services. It is both a socio-economic and sacro-economic system. For example, there is sharing of agricultural produce during a natural calamity and artisans are given rent-free land and grain along with equitable distribution of wealth. Thus, the continuity of tradition, social and sacred, implies the acceptance of non-brahminical types within the brahminical. Further, the criteria may not be external but internal, in the context of being and becoming. This is seen in the way knowledge is transmitted from one generation to the next, and connects thought and action (Saraswati 1973).

Civilisational knowledge is transmitted in three ways, viz., oral, writing, and revelation. One of these is adopted as an essential mode of survival. This transmission includes all the facets, such as the temple, image, content, social life and world view, and comes in the following categories: (a) collective memory, primarily *laukik*; (b) textual culture, primarily *shastric*;

and (c) self-realising esoteric processes, or the *naivritik*, i.e. those dictated by the concern of transcendental knowledge of 'transcendental culture'.

In 'Hindu' scriptures, there are two divisions of civilisational knowledge, viz., *pravriti* (this-worldly) and *naivriti* (other-worldly). The former is divided into *lokachar* (oral) and *sastrachar* (textual). The *lokachar* for example, is that of the potters. Their tradition is based on the collective memory of the elders. Crafts and their organisation are based on oral tradition that acts as a guiding force in the well honoured *jajmani* relations. Marriage and inheritance also are conventionally followed, as are food taboos, domestic rituals and festivals that are prescribed and conducted orally by community elders. Sex taboos, marriage ceremonies, the role of male elders for ritual ceremonies and females for traditions also come in this category.

The *shastric* is based on the texts of *nitishastra* and *dharmashastra* scriptures, which are followed by brahminical cultures. These prescribe not only social stratification of *varnas* but give clear instructions regarding *silpa, sangeet, sahitya,* medicine, astronomy, *sanskaras,* inheritance and marriage laws, criminal laws, and so on. In the *laukik* breaches are dealt with by caste councils. Among non-brahmin *jatis* purificatory rites are performed; and among brahmins, *prayaschitta* (penance of a sort) prescribed in the *shastras* is done. Whether among brahmins or non-brahmins, norms and values and the textual boundaries govern their life. The continuity of past thought, modified, reformed, is put in new words, but it is essentially the same (Saraswati 1973).

All three modes of transmission of knowledge — *laukik, shastric* and *naivritik* — are primary self-sustaining categories ideally; but operationally, they are a way of looking at the universe. There is interconnection among them. All have the same interconnecting circles, or spheres. Also, people following one category depend upon people following other categories. Thus *naivriti marg* people depend upon *pravriti marg* people for living. Thus, all arts, crafts, music, dance, etc. depend upon oral tradition and also textual culture. There is no hierarchy of the three; only, they are different. Scholars may 'sit at the feet of illiterate *sadhus* to seek transcendental knowledge. As such, therefore, it is immaterial whether we talk in categories of little and great traditions, hierarchy, percentages, universal and particularistic, local and regional and national or supernational, or the divisions of conscious and unconscious as against superconscious, self-conscious and the cosmic self.

In the peasant mode of transmission of knowledge, the whole community is involved in the pursuit of 'knowledge', not only for sharing a way of life but for survival as well (Singer 1959). Power is not a monopoly here, and it is open and available more or less equally since textual linkages are at the periphery rather than at the centre of ethnographic communities. Peasant and urban boundaries are fuzzier in India than elsewhere, since the emphasis is not on the texts but on their interpretation, which is by and large done orally, creating epic myths at many levels. Thus civilisation in India is both sacred and secular, textual and oral, not either/or. Of course, the see-saw between the *laukik* and *shastric* — *para* and *apara* — goes on. In this context, texts are traditional. They have absolute authentic names to which the members of the society concerned respond automatically. Also, they rely on transcendentalism (Being) beyond language, or external sense, or language (Saraswati 1973).

In the self-identification of cultures what is most important is the knowledge of cultural traits which people inherit from generation to generation. In this sense, pandits and brahmins, diviners, etc. are equally interpreters and transmitters of tradition, upholders of reality and presenters of opposing views. Debates are part of the *shastric* tradition, which is a reflection of intellectuals of that society. This is very different from our own notions of intellectuals — or academics as we would like to call ourselves — but do we really act as watchdogs? Very few answer to this description, as most óf us continue to perpetuate the same old reality at many levels, with compromises. In this way, the past incorporates itself as the present, remoulds it and suggests a future solution. But nothing new or radical really takes places since all 'action' is really a 'reaction' system — like cause and effect are an intrinsic part of each other. The very separation of the past, present and future is a subtle separation of one whole concept, which makes us feel it is different, while it is the same in essence.

2.11. *The Ethnographic Context*

India is a civilisation, not a mere nation-state. Its political boundaries have constantly been changing, but some basic ways of life, its style, levels of integration and world views have kept it up as a dynamic structure. It is a life of cultures, social groupings, in the context of families, neighbours, work, ceremonies, rites and rituals, rounds of life, etc. A village is a small community, with location-interaction in space, with a population more or less cohesive. India's half a million villages have traditional features like caste, joint family, festivals, religious beliefs and traditional knowledge and its media for transmission. Changes have taken place at various times — with adaptations and innovations, new creations — which have allowed this civilisation to continue. Western-industrial influences have, however, brought about changes much faster than ever before in all spheres, as they have done the world over. There is now more democratisation in the villages, rather than secularisation. Caste interdependence exists alongside domination/subordination principles. Land tenure is based on social structure which in turn affects land tenure. Within and between individuals status is maintained in terms of the influence — distorted or not — of ancient codes and ideas. There is disintegration of social systems, decline of occupational specialities, increasing use of money, growth of factionalism, changes in interdependence of castes and a tendency for repressed classes to find common cause in political/economic interest.

There are various dimensions involved in a village community — such as ecological, physical, social, political, psychological, economic, mythological — which intersect. One or more of these spheres may define the limits of the village community and may spill over to the boundaries of other communities. For the context is always larger than the unit and not all units have the same limits. For instance, there is a fantastic range of variation under the rubric of peasant village society, despite the underlying similarities in the material culture and technology or even economic levels of social groups. These variations cover such aspects as in values and personality, quality of social relations and mutual dependence and interdependence of power groups. Thus a village may be seen as a nucleus of activity, a stage of social activity, and — at the level of integration within the folk-rural-town-urban continuum — reflective of the basic nature of the indigenous primary civilisation. If most of India lives in the villages, the urban areas are a dimension of the village (Malik 1968, 1971, 1975, 1987).

The village, while it is a cause and product of our ancient civilisation, is also a division — a category — of a local community made by us. It is not a thing, it is a system. There are just as many aspects of peasant or rural dimension in the national life of a civilisation, as there are urban. Both the great and the little traditions lie in the village, one in the form of literacy and the other that of oral tradition, the latter being the more fundamental. As an element in Indian civilisation, a village may be studied from the State downward or village upward. For instance, the Indian government is very much a part of the growth upward from the institution of the local community through adult franchise, so that it includes the old style feudalism, rituals and beliefs. From times immemorial, these villagefolk systems of life and beliefs have contributed to sanskritic traditions and in turn modified local tradition through oral myths, bards, etc.

Thus, there may be seen even today the generic historic reinterpretative process of the interaction of 'whole-part' in the universe of Indian civilisation. A village reflects a distinctive aspect of its civilisation. Peasants are the old stable population of the land, depending on agriculture and yet are integrated into the larger socio-economic-political units of urban areas that in turn borrow from other rural areas.

i. *An Indian Example*

The Kuruvas (or Kaurabas) are a shepherd community inhabiting the semi-arid regions of Karnataka and Andhra Pradesh; some groups of Dhangars in Maharashtra have similar life styles (Murty and Sontheimer 1980). In either environment, they are neither nomadic nor practise transhumance, i.e. moving with large flocks of sheep from one pasture to another. They 'now' lead a symbiotic life with settled farmers and maintain themselves through the sale of sheep and goats. Each pastoral group represents a single community and forms an 'isolated' 'whole' — being a homogenous self-subsistence unit. But do they retain distinct qualities? They have been in constant interaction with the other predominantly Hinduised communities for the last 3,000 years or so. This interaction may be viewed as universalisation and parochialisation (Marriot 1963). All these pastoral communities are Saivites; they worship the different incarnations of Siva. Historically this religious affiliation may be traced back to a prototype god found in early Tamil literature of the second to fourth centuries A.D. One example of interaction is that of god having two wives, one from an advanced community and the other from a hill tribe or a pastoral tribe. This has been supposed to reflect acculturation of communities of different subsistence systems, who were drawn into the fold of each other in an eco-system which, as archaeological reasoning points, induced the development of an economic system that tended to be dyadic. This is further reflected in a corresponding dichotomy of traditions which are not only orally transmitted but have also found their way into the *puranas* or local *mahatmayas.*

A binary economic system embracing both pastoralism and agriculture may at times permeate through groups and even families. For example, Hatkar Dhangars are settled farmers, but one part of the group, or one member of a family, or a relation by marriage may be nomadic Dhangars. Ecological stress drove away a segment of the population into the interior forested zones and in due course, they lost trace of any links with the parent stock. There is evidence to this effect in the oral traditions. In becoming a distinct group in the forest, the pastoral system suffered degradation and ritual impurity. Thus, tribal groups need not represent an earlier evolutionary stage but a reversal from being sedentary or agricultural groups, on account of being pushed into the interiors by other groups. This is notable in the Himalayan Kanets as well, among whom it reflects the taking over of a higher caste ranking and status through kinship and genealogical reckoning.

The Kuruvas are spread over several villages, and are almost acculturated into the agricultural society, because of seasonal migration to the neighbouring villages within a radius of 150 kilometres. This kind of interaction between tribal and village communities in the region goes back to the neolithic-chalcolithic times. This is inferred from the similar subsistence levels of animals and plants; the way life is also inferred through actual study, study of the oral traditions and that of archaeological finds. The tradition of two wives symbolises the crystallisation of the forest and pastoral and the settled agricultural and merchant communities. The symbolism is also borne out by the *vahanas*; e.g. Khandoba rides a horse, Siva a *nandi* and Biroba tends to have a horse and/or ram. The oral system of the traditions and cults of these civilisational groups has preserved valuable information on them. Their origins and linkages go back to 3000 B.C. at least. Changes are always occurring among them: their existence has neither been static nor any less sophisticated than among other groups and in other times.

Again, in Andhra Pradesh the tribes of Yanadis, Yerukulas and Boyas were traditionally hunter-gatherers favouring forest or semi-forested scrub jungle riverine zones. But owing to encroachment of agricultural/pastoral and trader communities, there was interaction with advanced castes. Because of the consequent depletion of floral cover and the faunal bio-mass, there was a readaptation to a subsistence that reflects a symbiotic adjustment to suit the village-based economies. The former groups, for example, became subsidiary to the agricultural economy. Their chief occupations now are the sale of cattle and pig dung as manure to the farmers, for which they maintain cattle herds and piggery; at harvest time, they also work as labourers. While bird hunting also is their speciality, the former arrangement assures cash-and-kind returns (Murty et. al 1980).

In the Indo-Gangetic plains of north India, evidence of population migration settlements, of well-settled communities and villages and their movements, comes from early times even prior to so-called coming of the Aryans. These areas have seen the constant intrusion of tribes, and invaders that kept coming from outside, getting assimilated to settle down. But how has this changed; how were people assimilated in this melting pot; how much do we know? While the technological-economic patterns remain the same in a sense, social reorganisation has also taken place, say, with the introduction of iron, persian wheel and so on. In this way cultural expressions and idioms change, the socio-cultural content, the attitudes and values alter. But what exactly are the parameters to consider when we try to examine such changes? Very little study along these lines has been carried out, to understand continuity and change. In this process, is India different from other civilisations, i.e. do not the same laws and generalisations apply? Or, are we in this study deliberately trying to preserve our peculiar notions of cultural heritage, to bring out a post-independence identity — another psychological viewpoint of the subcontinental variety of the ego or the self?

2.11.2. *Summing up of this section*

The peasant dimension is the basic context that carries forward values, norms, materials; assimilating them, to universalise the cultural consciousness of persons and content that gives a corporate self-identity and widely shared common traits, mythology and oral traditions (Redfield 1956, 1961; Singer, 1959). Nevertheless, the above examples illustrate in brief that in terms of the variability and variables involved, a village cannot be seen as a standard microcosm — a unit — for any holistic study, since this would be posing the wrong question. There are limitations of the methods, too, as these are not always organised and totally coherent. For example, assertion about birth-ascribed stratification, no-conflict situations, being static, lack of aspiration and progression, etc. are mere assumptions about Indian civilisation. We know, for example, of several groups throughout history wanting to escape oppression and exploitation because of inborn stigma.

Oppression brings about movements — often violent — for mobility of all kinds, even if these groups themselves may become privileged. It is therefore not easy to accept the belief that Indians accept oppression, and the oppressed found an escape through conversion and the like processes. Discontent has always existed, and people do not want their low status to continue, they are aware of it. Many reform movements have originated in the villages, since the dominating powers seldom want to give up their hold.

Anthropologists have for too long relied on elite resources to understand the low, in more ways than one. Recent socio-economic changes have only secured the position of the haves — the *nouveau-riche*. If we are still carrying on the lament of the romantic vision of the village is it because as urban folk we suffer from a 'loss of innocence' or is it because we are guilty? In this sense the 'colonial' heritage continues. Perhaps, towns and cities are mostly conglomerations of expanded villages. There is hardly a claim for a truly 'modern' secular way of life in India. The so-called urban groups — and their counterparts in the villages — have monopolised control over wealth, power and services, and other subsystems, throughout the history of this civilisation.

Defining India or Indianness, spatio-temporally, is itself not an easy task, since it is a changing entity of both 'being' and 'becoming', both historically in terms of socio-cultural processes and the contemporary definitions of ourselves through signs and symbols in both universal and particularistic objectives. Many research objectives are unconsciously agreed 'games' set up by academics and the powers that be. For example, one dominant notion today is that India is to be preserved in its villages; its arts and crafts must be preserved as precious heritage not only in museums, but exported as cultural festivals. This endeavour surely suggests the death of the civilisation instead of its being a live tradition, which it has been for so long. Indian civilisation has maintained itself in a continuity that is dynamic, adaptive, innovative and creative, not static. Yet today, it depends upon who decides about whom and for what purpose. Covertly what really works is the deeply ingrained psychology of 'domination versus subordination' paradigm which has been running humankind for millennia. Even if we do not use the word exploitation explicitly, nevertheless we do 'use' each other at various levels.

Again, what is continuity, what is change, except what is seen, repeatedly within the paradigm of 'survival'? This is a century of rapid change, which is an apparent preferred value. But what this change is and what it is about is debatable; the whole debate being about developing and developed nations, and the impact of modernisation on preserving cultural and ethnic identities. In this sense conservativeness is part of modernity in as much as it is not found in traditional societies. Today, while there is glory given to the villagers, their crafts and traditions, power is not duly given to them — they are not made responsible for their traditions and empowered. What then is the meaning of tradition, heritage and so on, which we discuss in our concepts that are so subtle and sophisticated, if these are not related to our understanding of values, of the identity collective and of the 'me'? This understanding is crucial for this is what is projected on to the local, regional and national levels. Heritage is inclusive of one's mental and emotional states. The latter is seldom touched upon, as it involves asking fundamental questions about both epistemology and ontology. Anthropological investigations must take this into account, every now and then.

III

Rock Art: A Universal Creative Act

3.1. *Introduction*

Rock art research is a well-established discipline in many parts of the world — Asia, Africa, Australia, America and Europe — where specific aspects of this cultural heritage of humankind are studied in different countries. Of late, increasing interest in this subject has also led to a healthy questioning of certain theoretical frameworks that formed the unquestioned base for the study of rock art research. The old stylistic and other chronologies are being questioned, and there is a great deal of reliance on comparative ethnographic data in interpreting rock art. Equally important is the awareness of the constraints involved in reconstructing the past, especially the archaeologist's own viewpoint. Subjectivity here does not merely refer to the individual, it also points to the cultural biases, say, the Euro-centrism whereby all rock art traditions were judged from that angle alone, i.e. rock art was supposed to have emerged and spread in different directions of the globe from this geographic region alone, along with perceived cultural significances and attributes within certain 'evolutionary' schemes of the palaeolithic period.

This focus on Europe, along with the classificatory chronological schemes both in palaeolithic sequences and rock art styles were then sought to be duplicated in other parts of the world. Obviously, not only has there been little success in this enterprise, these inappropriate questions have continued to dog archaeological research in non-European cultural zones as well. Further, it has led to an almost total neglect of studying indigenous traditions, their theoretical models and the spatio-temporal distributions. The error is now being rectified somewhat, and with shifting interest — having gained freedom from colonial rule — one is seeing the beginning of a healthy questioning of older categories, the pigeonholing of rock art. The aim here is to indicate that in this movement to broaden horizons, rock art, perhaps, may be viewed within the framework of some overarching artistic — creative — act which runs as a common thread through various cultural communities. But the reference to this commonness is not necessarily restricting the idea to the lately evolved very sophisticated new classificatory schemes. For instance, is it not possible to understand rock art by approaching it from a cosmogonic universal act — Universal Consciousness — whereby this cultural manifestation, as creativity, is linked to all such expressions irrespective of time and place? Thinking along these lines may not, then, rock art research provide a crucial link for the understanding of various contemporary dilemmas?

This is not to say that researchers do not visualise rock art as a universal phenomenon, in the sense of its being a cultural heritage of humankind as such. Many different nations even lay claim to this heritage in terms of their cultural and political identity. Beyond this, the universality is also seen in terms of man's search for its common identity — psychological and biological — which transcends regional identities. In the application of sophisticated techniques, taking into account ecological conditions, archaeological correlates and contexts, the study of rock art cuts across various boundaries. It is not the intention here, however, to discuss these aspects of universality.

In rock art studies the use of the word art itself has been limited by specific concepts governed by various cultural connotations, e.g. more by monolithic definitions and the like rather than by other sensibilities and freedom of expression that may be common to all of humankind, remnants of which may be seen in non-industrialised societies at various levels. The modern notion of art as mere aesthetic beauty for its own sake, both

in terms of formal qualities and other social and functional purposes, is a limited way of seeing artistic creations. The perception of earlier cultures of their artistic manifestations was linked
to every other aspect of their life and the sacredness of the
world order. In contrast, modern man gives little consideration
to any form of cosmic vision. Access to this universal view is
available to all human beings, irrespective of time and place, to
keep them in touch with the supernatural or the noumenal dimension. This kind of knowledge was widely prevalent
amongst non-industrial traditional societies of the past which
manifested it on rock surfaces. Such akin traditions survive even
today. It is in this sense that ethnology, myths, beliefs, and so
on, in different traditions indicate probable alternate ways of
viewing rock art, supplemented with archaeological records.

It is in this context that there is a general need to reframe
the role of archaeology, history and culture understanding
Indian civilisation, especially in the light of recent developments
in the scientific world, which suggest holistic frameworks, converging with the ancient and recent indigenous world views.
Since far too long have we been following the Euro-centric orientation, long after the end of colonial rule. Understanding why
this has been so requires us to look into certain basic assumptions which were formulated in the European context, beginning with the modern era in the sixteenth-seventeenth centuries. These assumptions have greatly influenced research into
India's past and its culture, though they were set against a metaphysics and world view radically different from the Indian one.
The Euro-centric vision has also been the foundation of developments in science and technology during the past two or three
centuries, conditioning all educational systems in the colonial
world, and the intellectuals — the elite. As stated previously,
some of the important unexamined assumptions, which have
governed the study of archaeology, culture and history in this
subcontinent therefore need to be re-examined. We may then
be able to formulate holistic approaches to the knowledge of

the past, in tune with contemporary scientific developments, which are supported by the fundamental metaphysics of Indian civilisation.

Greater insights will be available into the past if such knowledge is related to our own psyche rather than the European one. For example, it is 'normal' for researchers to locate events within a past-present-future framework, at both the social and psychological level. Moreover, this movement of time is mostly considered external, outside the body-brain mechanism; or internal as a narrative dialogue within the mind-brain set-up. It is seldom noted that the external-internal movement is not only closely linked but is in fact one movement. It is split because of the social system, within the space-time symbolic-semiotic languaging terms that make up the framework of reference of most social and human sciences (Malik 1989a). Within the awareness of this holistic framework, which is a matter of introspection, the notion of culture in anthropology in general and rock art specifically may be viewed in the Indian setting. Here exists a tremendous variation of cultural configurations, along with a multitude of variables.

If the goal is to search for meaning behind rock art, in accustomed ways, there will be little success. Success has been poor so far because the accustomed ways of search have totally ignored a crucial dimension of the subject of study. It is only when the mechanistic, analytical, evolutionary approaches (which assume that the underlying significance of this kind of activity can be inferred by quantitative methods along with some intuitive-aesthetic or pseudo-religious explanations) are transcended that the complexity and richness of this tradition may provide a glimpse into the underlying philosophies and world views. The process of decoding the total symbolic system can only then begin to reveal the universal nature of this art.

3.2. *Rock Art qua Art*

There is growing realisation that any philosophy and explanation of art without an account and understanding of aesthetic experience is inadequate and lifeless. The trend of ignoring experience has also dominated, by and large, the phenomenology of aesthetics. The scientific theory of an expression of this directedness of consciousness upon an object is quite different from the universe of discourse that is given shape by artistic experience and expression. In the triad of consciousness, aesthetic objectivity and art expression, experience is definitely the primal source, common to all human communities. Art experience is an exudation of consciousness from the privacy of the inner, and cannot therefore be treated merely as a 'thing'. The language of art moves beyond the conceptual, semantic, and syntactic constraints, to cognise reality in silence. Art, however, does not fully relinquish the garb of ordinary language; the latter being more of an instrument and less an expression of being, that carries a deeper and new meaning. In other words, art experience, both for the creator and the spectator, is dialogic in all its pre-linguistic, linguistic and trans-linguistic aspects (Biswas 1995).

Art, viewed in this sense, signifies a continuity of reality through different spatial and temporal levels. In it, the range of human faculties like perception, reason and imagination are not confined to any particular hierarchical level of reality. The images of poetry, painting, sculpture and architecture, music, dance and all other arts constitute such items of knowledge. The questions which arise from such an approach may be as follows: 1. What is one's relation with works of art? 2. What is the nature of the creative process? 3. What is the relation between man as an artist and his creations? 4. How is the meaning of art determined? and 5. What is the ontological status of a work of art? (Biswas ibid). There are considerable variations and differences in the manner of presentation, in the degree of sensuousness, flexibility, opacity, materiality, and in the role of medium, etc. in the different art forms. Viewed within this general framework, however, the approach provides a common platform on which all arts stand together. There is then a sense also of indeterminacy in experiencing a work of art because when one creates, or enjoys or evaluates a work of art, there is an in-built awareness of something which comes to take shape and which is likely to change in the course of time. In the works of art there is an absence of 'fact', of a kind which is commonplace in the modern world — an 'I-It' relationship is replaced by an 'I-Thou' one (Friedman and Malik 1995). The appearances of things are abstracted from their material existence and trans-formed into visions, forms and images in art. For example, a picture is made with pigments on a rock surface, but the painting that emerges is not 'pigment on canvas'. It expresses its own space and a particular relationship between the human and the world; it is both significant and speakable in this sense. In short, a work of art has a continuous existence and identity, and like a human being it is 'no-thing', a non-factual order of be-ing. The modern world is dominated by a fact-ridden reality, beset with dichotomies and hierarchies which become irreconcilable. It is only when one understands this basic holistic vision which gives rise to a non-utilitarian attitude to man and his creative work, that any meaningful insight of rock art research becomes possible.

Thus, rock art *qua* art, as an artistic activity is intrinsically an act of creativity. But this may only be seen by adopting an approach that views works of art which are not dissociated from the life of any given culture and society. In this approach, the central concern of the integral vision of art is experience and creativity — whether it is termed art or non-art in conventional terms. This is a departure from such notions as 'art for art's sake', that arise out of such frameworks as conflict-confronta-tionist binary opposites (sacred-secular, high-low, literate-non-literate, urban-rural or tribal, traditional-modern, etc.), struc-tural-functional, uni or multi-linear evolutionary models and such other ways of investigation. The integral way suggests principles of complementarity, pluralism, concurrency, coexistence, polyvalence and synergy, to view works of art — rock art — within the framework of the universal category of a creative act; obviously implying thereby that there are no fundamental qualitative hierarchies amongst the spheres of creativity, often so assessed through the adoption/application of socio-economic yardsticks of 'development' and 'progress'. The concern of artistic manifestation is to focus attention on dynamic inter-relationships, towards what one may call 'integrality' as distinct from de-contextualisation of artistic manifestation and expression. This statement holds true for any work of art in the modern context (Saraswati et al. 1994).

While in this sense there is no distinction between what happened in artistic manifestation in ancient times and more recent eras, any evolutionary processes, or the archaeological records are not discarded altogether. Nevertheless, these areas of study may be seen as subsets of larger categories, as is being suggested by contemporary science within the context of principles of concurrency, simultaneity and space-time continuum in preference to linear progressive movements. In times when the written word, or thought, had not become so specialised, man was very much in touch with nature and the cosmos with highly sensitised senses. Experience — experiencing — both inner and outer, then played a central role, beyond words and beyond any idea of a sharply separated self, person or individual. The expression and articulation of this experience was through non-verbal images and symbols, artistic or otherwise. Thus, there was a balancing of the inner/outer, verbal/non-verbal and other dichotomies. This balance also led one to recognise fuzzy areas, twilight zones, beyond rigid clear-cut demarcations. In other words, art was an integral part of not only music, dance, etc. but also of social and economic (subsistence patterns) life. Seen in this light art is a creative act which takes into account some perennial common core principles that are equally valid for all cultures. These core principles may have evolved and may have been articulated in different ways, sometimes consciously as theoretical artistic/aesthetic concepts, and at other times, these may have been manifested themselves within a framework of existential-experiential states of participatory observation. The stress is on 'totality', wherein both or many of the ways are of not only equal value but may be considered as interdependent and interrelated.

The natural and social environment does shape artistic expression; herein may lie also the cause of creativity. Nevertheless, there is no linear — one to one — logical connection or explanation of this or any other order. The upsurge for creativity remains unknown, if it has to be understood merely at the phenomenal level. Its sources lie possibly in the noumenal dimension. At any rate, in turn, creative expression does affect the natural and human environment. In this way, life functions, life cycles, social needs, economic, political systems, mythical world views — all these are to be seen as symbiotic, closely linked relationships. This approach may possibly provide the context or several contexts of art, seen as creativity. Art in this sense is both a participatory, universal activity, and at the same time unique. It may or may not be nurtured by the natural environment. Creativity is timeless in this sense, since it springs from a still interiority, a silence that is a form of contemplation — an area from which urban modern man has moved very far indeed. Art, in this sense, as a manifestation of the unspoken and authentic experience, invokes, evokes, provokes, stimulates, sustains, disturbs the viewer. It has the ability to transform and recreate the natural and human environment.

Art may be seen in its forms, manifestations, and products as an integral part of the totality of life experience at an individual and collective level. Its playful or unpredictable quality is its power, poetry and potency. Artistic activity is correlated and integral to ritual, fairs, worship, beliefs, festivals — a very wide spectrum that includes all the material techniques. Under certain situations and conditions, forms of art reflect a plurality and diversity which also has specific functional context for the artistic products, albeit the aesthetic aspect is often transcultural spatio-temporally. Thus, there are different orders of experience, different levels of functional attributes, formal values and so on of art as such. All this is equally true for rock art, and valid for it.

Several questions may arise in the context of viewing art — rock art — in alternate ways. For instance:

a. What methodologies are to be evolved to avoid dichotomies and binary opposites?

b. In the holistic vision, how is one to divide and subdivide for purposes of analysis and classification — can one eschew analytical methodology?

c. How is one to define art, if one is to cover religio-philosophical-technological and environmental parameters?

d. How is one to relate to other cultures, to the language and non-language texts, to deal with the problem of translating non-verbal phenomena into verbal essays, without getting into non-linear narratives?

e. Is it possible to address different levels at the same time, or audiences at once?

f. Is it legitimate to take the non-European, say the Indian view of culture, in applying it to rock art, as organising principles in general? Is it all right to ignore twentieth century categories, since we are ourselves bound by the twentieth century; or is the Indian view universalistic in any true sense? If so, what may be the key categories and definitions for our purpose — as the rubric of our discourse?

To answer any of these queries, a different approach, as stated above, needs to be adopted to Art as such, outside the rubric of what is 'modern', or any nationalistic viewpoint. Rock art of course may be approached in a variety of ways; as art history, psychology and metaphysics, religion, utilitarian and functional, graphic representational motifs of some underlying 'material' aspects of social and cultural life, subsistence patterns and so on. But all this is still the fragmentary and partial approach which does not tell us about the global and universal phenomenon that art is, since most of all art, today, is not viewed within any notion of a sacred cosmic order from whence arises the Creative Urge, common to all of humanity, beyond place and time. The creativity of art is the silent common-communion-language of humankind, just as the silent puppets speak to all irrespective of any particularity. True, sincere and authentic art in this sense speaks of an integral vision, of a world vision which is mystic, mysterious, divine, supernatural, and so on. These are words used variously to express that which is not speakable yet which is communicable because it transcends individual man-centred modern aesthetic notions of art. This approach is beyond the questions of what, when, where, and why without excluding any of these, even if the latter are arbitrary classifications in terms of linearity, stylistic chronologies in a comparative and relative sense, and not in any inherent logical order except the imposition of the present 'subject', his beliefs and so on. The Creative-Urge approach has another dynamic and flexible frame of reference since it expresses different kinds of inherent cultural continuities in terms of myths, dream-times, and other motifs which exist in the entire species of *Homo sapiens*. It is like the common geometrical patterns, stylised lines, and so on which like the basic rhythm of sound and sight — music and dance — is built into the human being. This is a holistic notion of simultaneity, whereby even the style and form of artistic expression of rock art may be seen.

But none of this can be understood apart from an experiential level when one lives or is in touch with the sacred dimension, and certainly not within the desacralised 'modern' civilisation which has lost the lustre and significance of an integral life, since it treats art separately from life and all other activities. With his shrunken outlook, modern man is surprised that 'primitive' people could produce art! There is today an undue emphasis on the external, to the neglect of the inner experience and feelings that are considered to be too private to be expressed or trusted as intimations of another dimension. Whatever expression the latter finds is merely in terms of imitations, secondhand experiences spoonfed through the mass media and consumeristic reward-and-punishment competitive philosophies. There is a sense of disbelief, a lack of purpose and ideal, alienation and meaninglessness, because modern notions of art have no prophetic strength. The message of art is perennial and authentic because it is 'non-material' in its approach. Its continuity lies in the spirit, which does not depart this world like the body. It is the inner similarities — moral and spiritual — of art that coincide to make rock art a universal creative act.

3.3. *The Indian Example*

India has the third largest concentration of rock art, after Australia and Africa. Of the over one million motifs, animals are the most frequent, humans come next, and symbols and designs third. Various pigments are used, such as haematite and other oxides of iron to provide colour in red, yellow, orange or brown. There are also a few instances of black and deep purple, obtained from oxides of magnesium (Twenty-one colours for instance were counted from Bhimbetka — ranging from white, ashy white, creamy white, yellow, yellow ochre, raw sienna, raw umber, orange, dark orange, vermilion, scarlet, light red, dark red, burnt sienna, burnt umber, crimson, dark crimson, purple, chocolate, emerald green to black). Most of these compounds are available in surface deposits, found at a close distance from the paintings. Unlike elsewhere, there is little in India in terms of living tradition of painting on rock surfaces. But the fundamental art tradition persists by way of contemporary 'folk' and 'tribal' in oral ways, such as amongst the Warli, Santhal and Gonds. Thus, there is a great possibility of probable reconstructions about rock art in India within the context of several continuing living traditions, which tell one also about local — oral — histories; these may provide certain hints for understanding the psychology and motivations of societies of yore. Generalisations become possible because of the universality of the medium and the message within holistic thinking whereby alternate methodologies may emerge.

By way of a generalised illustration for the moment, rock art may be seen in terms of certain psychological-metaphysical meanings behind designs, symbols and signs — for instance, in terms of Jungian archetypes, as *mandalas* and so on. The paintings in this context may be seen to arise out of the common universal collective consciousness. They may be approached in terms of symbolic imagery that indicates inner feelings of various kinds, so that outward similarity becomes incidental. For instance, single-line drawings do not reflect the simplicity of 'primitive' people but in fact are representations of extreme sophistication; and the simplicity of the paintings certainly do not arise out of untrained 'naturalism'. The simplicity reflects the freshness of a childlike — not childish – vision, unencumbered by many associations and interests. In this expression of the movement of dynamism, the observer selects what is essential. Similar drawings are made and compared in terms of pre-and post-meditational states that create the same patterns, archetypes and *mandalas* among various cultural groups, including experimentation with schoolchildren in terms of pre-and post-meditational states (Kandinsky 1977; Saraswati et al. 1994).

At a deeper level of understanding, art is the mother of all human emotions, and every work of art is the child of its age. It unites all our senses — sound, sight, touch, smell are interwoven into each other. Painting — art — represents not a visual harmony but colours equally and significantly are also expressions of harmony in sound — music. Colours, as is well known, do trigger off emotional states, such as red may provoke anger, blue is for peace, green is for jealousy, etc. These colours also have sound impacts, and set off psychic vibrations of various orders, and the associated different permutations and combinations.

Paintings are thus symphonies of not only colours, but those of sound, taste, smell, feelings of warmth, coldness, lightness, and of darkness. These works also have the dimensions of horizontality, verticality, and so on. In other words, there is a grammar of painting which may be deciphered, say, in terms of:

1. musical movement,
2. pictorial movement in terms of melodic principles,
3. physical movement,
4. spiritual movement of a triangle, circles, etc., and
5. mysterious and secret manifestations of the unknown.

Traditional art, as opposed to modern art which is extensive and informal, generally has certain qualities, such as:

1. it is formal — it involves intensive laborious formality;
2. it is repetitive and calls for concentration,
3. it has an element of faith and obedience, and
4. there is respect and reverence.

Painting thus may be seen as a combination of a composition like music which is:

1. melodic and simple,
2. symphonic and complex, and so on (Kandinsky 1977).

3.4. *Summary*

The above are many areas which archaeologists and anthropologists, who mainly try to interpret rock art as a socio-cultural phenomenon, may explore the possibilities of seeing rock art in the light of a creative act. This viewpoint is supported by another kind of inferential evidence. A million years ago *Homo sapiens* emerged from *Australopithecus, Homo habilis, Homo erectus*, and so on. There is little evidence, however, that there has been any major evolutionary change in this context in the brain structure of *Homo sapiens*, or that intelligence has evolved from the 'primitive' to the 'modern' in *Homo sapiens*. In terms of technology and language, one may say that there has been 'progress' albeit towards violence — and the crisis of modern civilisation decries even this statement. In the case of art, specifically rock art, if it is seen as a creative act, is there any evolutionary sequence, in a holistic sense at all? The creative impulse is universal, non-hierarchical and non-linear. In this sense art is a manifestation and movement of archetypes of 'invisible' reality. But most academics are not in touch with this cosmic dynamism, this area of the sacred. Archaeologists, anthropologists and other social scientists, continue to be governed mainly by the western or modern alphabet of analysis, of serialisation and comparison of data, and so on, in the study of rock art. Today, humankind has lost touch with some internal truth wherein lies the seed of the future — art seen as an integral vision. Is it really possible to understand rock art as a creative act within this nightmare of materialism and the despair of unbelief that harshly divides life into various unrelated processes? The plea of this chapter has been to discuss these issues, and view rock art — *qua* Art — as integral to life within a non-hierarchical quality that exists amongst all cultures, both of the past and the present.

IV

Man in Nature: An Integral Universe

4.1. *Introduction*

Science, in its quest for a basic oneness of the universe, speaks of many unified field theories, such as symmetry, gauge symmetry, and supersymmtery, gravity and supergravity, strings and superstrings, etc. Basically it suggests that the constituents of matter are interconnected, interrelated and interdependent. The phenomenal world may not merely be understood in terms of isolated entities, because the latter are integral parts of the whole. For example, space-time and energy are inseparable aspects of a single reality, as are energy and matter, wave and particle. In general, without discussing each theory, it is clear that the physical universe is proving to be a seamless texture of inseparable events and entities, organised in accordance with a universal principle that specifies itself in innumerable forms. Now, coherence, elegance, and symmetry — the criteria of beauty and truth — are not only seen by the mathematician and the theoretical physicist, but even seem to be within the reach of the experimentalist (Gandhi 1990).

Physical sciences refer to certain well-known unifying theories in terms of processes that are mathematically describable by linear (and thus soluble) equations. But other, even more extraordinary, testimony to wholeness comes from a new quarter: the investigation of complex dynamic systems (or turbulence), which require for their description non-linear equations. This has given rise to a new department of science embracing mathematics, physics, and numerous fields — what has become known as the science of Chaos (Prigogine and Stengers 1980, 1984). New mathematical revelations have demonstrated in quite unexpected fashion that chaos is simply a superficial mask of the most intricate and entrancing forms of order and pattern, and that its occurrence in nature is determined mathematically. These revelations have been made in the course of new developments in the study of complex systems. In other words, the most important contribution of chaos, in seeking the whole, the overall structure, is to end the reductionist programme in science.

The world picture implied in the theories outlined above is one of a single unbroken whole, governed by a principle of organisation universal to a self-generating system. It specifies itself in a scale, a series of forces and entities, ranging from the simplest to most complex and opening the way to further development on a higher level of organic wholeness. Thus at the micro level, there is a continuous scale of 'complexification' from space-time to those forms transitional between the inorganic and the organic. It is a dialectic scale of opposing, yet overlapping, specific forms, which differentially exemplify a single universal principle of order in continuously increasing degrees of complexity and integral wholeness. But this is only half the picture, which is paralleled by the other half — the macrocosm of the expanding universe, of stars and galaxies — which apparently stands in contrast to the microcosmic level. But the two scales are complementary to each other, inseparable and indispensably linked to each other forming one systematically integrated totality. Were it not so, there would be no planets like the earth, no life, no biosphere, and no observers. In short, the microscopic sequence from hydrogen atoms to macromolecules depends intimately upon the macrocosmic sequence of stellar evolution — ranging in scale from planets, stars, galaxies, galactic clusters, continuously right up to the final hypersphere. Space-time continuum itself is created by the pervasive activity of energy and its complementary matter (Malik 1972).

Obviously, this physical base is intrinsic and has characteristics indispensable to the existence and support of living beings, intelligent creatures capable of observation and reflection; thinkers able to ask questions about themselves and their environment, and so on. One is aware that one exists here and now, and one is apprised of this fact by one's awareness. There is no astonishment to hear this necessary interconnectedness. It is not that the universe exists because one exists and observes it; but one exists because the universe exists and one observes it (Bohm 1980). What is of significance, philosophically or otherwise, is that physicists are discovering principles determining the structure of the universe to be so finely tuned, and the relations between its parts so minutely adjusted to one another that the emergence of intelligent life is incompatible with any other possible arrangement of things and events. Were one to find that the universe could not be other than it is, and that its being so is inseparably bound up with the emergence and evolution of life forms, that would be of the most profound importance.

The recent enunciation by physicists of the Anthropic Cosmological Principle marks a new revolution in the scientific outlook (Harris 1991). The principle states that intelligent life, its existence and observation of its surrounding universe, is essentially involved in what it discovers. This principle has immense philosophical implications, says Harris, as he traces it continuously through physics, biology and psychology. In short, intelligent life is necessarily involved from the very beginning of physical reality and the entire process of natural evolution comes to consciousness of itself in the human mind. This is what Lester-Smith (1975) also stated in his book — as part of the Theosophical Society's theme.

The wholeness of the universe is indicated by the intricate and intimate interdependence of physical and biological facts (e.g. the integral unity of the biosphere), as mentioned in another chapter, which is widely acknowledged today. New evidence of holism also has been disclosed by the study of turbulence and the development of fractal geometry. A contemporary concept of the universe therefore requires a logico-metaphysical theory of wholes. Harris has also thrown light on the argument for God from the fact of the design, which indicates the philosophical implications also of current scientific work.

What is important in current scientific thinking is that there is an intelligent observer watching the universe — man himself. The reason simply is that so far scientists had considered themselves outside the painting; that their observations impinged on the physical world without interfering with it — that it was an automaton that ran according to its own intrinsic laws, without relation to observers. This is the inheritance passed down from the Copernican revolution at the time of the Renaissance and its consolidation in the Newtonian system of celestial and terrestrial mechanics. Ancient or traditional thinkers considered the universe to contain human beings, and the cosmos to be a living organism with an all-pervasive soul — the human souls being individual participants. Modern thinking removed the earth and man from the centre of the universe which was now a machine, no doubt created by God but free of any divine nature, that worked independently of the human mind. Mind and body, Descartes decided, belonged to two separate substances, which had nothing in common except their creator, God. In these circumstances it would indeed have been surprising if a human being found the physical world to be such as to provide the conditions necessary for the existence within it of minds. Intelligent observers — their existence and consciousness — were thus an impenetrable mystery unable to explain their own awareness. These were the metaphysical presuppositions of science in the seventeenth and succeeding centuries. In the mid-nineteenth century, Darwin's theory of evolution changed all this, since human beings were now considered to have evolved from non-human beings or non-living matter. A bridge between matter and mind began to be conceived albeit still in terms of chance variation and natural selection.

It is only in the twentieth century that a revolution in physics has changed all this. The universe is no longer conceived as a machine. Life can now be more easily understood as a development continuous with the non-living. The world so observed provides the conditions for the emergence of intelligent beings. Were there no Intelligence in the universe, there would be neither observers to pronounce their theories nor any who might question their validity. In short, one exists because the universe is the way one observes it to be, and one could not observe it otherwise. What one observes is conditioned not only by the fact of one's existence, but also by the nature and capacities of one's perceptive and intellectual faculties. Thus, observations reveal one's nature, more about the authors than about the subject matter. This selective effect — the limitations of the apparatus, human or otherwise — is true of scientific matters as well.

It is well to remember that one cannot, by any conceivable means, transcend one's own perceptual and intellectual capacities. This suggests a subjectivism for which there is no remedy. One cannot, therefore, have true knowledge even of the physical world. But this leads to an epistemological disaster, and solipsism is all too imminent. Solipsism is however contradictory. It asserts the existence of a self alone, but this assertion has meaning only through a distinction from another. In splendid isolation, therefore, no self can exist — not even God who would be neither infinite nor omnipotent without his creation of the universe.

If Quantum Theory and Relativity undermined the classical dichotomy, it was because they involved the observer inextricably with what was observed. There is no absolute frame of reference, and the observer was a fundamental factor, affecting every measurement whether of space or of time. But observers are human beings, and human beings are animal organisms, evolved from other species under the influence of environmental pressures. This is to say that the conditions of human evolution are contained in the physical world, the nature of which is known to us through human observation alone.

Science now talks of the wholeness of the universe, in which human and all other life is included, dependent on the fundamental physical constants of nature. This interrelatedness has resulted in the pronouncement of the Anthropic Principle in which the unity of the universe — its wholeness — is a basic feature. The Participatory Anthropic Principle was prompted by the Copenhagen interpretation of the Quantum Theory, initiated by Neils Bohr (Kothari 1990). The Anthropic Principle holds that intelligent beings, through their observation and measurements, must participate in the actualisation of the universe at large. The difficulty with this contention, however, is that human bodies and their sense organs, as well as the measuring instruments and any apparatus they may use for experimentation, are macroscopic objects made up of the microscopic entities that quantum physicists investigate. The physical universe could not, therefore, come to be until observed. On the other hand, until the physical world existed there could be no observers because they are consequent upon the generation of life, which again is dependent on the prior occurrence of physico-chemical processes. If physical reality depends on the existence of the mind, and mind depends on the prior existence of physical reality, neither can exist unless both can come into being simultaneously. For, although measurement requires that the quantum system to be measured is coupled with some macroscopic instrument, once this is done, the entire system, including the measuring device, can be regarded as a single quantum system, indeterminate as to its state until the measurement is made and observed. But this again is a subjectivist position. At any rate, scientists have finally realised the obsolescence of the Copernican outlook with respect to human mentality, and the implications of recognising the continuity of matter with mind in a unified world (Harris 1991).

4.2. *Wholeness*

Every whole is a system, however primitive; every system is a whole, structured in accordance with a universal principle of order. That, in consequence, specifies itself in a scale of forms that differ consecutively in the degree of their adequacy to its explicit wholeness. But we are speaking here not of abstract universals, say represented by a genus under which particulars are contained. Undoubtedly this logical schema has useful applications, but its underlying metaphysical assumption is that the real consists of a fortuitous collection of atomic particulars, mutually related externally only. There may be common properties but the elements are related externally only. This kind of assumption was encouraged by Newtonian physics, followed by the empiricist philosophers of the seventeenth and eighteenth centuries. But contemporary physics has abandoned this view, and has adopted one in which the relations between things and processes and the terms in which they relate are intrinsically dependent upon one another, so that they are inseparable in a unified system. A principle of this kind is universal because its influence prevails throughout the system and is universal to its parts. There is thus immanence and transcendence in this concrete universal system (Harris ibid.).

Relations of any kind, whether they are internal in this or are external — in the sense that they fall between their terms and leave them unaffected — can be apprehended only by a conscious subject, because what stands in relation must be grasped all together and as a whole. It follows that elements in a relation must either be objects of some consciousness or must, as a complex totality, be conscious themselves. This is strictly correct, if by existence one means fully actualised being; but, although a relational complex is explicit only at the level of consciousness, there can be lower levels, prior to consciousness and requisite for its emergence in the order of nature — existing implicitly, having potency and latent inter-relativity. These are phases in the dialectical scale prior to the mind, through which the natural whole brings itself to consciousness by its inherent nature to self-completion (Harris ibid.).

Thus, when anything is said to be a whole, it implies not mere congeries of disconnected and separable items, or even just a loose collection; it also implies that the thing spoken of is a unity of coherent parts. Every whole is made up of differences that are combined within it to constitute one totality. A purely blank unity is virtually impossible to conceive. Even the simplest of wholes, therefore, is a unity of differences which in some discernible way intermesh, interlock and interrelate systematically. There is essentially an ordering principle universally determining the interrelations of the elements so that it determines likewise their intrinsic natures, for each must be adapted and adjusted to its neighbours, although they must inevitably differ from one another to avoid complete coincidence.

Within the whole, however, the elements contrast with each other, and therefore inevitably lead to internal conflict and provisional disunity. Finite elements naturally tend to shun one another, emphasising their respective exclusiveness in order to maintain their self-identities. This conflict leads to relative chaos and contingency. This is soon overcome, and unity re-established, only when identity in and through differences is acknowledged. Nevertheless, each identity is defined by the mutual relations and differences, and they are inseparable from one another owing to their mutual implications. This overlap despite difference is what effects their integration into a single whole.

Overlap together with integration of opposites in a wider whole involves self-enfoldment, because the wider whole includes the more fragmentary parts, each implying the other in its own self-maintenance. For example, in a growing embryo, the mutual implication of successive stages is more apparent, as is its explicit realisation in subsequent phases of development.

The self-enfoldment of the earlier forms and processes to create emerging complexifications is also unmistakable. Segmentation of primitive cells continues at the stage of specialisation and functional differentiation, which again is repeated and internalised in each limb and organ. What ensues is a continuous succession of provisional realisations of the organising principle — in this case the mature organism for the embryo — in a series of wholes increasing in complexity and integration.

In other words, elements are double-edged, in at once excluding each other in mutual opposition, and also being complementary to each other in mutual determination and dependence for their several identities. In each, the other is implicit, representing the wholeness principle in a comprehensive way. Such a system is 'open' and cannot thus be present in any one instant or at any one point. It is not a static but dynamic principle — forbidding both isolation and repetition in an abstract manner. The finite element drives itself to transcend its own limits in order to persist in its own being. This dynamic organising principle of wholeness, inorganic or organic, is operative and directive throughout the hierarchy of forms and phases, impelling its partial elements and rudimentary phases towards completion and fulfilment. In this way it leads to the emergence of intelligent behaviour and interpretative understanding, which is the activity of awareness. It is this self-awareness, and the ability to comprehend the whole as a cognitive state of coherent experiencing, which is reflected in thinking processes. Both ontology and teleology — dialectics and holism — are thus necessarily inseparable concepts (Harris 1991.).

Traditionally, teleology referred to some final end. Today, however, because of the ordering principle of an organised whole, teleological explanation is one in which the parts are seen in terms of the whole and not vice versa. It is the opposite of reductionism, requiring conscious intention, deliberate choice, towards completion and fulfilment as a whole. Thus purposive action, described as action by design, is revealed as the endeavour to complete a whole and to bring it to fulfilment. Processes below the level of human purpose, however, may well be teleological without involving any consciousness, but are determined nevertheless by the ordering principle of wholeness, towards intelligent self-awareness. The universe is designed with the goal of generating intelligent observers, leading logically beyond to some supra-personality. This now is exemplified and seen in the relationships between the parts, between energy and matter, between the inorganic and the organic, between body and mind (Harris 1991).

The unity of the universe and the exact nature of the organising principle that governs its order and structure are clearly not indifferent to the emergence and the existence of life and mind. Of all this, nothing is brought home to us with greater force than our ability to discover it. It is not because one is here that the world comes to be so disposed. The reality is the opposite: it is because the world is thus ordered, because the terrestrial environment is so precisely suited to the emergence of life and the development of a biosphere, that human beings have evolved and one is able to investigate the conditions of one's own being. One's observations and reflections are not the efficient cause of what they reveal although, perhaps, these may well be their final cause.

The unity of the physical world seems, as it were, to focus itself on the implication of this intrinsic order from the very start. The point to note is the concurrence and convergence of conditions for intelligent life within a coherent system. The explanation for these interrelationships may be attributed to a divine creator, or to natural explanation; but that is not the point. What these interrelationships show is that there is an interdependence of fact — things — and processes that forbids any attempts to explain matters purely by analysis and reduction to detail (necessary though it may be). One must, therefore, look at the whole for an understanding of the parts. For example, one may see the unbroken continuity between the inorganic and the organic, in a way opposites yet complementary. The influence of the universal is transmitted uninterrupted, through forms of growing complication and self-enfoldment, along a scale of increasing degrees of adequacy in its exemplification, which guarantees that life is the fruition of what is already potentially present in the physical. Its emergence is simply the continuation of an already-evident tendency to build more integral, more versatile, and more self-maintaining wholes.

4.3. *From the Inorganic to the Organic*

It is clear that the systematic wholeness of the physical world is governed by a single principle of order. At the inorganic level, however, its unity is merely implicit since the ordering principle is immanent in its elements; it is not explicit for itself and self-reflective. It comprises elements manifested in the mutual adaptation of disparate elements that register its influence, while they are not apprised of its nature, or otherwise cognisant of each other. If the unity becomes apparent, it is because of the fruit of observation, inference and interpretation as one studies it; it is not apprehended by the physical reality, extended in time and space, merely as such. This ordering principle is dynamic; beyond the physical scale of forms from elementary particles to atoms, molecules, macromolecules, and crystals, the next step is to the living cell, the organism.

An organism is distinguished from the inorganic by the manner in which the organic being maintains its identity, the effect of which is to create and sustain an individual structure. The system of the organism is an open system in dynamic equilibrium with its surroundings. It is a cybernetic system, which maintains itself in a steady state, or homeostasis, by means of a complex and intricate network of negative feedback, or servo-mechanisms. Consequently, with an organism the concrete universal has embarked upon a new phase of self-specification, at a higher level of individuation and integrity, constantly exchanging matter and energy with its environment. Some self-maintenance of form within an energetic flux has been suggested even within the purely physical realm, but the organism is the result of intricate self-enfoldment of the physico-chemical basis by spontaneous adaptation to environing conditions. It is a system containing information preserved by natural selection, which is capable of self-reproduction. This is not to say that physical laws cease to apply or physical forces to operate in the organism. On the contrary, they are essential to its self-maintenance to preserve its dynamic equilibrium (Bateson 1984).

It is still a mystery how organic wholes of this kind originally arose within an entirely inorganic environment. Nowadays it is often maintained that the problem has been solved by the discovery and interpretability of the genetic code. But this certainly cannot explain all regulation, because the genetic code is reduplicated identically in every cell. It cannot account for the ability of the cell to develop differently in different situations. This, it is suggested, may be controlled by something in the organism analogous to a computer programme; the source of which remains totally obscure. Programming a computer, normally, presupposes a human agent. In principle, it may be said, self-reproducing, self-programming computers are possible. But even they would initially require a human or divine inventor and programmer. To contend that such genetic machines could have been evolved by random mutation and natural selection would beg the question because selection can only operate on a self-regulating organism already in existence. Can it possibly arise from unregulated chemical processes through a series of accidental changes, however selected, at that?

The idea of morphogenetic field has been developed in detail and with sophistication by Sheldrake (1980), of formative causation by morphogenetic fields — non-energetic cause of form, beyond physico-chemical explanations of biomorphogenesis. What is significant in all this is the appeal to the notion of field, as is already the case in physics, giving priority in explanation to the whole over the part, in opposition to reductionism. The idea of a field is primarily a structural concept, a formative whole to which the notion of force, or energy, is subordinated. If Einstein geometrised mechanics, Sheldrake's hypothesis seeks to geometrise morphogenetics. It may very well be that the appropriate type of geometry is that discovered by the scientists of Chaos, who have examined complex dynamic systems, to find them to be ordered by 'strange attractors' and to exemplify fractal curves. And so on. Can it therefore not be admitted, surely, that the organising principle of the whole is not a physical or chemical force but a different kind of effect?

4.4. *Organic Evolution*

The unit of life is the cell, which in itself is a highly complex structure, differentiated into proteins and nucleic acids, cytoplasm and nucleus, and containing many other specialised organelles, ribosomes, and so on. This microcosm of life is an unceasing activity, a constant movement of concerted and concatenated cycles of chemical analysis and synthesis. Although each step is understandable chemistry, the integrative organisation is not chemistry at all, but must be explained, if it ever can be, in terms of some holistic principle. It might be referred to the genetic code in the DNA of the nucleus, but whence genetic code originates, or how, nobody yet knows. It is itself an organised system the source and principle of which has still to be discovered.

Evolution of life progressed from such unicellular organisms, from relative uniformity to differentiation and specialisation of organs, which represents an advance in the degree of complexity and organisation, marking another step forward in the scale of forms. The accumulated evidence is so massive that living species have evolved from progenitors of different genotypes, and are still evolving, that the theory is now firmly established and its truth is automatically assumed by biologists of repute. Likewise, the evidence is ubiquitous and copious that evolution is promoted by chance mutation and natural selection.

The reference now is to organismic genetics, for which there is enough evidence, say adaptation and adjustment to environmental conditions is inherent in the very nature of life. To be selected, a system must be better adapted for survival than others with which it competes for the available energy and sustenance. Moreover, geneticists have established that single genes do not control or determine single characteristics, but that the chromosome functions as a whole, as does, in fact, the entire genome. It is now apparent that 'survival value' is equivalent to more efficient self-maintenance and more completely self-determining wholeness. What evolves is always the organic system and nothing less; and what evolution produces is increased self-determining adaptation, increased capacity for relevant variation and selective reaction to circumstances, in short, increased versatility and freedom. A whole with these characteristics is a more adequate manifestation of the self-specifying universal expressing itself in the organism as well as in the cosmos, than is any inorganic purely physical or chemical whole. Organic systems of this kind more fully reflect the nature of the principle of organisation immanent in life and in the universe as such, and approach more nearly its free self-determination (Harris 1991).

Basically, all behaviour is instinctive, and purposive in that it pursues a definite goal characteristic of the particular instinct — eating, mating, migrating, nesting, etc. Behaviour may be characterised by relevant variation, as it blossoms in the higher species, into sensory-motor, perceptual, and intelligent learning. It is an informed activity, in terms of structural organisation and perceptual enlightenment not to specific stimuli alone but a response to a total situation, which must be grasped as a whole if the behaviour is to be appropriate. The inner, mental aspect of instinctive behaviour and its intelligent outcome belongs to a further phase of the self-differentiation of the universal whole;

one that renders it aware of itself and its own relational structures. Behaviour is foreshadowed below the mental level in the living processes of metabolism and physiology which, as they evolve, fold back upon themselves to produce new wholes and more developed forms. When the human level, with its cognitive capacity of discrimination, definition and comprehension is reached, this aspect attains to the pitch of explicit self-consciousness, thought. The principle and agency of organisation is inherent from the start and is itself the immanent principle ordering the cosmos as a whole. To understand behaviour in the context of evolution, it is important to understand the part played by consciousness in animal and human activity. (Harris 1991).

The biosphere differentiates itself, through the process of evolution, into a scale of forms that are mutually opposed, mutually complementary species, genera, orders, and classes — distinct examples of the universal organic system, in differing and progressively intensifying degrees of integrity and complex unity. But is evolution 'progressive'? Some have argued that it is not, that it is simply the constant change of living forms subject to natural selection under environmental pressures. There is general agreement among biologists that evolution has not proceeded in a straight line. There is equally widespread agreement that different species have descended from common ancestors, and that orthogenesis must have occurred in ramifying directions.

The gamut of living species constitutes a dialectical scale of forms that progressively express with increasing adequacy the principle of order and unity immanent, not only in the organism, but also in the environment, in the biosphere as a whole. The scale proceeds towards more intelligent and self-conscious forms by way of the development of yet another aspect of its evolutionary advance, namely, behaviour. Both metabolism and physiological process are continuous with behaviour, as is apparent from protozoa onwards, directed to the protection and care of the young. In later stages, the behaviour tends to become more and more gregarious, as is to be expected when it centres on the family group. With *Homo sapiens* all this blossoms out into vastly more complex and significant behaviour, and only at the human level is social conduct organised in that distinctive fashion we have come to recognise as political or civilised.

4.5. *Biosphere, Organism and Environment*

So far one has considered evolution as merely concerned with the organism and its changing form. Life, on the other hand, is a dynamic equilibrium, maintained between organism and environment, so that there is continual intercourse between the two. They form one organic whole and cannot be strictly separated. Evolution is a process involving both together. The evidence is widespread, of this mutual interdependence between living forms and environment. Organic wholeness is not confined to living units. A drop of water can contain a miniature ecosystem, as does every natural pond. But no such ecosystem in turn is altogether self-contained, it is further linked to another system, and so on and on. In the end, the planet as a whole is one ecological totality, changes everywhere affecting conditions everywhere else. This is limiting one's context to organic earth; but one could link it further to the solar system, and other stars and galaxies — the cosmos.

The earth as a whole presents the characteristics of a living being, which in the scientific tradition of the West, has been proposed by James Lovelock (1979, 1988) as the "Gaia hypothesis" which is fairly wellknown by now. It is the biosphere which actually is a living whole cybernetically controlling its earthly environment to maintain the conditions most favourable to its own preservation. The idea is not new whether in the eastern or western tradition. Without giving details of this hypothesis, the evidence offered leaves one in no doubt that biosphere, hydrosphere, atmosphere, and lithosphere are all in intimate organic relationship and interchange, and that they constitute a single organic whole. If the hypotheses of Lovelock and Sheldrake are taken together, very promising and intriguing consequences emerge.

The concepts of the Gaia and morphogenetic fields together would contemplate a field covering the entire planet and directing all the fantastically complex interrelated levels and phases of morphogenesis, with their cybernetically controlled homeostases. It would make the whole earth one organism with an eminent degree of autonomy and self-determination — a freely acting individual. In that case, a planetary field would be the source of all subordinate fields, and the question of origin would be pushed back to become one of cosmological evolution. As suggested above and elsewhere, the earth cannot be treated in isolation from the solar system, nor the galaxy, or the galaxy from the universe. This is what physicists suggest also, that the universe is one system and its fundamental laws and forces can be traced back to a single principle, immanent at its origins in the Big Bang (Malik 1989a). If so, then we must presume that there is ultimately only one universal morphic field. It would be a universal morphe, pervasive over and regulating all subsidiary fields — such as notions mentioned as metaphysical options and theories of traditional speculative philosophy, Plato's Idea of the Good, Aristotle's Form of Forms as eternal activity, and in itself an active reason.

Evolution, in this context, assumes the aspect rather of a process of maturation, in which the development of sense organs and perception in symbiotic organisms marks, as it were, the way in which Gaia gradually, and, by dialectical stages, brings herself to consciousness of her setting within the world and of her own integral unity. She brings consciousness in the mentality of her member organisms, and this is at the same time the coming to consciousness of the entire cosmos, of which Gaia herself is a specific phase. This again conforms to the account given above of the nature of the whole. It must in principle and in fact be complete, which cannot be totally fulfilled unless it is fully and explicitly for itself (self-aware), i.e. it is in conscious knowledge — the realm of self-reflective intelligence. The unitary whole that the physicists have discovered the universe to be is now revealed as not simply physical but also alive.

To sum up, so far, the universal organising principle has specified itself in an extended series of subsidiary and provisional wholes, from elementary particles, atoms, and molecules to viruses and bacteria, to sentient and conscious organisms, each in its own degree expressing the implicit order and exemplifying the totality of which it is a dialectical moment. In this way, the succession of phases constitutes a graded scale of overlapping, mutually implicating, and interrelated forms issuing as intelligent minds. The major divisions of the series are thus themselves continuous, each incorporating its predecessor and each, in its continuous outgrowth from its forebears, is dominated by the ordering principle. It is first manifested in the physical world, then in the biosphere, and subsequently in the noosphere, where it becomes aware of itself in explicit conscious knowledge. To achieve the capacity for more self-determined action, intentionality and a higher degree of internality and centralisation of external differences is necessary. Now, a further phase transition is required, leading to a new threshold.

4.6. *Beyond Duality*

If the life-world is all-inclusive, and normally the world, as perceived by common sense, is regarded as 'external' to the mind, it is because at that level 'the mind' is imagined as a function of the brain and is objectified along with the body. The subsequent attempt to explain consciousness that is seen as a result of the transmission from external objects of physical impulses through the senses to the brain, therefore naturally proves incoherent. Consequently, it has brought in the history of philosophy only epistemological disaster. What has been overlooked is the self-transcendent character of Consciousness, aware at once of the presented object and of its own relation to it. Thus, as it distinguishes subject from object, it also grasps their relation within the whole, which together they constitute. The mind, becoming self-conscious, is capable of developing the implications of such holism in philosophical reflections.

The world disclosed in observation and interpreted in science and philosophy reveals itself as dialectical scale of forms, primarily in experience, ranging from sentience through perception and reflection to comprehension. This is why we cannot get outside the consciousness that arises from primitive sentience. But why is it that the life-world is an all-inclusive whole? It is because the physical world, not speaking only of science, is indeed an all-inclusive whole — finite but unbounded — outside of which there is nothing. The experienced world is that same whole become aware of itself. What 'corresponds' to it, therefore, are simply the prior phases of its own development. These go back beyond sentience for the very reason that sentience has revealed itself as the form of the body, the reflection and registration of organismic activity, integral to the biosphere and rooted in a physico-chemical environment. The object of the mind is, therefore, its own self in becoming, and the subject is no less than the world become conscious of itself. Subject and object are identical, and fact corresponds to theory in so far as the theory is what the fact itself has become in bringing itself to consciousness. This conclusion reveals itself in reflection upon science and experience in general at the philosophical stage.

Throughout the course of the above argument one has traced wholes in hierarchical progression, and each succeeding whole has brought with it a new form — in the scale of forms — carrying a supervening quality not displayed at previous levels. The complex wholes that appear at every level display the emergent quality and the new capacities of life, impossible at any of the prior stages. Life is the form assumed by the integrated metabolic processes (Harris 1991).

When these wholes develop and combine as physiological

processes, integrated by vascular and neural functioning at a new threshold of intensity, a further form emerges, namely, sentience. Atoms and molecules are energy systems, and it is the form of the energetic complex that displays the peculiar properties. The proposition now being advanced is that this integration of physiological processes at a high degree of complexity and intensity assumes a new form, the experience of feeling. And this new form is sentience or feeling. Perhaps it could as well be called a distinct 'state' of the system, as gaseous, liquid, and solid are distinct states of chemical substances.

This doctrine has the advantage of disposing once and for all of the problems attendant upon body-mind dualism. There is indeed only one reality but it displays itself in a series of forms with different degrees of unity and wholeness. At each successive level, the entity or entities concerned display different qualities and capacities, although they presuppose and involve all the prior forms and degrees of actualisation. When we reach the level of the mind, these qualities are sensory, as at every prior level they are not. In this way one may say that there is a duality of degree in intensity of integration between the exclusively physiological, and a corresponding duality of qualitative form, but there is no dualism of substantive existence. The reference is to the continuity of the dynamic principle and its energia, its organising activity, operating at successive levels — becoming aware of itself and its own spontaneous activity at every stage structured as a scale of forms — the physical spatio-temporal field, the biotic morphogenetic field, and now the psychical field (Stiskin 1972).

4.7. *Self-reflection and Self-transcendence*

In the scale of forms that constitutes the self-differentiation of the cosmic order there are two critical transitions. The first is from the physico-chemical to the metabolic, marking the emergence of life. The second is from the sentient and perceptive to the fully self-conscious and reflective. Neither of these is abrupt or unheralded. Life is foreshadowed by crystalline and organic molecular structures; reflection is preceded by immediate perception. But the crucial awakening is that of reflective deliberation, because here for the first time the universal principle of organisations, as such, begins to become explicitly aware of itself as reason (Harris 1991).

The universal principle is dynamically self-specifying. It manifests itself first in a physical universe, then in an organic totality, and subsequently in a known world or noosphere (de Chardin 1959). Only then is its concrete potential fully actualised, because only then does its systematic structure become explicit. It becomes aware of itself as conscious subject, reflective upon itself, upon its own experience of itself and of the world. This is self-transcendent awareness, that comprehends its own finite limits and its own infinite scope and potential. The miracle of consciousness is self-transcendence. It must, as it were, project itself beyond itself and alienate itself from itself. Moreover, to be conscious of an object is to cognise it in a context both spatial and temporal. But to be aware of a temporal context is at once to remember and to anticipate. For instance, all consciousness of time involves such transcendence — as does space — because the succession of events can be apprehended as a succession only if the series is grasped as a whole, which means that the apprehending subject can never be confined to any one event, past, present, or future. It must be transcendent above, or beyond, all of them.

Without getting into a long and detailed debate about the self, 'I', self-consciousness and so on, we may note that while awareness happens in our nervous systems, it is happening not just there. While happenings do involve one's body, they involve an organic whole, and the awareness of the 'happenings' is the form taken by that wholeness at a high degree of integration. The form of feeling, becomes consciousness when it is organised by attention and judgment, identifying, distinguishing, and relating objects. This involves the ego, which is the whole come to consciousness of itself as 'I'. As such, it can and does distinguish itself from its objects, including its body, in which the neural happenings occur, in order to be aware of them as physiological. Indeed, one is not a separate or separable entity from one's body. One is identical with it, or rather one is its identity as a functioning whole — the self-cognisant form of the principle of unity and organisation immanent in it. As the self-awareness of the universal principle of wholeness in the body, the 'I' has become transcendent over the objects of its consciousness.

Awareness of self is reflective consciousness, in which the subject becomes its own object. Reflection leads to deliberation and criticism. It is essential to all morals and politics, thought and action. It is what gives rise to questioning and wonder, and so is equally essential to all science and philosophy, and because it is the root of the awareness of the distinction between the finite and the infinite, also to religion. This self-reflection is the outcome of the bringing to self-consciousness of the organising principle of the whole through the process of its own self-specification. Consequently, its self-awareness is the awareness of that process, its knowledge of its own concrescent nature and the way which must specify it is universality; in other words, it is the knowledge of the world of nature.

4.8. *Nature of Science and Wholeness*

Science begins in wonder and the interrogation of nature, which presuppose reflection; without reflection there can be no science, and without science knowledge of the world remains in its infancy. The self-reflective character of science is often overlooked. The Newtonian world view provided no mechanics of the mind, and the celestial mechanics made no room for consciousness. The scientific observer viewed the world from the outside, and within that world no provision was made for any consciousness. The fruit of this in philosophy led to materialism and dualism; but both may be refuted by the fact that these theories would not be possible without self-reflection. Both, whether rationalist or empiricist, fail to provide a viable theory of knowledge, of how the mind, in its separation from matter, can encompass a representation of an external world, how the world can get into the mind, or how a mechanical material process can be miraculously converted into a cognitive awareness. Meanwhile, the scientific disregard of the observer leaves science itself beyond the reach of scientific explanation.

It was at the end of the nineteenth century that the Newtonian 'paradigm', which was obstructing scientific progress, was broken by a new revolution, which required a more holistic approach; and this came with Relativity and Quantum theories. Neither of these could disregard the observer. For Relativity, the relative velocity of the observer determines the value of every measurement, and for Quantum Theory, the observer and the measurement of specific quantities have become inseparable from the very actuality of elementary particles. The reality of elementary particles is restricted to the act of observation by means of instruments that are themselves composed of multitudes of such particles, and by observers who have evolved from organic species similarly composed. Thus the reality of the elements is made to depend on the activity of that to which they are elementary. (Reference is to Copenhagen interpretation of the Quantum Theory — Neils Bohr, Schrodinger Wave Function, Heisenberg's Indeterminacy Principle, Bell's Theorem, Henry Stapp's work and so on; all these works show that the unity of the universe and the apparent dependence of physical reality upon subjective experience are two aspects of a single fact). It is now being suggested that reflective awareness, in the guise of observation and interpretation, is constitutive of the very being of the universe. It goes beyond both subjectivism (dispensing with physical reality altogether) and phenomenalism (that leaves reality beyond our ken as an unknowable thing-in-itself).

If the universe is an indivisible whole, and as such must by its very nature be complete, and if, as has been argued, the completion of a whole necessarily involves its being brought to consciousness, the danger of falling into solipsism is averted. For although hidden variables have been ruled out, the indeterminate properties of particles are admitted by the Copenhagen theories to be latent, or potential, before they are observed. In other words, the actualisation of what is potential at the physical and biological levels should await the activity of observation and the efflorescence of knowledge. This in no way precludes the prior reality of the physical and biological world, because the very experience of a physical and biological world as an indivisible systematic whole implies and necessitates the self-differentiation of that whole as a scale of forms, in the more elementary of which what emerges at later stages is already implicit. The existence of both macroscopic and microscopic worlds is thus established. Of course Quantum Theory, with its principle of indeterminacy and theory of probability has led some reflective scientists to conclude that physical reality may well be a welter of energy on which the appearance of order supervenes only because we impose upon it a stochastical mathematic — the universe is thus a subjective fabrication, the actual nature of which we can never discover. If that were so, how would one explain one's ability to discover this, that one is emerging from an allegedly chaotic matrix?

If reality is in principle unknowable, one is left solely with what one's own consciousness presents. In the history of science, a number of worldviews have arisen in succession, each to be rejected by subsequent thinkers, often as palpably false and ridiculous. Instead of seeing this succession as a series of fantasies, one may see it as a dialectical succession of provisional conceptual schemes, unfolding as a scale of forms, in which each progressively more adequately explicates a conceptual whole; and each scheme is itself a particular stage in the self-discovery of the actual world. Scientific discoveries are no more than approximations, and yet each series of scientific revolutions deploys a series of worldviews that increase from each to the next in coherence and unity. The cosmic whole differentiates itself and brings itself to fruition in self-awareness. The universal principle of organisation immanent in all things manifests itself in a cosmic pattern, in which it is particularised in successive wholes, constituting various scales as self-enfoldment. In this way the world comes to consciousness of itself and explicitly realises its essential nature, in its reflective awareness and interpretative conceptualisation by intelligent human beings.

This world-concept is of a universe continuous and indivisible in space and time, deployed as a scale of comprehensive phases at successive levels; physical, chemical, biotic, sentient, and noetic, within each of which there is an analogous subordinate scale. All subsequent phases embody all their predecessors, and the latest sublates the whole prior scale, which in it is brought to a higher degree of actuality and self-sufficiency. The noetic level reflects all the rest, for not only does it envisage and comprehend all the prior phases but it is also realised in the practical and intellectual activity of living beings, who are at the same time both organisms and physico-chemical systems, each drawing to a focus within itself its total environing world.

4.9. *Conclusion: Context of all Contexts*

The most significant revolutionary effect of the physics of Relativity and Quantum Theory has been to generate a new view of the physical universe as a single, indivisible, generate whole, in which phenomena and events are necessarily interdetermining. It is a single system governed by a unitary dynamic principle, augmented by the results of findings in biology and ecology. The whole is not an undifferentiated unity, a blank; its integrity depends on the interconnection of parts internally related one to another, in accordance with an organising principle. In the dimension of time, this principle is dynamic, generating a graded scale of subordinate wholes in which it is specified. The dynamic dialectically related forms are specific exemplifications of the universal dynamic principle governing the whole. A design in the sense of pattern or structure, is obviously such a whole. Its parts and elements are interrelated systematically according to some principle of order and arrangement. The whole which contemporary physics has revealed, therefore, necessarily involves the generation of its own observation by intelligent beings, in whose minds it brings itself to consciousness.

The whole or design is not ultimately fragmentary; in principle it must be complete. Deployed in scale of forms, it must ultimately culminate in a completed totality. Nor can its self-manifestation be only partial. In principle, and in fact, there must be a culmination of the scale that is both its final phases and all-encompassing — an absolute, actual whole, totally self-contained and self-sufficient, and completely realised. It must sublate in itself the entire process of its self-specification, so that end and process overlap. It would be a mistake to imagine that this culmination can, or needs to, appear in time, for it must encompass all time in itself while nevertheless enduring throughout time. It does so in the same way as human consciousness transcends the present and includes at once both the present and the past while it continues to endure and participate in the flux. The culminating phase of the scale does this likewise, for it is the fulfilment of the organising principle universal to every phase and every existent. It is immanent throughout all process, for every process is a manifestation of its self-differentiation, contributing at its specific level and in its peculiar degree to the final consummation (Harris 1991).

Finally, there are three characteristics of the universal principle of organisation that need to be emphasised:

i.   It is in principle absolutely complete.

ii. Its completeness involves total explication in absolute self-consciousness.

iii. The final phase, like all others, must transcend and at the same time include and comprehend all its predecessors, that is, the final phase must be, and yet transcend, the sum-total of all the parts (Harris 1991).

The final phase must be such as no conception or existence can exceed it. This is the perfect being, totally complete, totally self-sufficient and self-sustaining — than that which a greater is inconceivable. As totally explicit in transparent self-consciousness, this consummation of the cosmic scale is an omniscient mind — the Alpha and Omega of all being. Because the universal principle is immanent in every part, it is what generates and determines the nature of every entity, and its activity is nothing more nor less than its own self-differentiation in and as the spatio-temporal world. But its ultimate realisation is a transcendent comprehension and self-conscious realisation of the whole. It is thus all-creative and all-powerful, as well as all-knowing and absolutely self-complete.

All this is necessarily entailed by the very concept of design. If God — *purusha* — is conceived as the absolute universal principle of order, its manifestation *prakriti* — is in and as the universe, and transcends all finite phases. The argument from design, as a proof of God's existence, can be justified in this manner, without any inference from a contrived plan to a Supreme Architect (unless these phrases are used metaphorically). God's knowing and conceiving are immediately and simultaneously his/her self-manifestation in and as the whole world — his/her creative power, his/her self-revelation. This conclusion has the rare advantage that it is not a resort to God as a cloak to cover our ignorance, but it is the logical consequence of the very nature of our knowledge and of the structure of the universe as discovered by empirical science. The latter, however, is not the eternal truth, or at least not all of it. Whatever the alternate theories which replace one another, it is still a unitary system, this universe with its dialectical series of ascending forms. Moreover, science is but one facet of a wider and more complex noosphere. It is inseparable from society and all that it entails. Humanities and social sciences, with philosophical systems in conjunction with science, need to pursue the deeper implications of the organising principle.

V

A Question of Consciousness

Consciousness as the basis of all existence has been referred to earlier in various contexts. This chapter elaborates this general aspect, raising some questions which the reader may like to explore further. Consciousness is not a thing that may be intellectually grasped or is easily definable. One is in it, like one is within the painting one intends to draw. It provides the matrix within itself for an infinitely vast and dynamic dimension which manifests and expresses itself in a myriad ways. It could, perhaps, even be viewed as a kind of perception, an awareness which allows one's being to function — in as wide a meaning as possible; or as an energy which may be channelised in many ways, depending upon the individual or collective mind-brain set or subset or even a no-set. Consciousness in its manifested form appears as a narrow version because it identifies and locates itself in terms of the bio-social memory patterns symbolically encoded. It continues, however, to retain the ability to create and imaginatively manifest further. Intellectual-cerebrating activity too is governed by the presence of primordial awareness or Consciousness. Nevertheless, while it includes all these realms of existence, and forms the basis of every phase of mental intelligence, intuition, insight and a psychic life, neither all of these areas put together nor existence jointly or separately is definable as or refers *per se* to Consciousness.

Consciousness is beyond all of its encompassing nature, as it refers to an essence. It is beyond words, being sometimes indicated intimately in one's existential-experience states; e.g. as expressed especially in works of creativity, such as poetry, music, works of science, and even in the mundane life during intense aesthetic experiences. One is told that these intimations are closely akin to, if not the same, as mystic states, that they are revelations expressed variously in many cultures, in the Jungian sense of appearing from the Collective Unconscious. It is during these momentary states which many dismiss as merely subjec- tive auto-suggestive experiences not worth examining, that the limited subjectivity of the everyday 'I' — the ego — disappears, bringing immense peace and tranquillity. In that state, there remains neither the experienced nor the experiencer (both ac- tually are the same). There is a totality of experiencing by itself, minus the little self. This is an intimation of the personal-im- personal Consciousness. In a way this total Subjectivity, this One-ness is true Objectivity, and is universal in character. In these moments of stillness of the mind, or no-mind state, dis- cursive thought as time and as ego is non-existent.

Such impersonal revelations of Consciousness are truly ob- jective, speaking in phenomenal terms. In matters academic, intellectual, objectivity is stressed emphatically. But objectivity is a relative matter, its existence and nature being dependent upon various attachments and affinities of the ego, individually or collectivelly both at the descriptive and analytical level. All analysis, of necessity, has to divide reality into binary or other fragmentary systems temporarily, for operational or contextual purposes. Language systems, too, can function only by splitting reality into the subjective and the objective. But the fact that these divisions are provisional is often forgotten; and arbitrari- ness, over a period of time, comes to be taken as reality. In contrast, in Consciousness there is only the One, call it Objec- tivity or Subjectivity. The moments of Consciousness are authen- tic moments; the pseudo-empiricist scientific ones are not. In the moment of Consciousness the person does not exist. Existence begins once again when thought re-enters — a com- mentary afterwards — about that moment and it is recorded in

the brain within a particular cultural context. Despite the varying cultural expressions of these states in different contexts, the
experience is verifiable and comparable, perhaps at the non-
verbal level. It is so subjective as not to allow one to compare
and discuss it, as some would have us believe.

The assertion, therefore, that raising questions about Consciousness is not scientific, and therefore Consciousness cannot
possibly be discussed, does not hold water. By analogy, any
experience, say the taste of water, eating, loving, swimming,
any aesthetic experience cannot be described in words. Yet it is
possible to explain these states through symbols, signs, images
not only from within the culture but through universal metaphors, or archetypes. In this sense, Consciousness is explainable. It is of course unique every time, both unique and universal. These 'mystic' moments of Consciousness are known
only when Consciousness is free from the erroneous identification with a person-hood. In this revelation of the universe, its
intrinsic nature, Consciousness attains a joyous state, and is
once again itself. Freedom, that humankind always speaks
about, is not available for the person, which is a mere shadow,
a false entity (Malik 1989a). Freedom is not for the person but
from person-hood. It is attained through an aware negation of
all limited but engrossing identities.

Consciousness is always present. One lives in certainty of it,
just as once having seen the sun, even when the clouds cover
it, one lives in the certainty of its existence. One becomes aware
of this state when one becomes totally attentive, in the moment
of 'what is'. These reflective or contemplative states are not
quantifiable, yet have a quality that is undoubtedly knowable
non-intellectually. In this Witnessing Consciousness, one dis-
tances oneself both from the self and the other. These states are
available to all, and they are the creative states that produce any
authentic, lasting results in everyday life.

Apart from aesthetic experience, this awareness allows one
to distance one's self from the impulsive reactive unconscious

state and, thereby, cuts off the chain reaction within which one is normally caught. Anger, for example, tends to fade out when one becomes conscious of this emotional state. This is true of moments of pleasure as well, which as thought-forms tend to continue, while trying to get out of them at the same time. These moments of awareness allow the task at hand to be completed, and the results wanted happen faster. This is simpler than is thought normally, when one feels 'involved' — the latter being a kind of entanglement even according to the dictionary meaning! True communication thrives at this level of awareness, which is impersonal, and it is during these rare moments that one feels as if true understanding happens with regard to the subject, situation, or the person. Without it, one is asleep, distracted by circumstances, conditions of life, clash of egos, etc. This is true even of the so-called rational actions of man, which are inevitably intertwined with emotional, instinctive and intuitive forces that one is not aware of. To free one's self from any of these negativities, any or all of these experiences need to be accepted, and acknowledged consciously — not self-consciously. Denial of them makes these pain-pleasure experiences not only to disappear into the unconscious but remain there in fermentation to worry one every now and then.

Consciousness, which governs all of one's activities, needs to acknowledge itself. It is the whole, unified, absolute omnipresence, omniscient energy. This is why whenever one focuses on whatever one chooses, it grows. For example, if the focus is on negativities like anger, they grow; if on positive areas like a smile or joy, these also grow. This is because it is an actual energy that permeates every aspect of the universe, visible in its effects, just like electricity or light which is known only through its manifestations or the media of manifestation. Person-hood obscures all of these insights, limiting one through the various cultural forms, and making one myopic in one's expression. Fragmented manifestation of Consciousness causes agony, anguish and alienation, because knowledge within the perspective of Consciousness is unified and related. This interconnectedness and relatedness is Divinity, or Pure Activity, of the Self, Consciousness minus the self.

* * * * * *

Why is one aware, of anything at all? Would it not be simple without Consciousness? What is awareness, consciousness? For many decades science has ignored any inquiry into this energy, or its process. And anthropologists, sociologists and others who deal with the human phenomenon, do not even consider it fit to be taken into account within their respective subjects; either it is taken for granted as given, or is to be dealt with by religious or philosophical disciplines. At best it is dealt in an evolutionary sense as an epiphenomenon of the increasing complexity of organic matter, as a growth through time with man at the apex. This is similar to the view of intelligence, which also is considered to be a gradual outcome of evolutionary, material organic process. The view that intelligence, consciousness existed first as a primordial substance so to speak and manifested itself in different forms is seldom entertained within the social and human sciences, being dismissed either as a non-scientific or non-empirical assumption, since scientific 'evidence' is to the contrary. In such dismissive attitude, the fact is ignored that science is itself based on certain a *priori* assumptions that are questionable but seldom looked into. Consciousness is mainly considered to belong to the realm of mysticism, occult, philosophy, ecstasy — some airy-fairy area of a meta-realm discourse.

In recent years, however, Consciousness has come under the increasing attention of the neuro-sciences and of those who are scientifically studying the phenomenon of the brain as a physio-neuro organ. Considerable literature is available in the medical sciences on the experiment, done in this field, but anthropologists do not consider these studies imported enough for the understanding of man. It is as if the socio-cultural aspects are independent of the neurological-psychological and their chemical processes which in fact are at the base of the mental activities in the individual and the collective.

Taking these processes into account in our study of man and society would help us explain some phenomena. For example, at the level of social behaviour, consider dual social organisation, moieties and such other recorded social units. These peculiar functioning groups appear contradictory to the common norm. One might, however, explain these social groupings as outward expressions of the internal dominating binary system which governs human psychology in general. Some have indeed tried to explain these systems in terms of binary systems (Louis Dumont and Levi-Strauss talk about them in structural-functional terms), but generally see them as irreconcilable opposites, confrontational dualities. Hardly any effort has been made to view them as reconcilable complementary modes that leave alternatives open for societies to function in different contexts. It is important to note, beyond the controversies of social scientists, that all confrontational dichotomies functionally arise, in all probability, from localised area and not the whole of the psycho-physiological brain system. But this system of dualism, built into the brain in the evolutionary system for operational and appropriate purposes, has in modern man become the dominating theme of overspecialisation at the expense of the functioning of the rest of the brain. Hence have arisen the various external social and cultural manifestations in systems that operate within the dual system.

One neuro-physiological study suggests that on stimulating the brain, it takes half a second for consciousness to appear, i.e., one is aware of the stimulus which has already taken place as a reaction or response when electrodes were inserted in the cortex of patients. This is to say, when someone taps one on the shoulder, one reacts immediately; but one becomes aware of the whole thing a while (half-a-second) later, and turns around. This kind of consciousness, which has been called an afterthought, may possibly be seen also as a process of verbalisation, thought-process, languaging, the symbolisation of the entire process of neuro-physiological stimulus-response situation which has already taken place. That is to say, as socio-cultural beings we symbolise everything in order to record and then react from the stored memory as cultural response. These are conditioned responses which are dependent upon the ability to interpret, to comment through compare-contrast processes. Everything functions during such a 'stimulus-response' situation within the framework of thought or a linguistic symbolic statement which appears as a commentary or, to use a more picturesque phrase, a chatter in the head. The awareness of the 'me' also follows a similar pattern. The situation of a reflexive nature becomes immediately a thought, feeling, experience; it is no longer consciousness, but self-consciousness. This is what one normally calls being aware. In the existing cultural set-up, while neuro-physiological 'stimulus-response' processes are going on non-stop at many levels (otherwise we might consider ourselves dead!), their perennial translation into symbols restricts the entry of a great deal of information into self-consciousness. This may be verified in one's daily behaviour within known — secure — categories.

In the unconscious or subconscious, vast amount of processes go on non-stop, trying to sort out the bombardment of 'stimulus-response' activities at both the macro and micro levels — sub-cellular, cellular, neurophysical and even thought processes. One is seldom aware of these goings on, which are very deep rooted even psychologically. The division between consciousness and unconsciousness also is neither clear nor well-studied, easily known or understood. Along with this vast area of ignorance, little is itself known of the large canvas of cultural-philosophical general assumptions of world views and so on which are input from one's birth onwards and thereby govern unconsciously one's behaviour. This cultural-cumulative inheritance interconnects the various ways of all human communities. For example, fire, language, food, etc. are the common heritage.

They are separate culturally but are diffused and have been carried across communities for a long time within a vast cultural umbrella which may be labelled as cultural-magnetic field.

The self-consciousness of the person, his will or choice, is generally a mere surface ripple of the vast ocean of physiological-psychological processes. One's reactions on the surface are often a cover for what is hidden in the unconscious, like the surface waves that belie the vast turmoil within the vast ocean. A person is a collectivity after all, and his thoughts are conditioned in the symbolic-psychological sense within the binary framework of the 'survival' model which governs the reptilian-mammalian brain. My self-awareness also is not a straightforward knowledge of me. For instance, whether I scream on being hurt or growl or hold my peace depends on my cultural conditioning. If I have a case history of repeated conditioning with regard to a psycho-physical hurt, my personal response is likely to be to hide my reaction.

While ignoring the fact that we are utterly ill-informed about Consciousness, social sciences also overlook the fact that today more and more of the mental states — the symbolic structures — govern the functioning of the physiological organic self. In the sciences — such as that the dichotomies and dualities governing modern man's life and thought are being questioned — fundamentally one is a psycho-somatic self; the division between the mental and the physical, material and non-material, empirical (practicality of facts as given by the gross senses) and philosophical, brain and body. These basic questions are being raised in the sciences because the two — the within and without — are intimately connected in physiological processes. It is increasingly becoming clear that the psycho-somatic being is a package deal, and in the modern world it is the mental, symbolic-languaging process that dominates life. To continue to believe in pure matter, physico-chemical interactions to the extent that one cannot discriminate between pure experience and thought is to be closed to the new discoveries. Perhaps, thoughts and feeling are not two separate areas really, since feelings are expressed and translated into words which trigger off physiological processes also. For instance, thinking of a lemon makes one salivate even though there is no lemon in sight; or the word 'anger' triggers off a chain of chemical reactions that are released as conditioned responses. These are cyclic processes, intertwined always.

Then there is the relative nature of subjectivity-objectivity. The subject affects and alters what is external to him/her, as much as the external affects him/her (in fact he/she is always at effect, unconsciously in his/her behaviour pattern). Whether it is man and man, man and nature, nature and nature, science tells us of the ever dynamic state of order-disorder-order states, of change and flux, of constant motion, of unpredictability, uncertainty and in a sense even of inevitability; all these form the basis of the structure-function of all in the universe. Professional scientists know this. But one may realise it also through the study and observation of the personal self, and of the ancient texts all over the world, both textual and oral. The Buddhists, for example, point to the 'non-self', which is not a permanent self since at every moment it is changing, becoming a new aggregate of functions and characteristics albeit 'normally' one functions through this culturally conditioned self which is taken to be an enduring entity. (It is really a state of stupor, sleep, an unconscious state in which the bottom-line or the paradigm itself becomes one's addictive identity).

The identity of 'me' has both negative and positive psychological states that appear as true, enduring, permanent in the sense of being in time and spatially located with reference to the body as the 'me' and 'not me'. This is so ingrained from the time one is born that one clutches to it despite evidence to the contrary, such as that there is no proof of this psychosomatic apparatus belonging to 'me'. The notion has been reinforced by one's being told from childhood that one is this body and name, repeatedly. Science tells us that all energy (The First Law of

Thermodynamic states that no energy is lost in the universe, it simply changes form) beginning from the subatomic level is in a dynamic state, it is all fleeting in this particle/wave state that depends upon the context. The fleeting nature of thought is the same, if one cares to contemplate a little, like the physiological passing away of phenomena. The cultural and psychological states are the same, indicating that the self one speaks of is a movement — there is nothing static. One cannot step in the same river twice. But the illusion of permanence is so strong that the falseness of this permanent entity is unbelievable. It is even difficult to entertain the possibility of it for a moment. This is despite the fact that all around one there is incessant coming and going of bodies in all kinds of manner. The immediacy of it happening to one's self is not evident, in this illusion of linear time where the desires and hopes veil the actual, and the pleasures hide the painful consequences of these repeated addictive pursuits that promise a one-day hope of heaven here or beyond. Such is the individual and collective notion of progress that it creates the mirage of an ever-receding utopia.

* * * * * *

How is one to understand Consciousness, when social sciences, which claim to be the total study of humankind, seem to ignore the basic source of it all — call it brain, mind or consciousness? If the basic unit, this self, is unknown, how is one to proceed to know the rest of the universe? Social sciences and other allied disciplines continue covertly to follow the Newtonian approach to knowledge, which holds that the accumulation of sufficient information will one day allow one to predict and control and plan human communities. Even in the case of nonhuman entities this has not proved quite satisfactory. The prediction of weather, for example, is well-nigh impossible except perhaps through the use of super-computers. So, is the old approach really helpful? Could it be that this search is merely a garb for certain vested interests to dominate the system by sheer force of authority, or to maintain the position of experts?

Even as an experimental neurological issue, the question is of the ever changing quality of Consciousness. What is it like to be 'me', being here and now? Yet, as soon as one thinks of it, it is gone, the world around one has changed from a moment ago. The Now turns into a thought of the past-present-future instantaneously. Even space-time concepts, according to Einstein, are concepts that are modes/vehicles of our manifest expressions. These are not, he says, the conditions in which we live in! It is much like the current saying that one is under the spell of a dominating notion of being a body, a mental set-up with a brain and memories, etc. in which consciousness is an epiphenomenon. One is not aware that Consciousness has bodies, brains and the rest of it within its functioning. The body-brain system and so on is not me; rather, I have a body, memories and so on. I am not to be identified with any of these except for appropriate contextual, operational occasions in the phenomenal world. The complete reversal of perceptions, which enables us to see what we normally call real — the notions of time and space — to be abstract and what we called abstract to be real will release a different set of manifestations of self-expression and way of life. For example, it will be realised that the past-present-future idea of time is only a limited concept; that there is no reality to it except as a subjective cultural systemisation of a specific universe which, under the spell of conditioning — *mahamaya* — seems like reality, not a belief system but the truth. It is Einstein again who says that the personal self, seen as a separate enduring entity rather than a merely functional psycho-somatic state, is an illusion.

The state of flux, where the present turns into the past immediately on being conscious of it, has been called by William James, Krishnamurti, the Buddhists and others, as a 'stream of consciousness'. It is like a stream, flowing; and while it flows unbroken, it never repeats itself exactly. While science seeks regularities and patterns, which is also what some social sciences seek, in this study of Consciousness where does one begin, with what does one start, since one is also part of that change? It can only be a hypothetical working statement. The difficulty is even greater when studying man, who is himself part of the picture he intends studying. One may perhaps start by saying that since consciousness is not a thing, there is no point trying to examine it as such, with the tools of empirical science; maybe it requires another set of tools, another language of discourse, another shift from the hard sciences to the soft areas of the broad canvas of the arts and the humanities, because it deals with the ontological-experiential states of existence. Maybe the science laboratory is not the place for this study, but the anatomy of the mind examining itself, like consciousness looking at its self in its creations, as reflections. It is like talking of the universal energy at the subatomic level, which may be examined only by the way it is manifested in the particular context, not for all times.

One may also ask, why do we have to need Consciousness? Like animals (?), one could carry on without such self-introspection — being blissful in ignorance, an addict of one kind or another. In fact, much of one's life is spent either in this state of stupor, or striving to establish routines, disciplines, techniques and so on to get out of it. These automatic, reactive states appear as spontaneous behaviour, but are not. They only falsely appear as actions in one's chasing after a never-ending good life. One knows in moments of waking up from the stupor that all the effort is of no avail, that it leads to more suffering and pain since it goes against the deepest states of a holistic existence, with their demand that it functions as a dynamic organ in tune with the general principles of the universe.

The questions related to the 'whys', have many answers and explanations, depending on one's cultural conditioning, circumstances of birth and circumstances of the moment. Scientists are not free of subjectivity, their framework at the present being an evolutionary one which dominates humankind today, assuming Consciousness as an epiphenomenon. If one were to see that Intelligence, Consciousness was ever present, the all-pervasive energy, one's perspective would be of an entirely different order. All researchers before Einstein were trying to understand light but were getting more and more confused as to its nature. Einstein took light energy as given, the baseline against which all was, or is to be explained. Suddenly, a whole new area, a new dimension of understanding the universe came into existence, taking light to be constant. Einstein had hit the jackpot, quite intuitively as one knows; it was a revelation.

Similarly, if one states that Consciousness is the baseline within which everything, every situation, physiology, psychology and so on functions, then the evolutionary model is not valid. Social scientists might suggest that any questions about Consciousness are irrelevant; that it is their business to study manifest behaviour in only socio-cultural terms. But Consciousness in whatever form it takes is neither purely external nor purely internal; it is neither merely transcendental nor merely immanent. It is not a question of either/or, it is both and neither/nor! Psychologically, has it ever been considered that consciousness may be a form of energy which not only manifests but also gives energy to form, especially in symbolic ways? As stated, focusing on the word anger, analysing it, seeking its why, etc., gives it further energy when one is in a state of anger — it allows anger to grow and expand. Focusing on a smile, on the other hand, increases that emotion all around. Focusing on negative thoughts, on dirt, gives it energy, while focusing the energy of consciousness on the beauty of flowers or positive thoughts expands them. These examples may be seen as metaphors, since at the moment, the language of this level of consciousness as energy is nameless and formless; like subatomic particles/waves it becomes whatever is appropriate in that specific context for that moment.

Several 'whys' of Consciousness have been studied, in the

evolutionary context. Thus, it is said that man had an adaptive advantage over animals because he was conscious of being conscious, of having a self-identity and power over his actions. It is also said that all this arose because of the ability to symbolise, to create culture, etc.; this in turn arose from his ability to make tools in the early evolutionary developments which further stimulated certain areas in the brain, the cortex. The tools expressed knowledge of a time-past and a time-future, giving man the ability to prepare for future eventualities. Man also attained the awareness of being conscious, of a self-identity vis-a-vis another person or collectivity because information of the external world was stored symbolically, to be used and communicated when required. The same argument, according to the evolutionists, may be used to state — not for sensory motor functions but for psychological reasons — that self-consciousness, self-awareness emerged for social reasons. Man became a *Homo psychologicus* in a cooperative society wherein symbols, models and thoughts became important. These could arise only in a collectivity where they could be controlled and predicted in the paradigm of 'domination-subordination' both at the social and personal level.

Even on these evolutionary theories, however, psychologists, neurosurgeons and anthropologists do not agree among themselves. For instance, some psychologists say that consciousness appeared in historical times, since the early Greeks and the Hebrews of the early period of the Old Testament did not experience themselves as 'thinking beings'. Their verbal images they attributed to voices of Gods (May be they were right!). For example, the *Iliad* has no reference to mental concepts such as mind, thought, feelings or even a self. The understanding in those times was that people were not to be blamed or held responsible for their actions, they were only instruments of external forces. It is an interesting theory, comparable to the idea of various *lokas* in Indian tradition, the notion of *akshic* records or morphogenetic fields, or the theosophic notion of man covered by an all-pervasive thought-field and that beings are expressions of thought-forms. Like the evolutionary theory, these are alternative forms of explanations of ourselves, the self or consciousness. A theory is as good or bad as any other explanation; it is good if it is useful and any human society has reached agreement on it. Just like a good theory, reality too is nothing but a consensus, a question of agreement only.

In some ways, all things are different 'illusions'. Like the universal energy of physics becoming anything in terms of the context, the mind also is an open-ended imaginative system — often a mechanical one — creating all kinds of fiction. In identifying with the universal mind and allowing for various possibilities, the individual has the ability to create anything any time. But even if the universal mind is consciousness, we have not yet located what consciousness is nor for that matter what the mind is - even whether there is such a thing at all! At any rate, there is some power which has the capabilities to create continuously new names and forms and thought associations. Among these thought associations it asks, under various garbs, questions about itself, its own creations through them and their attributes. This is how it keeps the process of creation moving, albeit it is labelled as illusion or imagination, since there are no final answers, no final solution to the mystery of life — there is no pot of gold at the end of the rainbow!

Many theories exist to explain various kinds of human and non-human behaviour, to predict and control. If one has faith in all these assumed world views, they appear to work; they give one the feeling as if the explanations given tell one about consciousness, self-identity and so on. But directly, experientially, does one know anything about consciousness, does one have proof of it? We know about consciousness like we know about light, indirectly. In some ways one cannot see one's own body as fully as of another person neither can one see one's eyes directly and empirically as one does of another. Does it mean that there is no proof of their existence? The external world is a proof, and reflection of one's self and of one having a body, eyes, and so on. One is not an unconscious automaton, since consciousness and awareness is always there and in rare moments one becomes conscious of being a witness to both the self and the other. In this state one has the ability to be consciously in control of events and circumstances, taking full responsibility for one's actions and one's universe, including the non-humans who exist there.

The reality of Consciousness directing human and non-human behaviour may be questioned by the human mind. Split-brain patient research has shown that the leftbrain of reasoning may give any 'reasonable' account of action, while intuitive action is taking place in the right brain. But the right brain could take over the verbal abilities also. Moreover, our verbal selves may take up plausible reasons for the actions they observe the body making, though the commentary of the experience may have little to do with the action. In the head often the distinction between the commentary and the experience is not kept clear and often the commentary is mistaken for the action. Split-brain research reveals that each half displays its own desires, intentions, and even hopes for the future; and when the two halves go their own way with out exchanging information and coordinating the effort, perhaps the neurotic states in general in which humankind is caught up, and schizophrenic conditions take place.

Consciousness, after it has split itself for practical, conceptual, reasons may forget its own unity. We have seen this happen in other areas, say, technology going berserk, the specialisation of thought and abstract symbols and signs, etc. The mind, too, may just keep going in separate directions out of control, as a self-generating system without any self-awareness. This rudderless situation, of just going on and on in one direction becomes an easier way of living. The direction taken usually is into negativities, destructive tendencies and towards entropy, through sheer thought association that is very addictive.

Split-brain research reveals that human minds are multiple entities, consisting of several subsystems, sets and subsets. They are like the multiple social roles each of us has depending upon the context. The universal energy one knows at the subatomic level is also creative in multidirectional ways. But it is only the ability to put things into words, as working hypothesis, that creates a personal sense of conscious reality out of the multiple systems present. The idea of a single conscious will is therefore not reflective of reality. Experiments again show that spontaneous voluntary acts of the unconscious take place well before any conscious desire or decisions to act take place. Self-consciousness is, thus, an afterthought although it gives rise to the false notion that there is some 'will' to choose. Even this secondary response to act in certain ways, it may be noted, is conditioned culturally. In this sense, it is the unconscious activities including *sanskaras*, genetic potentials, and so on which govern behaviour.

There are long philosophical debates about mental events, and science is taking interest in these areas, as empirical statements. There is, of course, the ongoing debate about artificial intelligence, of the brain being a computer, a complex computing information system at the highest sophisticated level unmatched by the machines man has created. This view does help to see the working of the brain, but it still does not tell us why it is so, and least of all about consciousness. Information systems and models do exist, and there are many constructs since that is the only way one knows another. But this implies that 'I' am also one model among many, an image of my brain-mind construct built largely by language-symbolic — semiotic? — systems. This self-image which in turn is connected to the social image of approval-attention from childhood. In other words, everyone in that cultural mould is stuck to some self-identity mode vis-a-vis another. But all this 'vis-a-vis' is still unconscious, reactive, as far as the making of the 'I' is concerned. One believes, however, that one is self-conscious, little realising that it is another unconscious state ignoring the rest of the conscious system. It is a self-reflective, self-generative and self-perpetuating system. Included among its possibilities is a self-corrective and self-destructive behaviour stored in coded words and engrams in the brain cells.

When the ego, which is only a part of consciousness, pretends to be aware individually and in the collectivity, to be independent of the rest of the picture, and instead of being an instrument takes over as the self-governed doer, it becomes a cause of destruction. It is destructive, to reiterate, because it is no longer a part of the whole, of a dynamic Consciousness. The ego, me, has to be aware of its limited role as an instrument, specific to certain models and roles. Problems begin when there is interference in switching from one role to another. The same boss in the office has to be a husband at home, and a father.

Consciousness as a mental model is not a thing, a place; its action is to be appropriate as a model in the appropriate context. Consciousness has not arisen because of the arrow of time in an evolutionary sense, with any one purpose. Consciousness has been and will be, and is there always. It is primordial. There is therefore, no primitive consciousness and no advanced one, as one may speak of technology. At the level of Consciousness all societies and all human beings are equal, always. Consciousness itself, the Self, Mind is self-aware of itself, it is self-connecting, not disparate. This viewpoint and perspective will transform the way we see the world around us. The essential point is to see the unity, to be awake completely in a mindful-mindless-choiceless way whereby this Consciousness, this energy, cleans itself of all the false notions it has subscribed to in identifying with a limited aspect of itself. This clearing up of all the dust, false identifications, the illusion of narrow visions takes place effortlessly, on being wake. But who is awake? It is not the person as such, it is the personal-impersonal THAT which does it all in moments of HERE and NOW, the timeless portals

through the intellect and thought. Being awake means not clinging, to models and concepts as realities, but to be with the BE-
ING, that leaves no residue of thought. It is pure perception and
nothing else, no me, no model, NO-THING.

* * * * * *

To conclude, in the modern world most explanations are
mechanistic interpretations of the processes of life, such as, that
it is in the brain that consciousness appeared as an
epiphenomenal process occurring in evolution. But this is like
a dreamer explaining a dream while asleep. It is explaining
consciousness through the mechanism of the brain, which itself
is the product of the mind — Universal Mind or Consciousness.
It is like looking for the programmer in a television set or a radio
set in its tubes or circuits. The analogy between Consciousness
and a radio set however, is apt only to a certain extent. For the
radio is only a receiving set. But where an individual is concerned, all the problems, conflicts about the brain, soul, existence and so on are parts of the individual mind's own firma-
ment and have no existence apart from Consciousness or Intelligence. Those who try to prove that the mind begins and ends
with the brain can testify to it with the mind alone.

The widely held notion that the mind is a mere bio-chemical
activity has never been proved, demonstrated or analysed. The
linguistic and languaging powers located and residing in the
brain the tape or commentary, and the audio-visual apparatus
— are also not the mind or its dynamics. The enterprise of social
sciences and sciences is based on this notion of the mind —
again a statement of the mind, counteracted in the mind itself by
an opposite statement! This is the game a language plays, as
mentioned elsewhere regarding the dual nature of thought
(Malik 1989a). In any case, consciousness cannot be known
through rational language left-brain activity, which cannot grasp
the ineffable and indescribable. The intellect, too, can only deal

with matters agreed upon by the social set-up. Whatever experiential states we have are possible only through an intuitive
mystical knowing and not by the left-brain language categories.
Is this knowing located in the individual brain or the mind? The
brain-body mechanism is an instrument, a very sophisticated
one at that, but self-referentially, it is like a computer. It cannot
know about these intimations which are beyond its limited
sphere.

There is a possibility of all brain activities being seen as
biochemical workings. But if all brain activity is the by-product
of such mechanical functioning, who or what is the knower?
Surely, the knower cannot be a transient derivative, arising out
of the atoms or molecules of lesser known matter. Were it so,
it could not answer questions regarding creation and existence,
or what is real or unreal. All this occurs in whatever this mind
or no-mind may be — the questions and answers in the mind-
stuff itself, its debates, the arguments, the verdict and those
against it. There are in this sense no others actually, it is all ME,
the Self or Consciousness which is the sceptic, the judge, the
opponent, the believer, the non-believer. All our hopes, ideas,
theories, doctrines, concepts, etc. arise in the mind and subside
in it only. It is like lines drawn on water, vanishing as soon as
they are drawn. All the stuff going on is the universal stuff itself
— the rays of sun are the sun. Is not matter then nothing but the
Universal Mind or Consciousness?

What is mind without Consciousness, that shoreless, mea-
sureless ocean on the surface of which it arises like foam. From
the mind arise various universes that appear very tangible,
which they are not except to be seen as metaphors of another
dimension, another reality. Both the universe and our personal
observing minds would not exist but for an omnipresent Intelligence. But all modern goals run counter to this embellish-
ment of the desire of the brain for spiritual needs; they cater
merely for the food needs of the body, bodily comforts and
material wants. The current trends thwart the opening of

supersensory channels. This course of collision is malevolent functioning, not the benevolent plan of nature to move to the Omega point of de Chardin (1959).

Consciousness may be seen as transcendental and immanent from the human viewpoint, but this is not so by itself; like air, it is everywhere. The space inside and outside the building is not different, except after the building is erected there. If the building falls, the space is once again one. It appeared like two, inside and outside, only because of the building being the focus of attention.

Consciousness is known by Consciousness (the mind-stuff); it partakes of itself in various ways in the confluence of the brain mind. Consciousness itself is the knower, the known and the knowing of its significance. It is known or seen when the general faculties are open in the brain-body mechanism, which is the vehicular instrument. The occurrence of paranormal telepathic communication is an example of this. We have the case of the photographer who got lost in the jungles of the Amazon and began to communicate with the Shaman of a tribe nonverbally. (One of the ideas communicated was that the tribe was moving away from civilisation since the greater its contact with civilisation the less ability it retained to communicate nonverbally! But much the same fate awaits them, as has happened with other non-western cultures in America, Africa and Australia.) Contemporary science, despite evidence to the contrary in even one's personal life, is ignoring the reality of Consciousness. This is, perhaps, because it has neither the tools nor means to verify it, with its rational-theoretical models limited by their own frameworks of scientific instruments, which are extensions of the five senses only and cannot detect the sixth sense areas. The laboratory and its verifiability would come from another area or dimension, beyond current scientific vision. When the essence of Knowledge, Mind and Consciousness, and of the notion of Self, is absent from the entire universe of discourse, can one really get at any other actuality, a dimension of reality, leave aside Truth? But then, if such extra-sensory perception was amenable to empirical scientific verification, especially moments of personal-impersonal existential-experiential states that are taken to have some validity, it would become a fearful threat to all that has been invested all these years all over the world into the current state of knowledge — theoretical and practical. It would shake the foundations not only of social sciences and anthropology, but even one's life at all levels, individual and collective, and especially one's relationships. To point out the reality behind our obvious phenomenal world would be to create a void; one would be in limbo, a transitional state between the known and the unknown. One is referring simply to the mystical dimension, not the mysterious, that is known and knowable but not by any so-called concrete means. These are areas which are governed by laws beyond those of space, time and causality; states which one may call meditative ones. These are not beyond anyone's means, or beyond directions of research separate from the 'material' empirical one of science and social science — beyond one's scope as one may imagine. The primary aspect of consciousness is crucial. This part of human being, the mental-experiential-aesthetic states, were familiar to the pre-industrial man as a way of life and still are to today's non-industrial communities. These states are expressed in their lifestyles, states of mind that manifest the grand creations and expressions seen in all civilisations. All this is beyond the rational-empirical methodological positivistic and reductionistic philosophy that has so determined modern life to its own detriment.

Obviously, Consciousness exists in all states, during wakefulness, dreams and in sleep — since there is a knowing even while dreaming, even in dreamless states when one gets a feeling of freshness, when even one's name or problems of the body are forgotten. Were it not so, one would not know that one slept well and it would all switch off, if it was only an epiphenomenon of the brain's activity. It would seem as if there is a kind of Witnessing to various activities by Consciousness. But we dismiss all this since we have separated the observer from the observed. The external evidence of the study of societies may not indicate all this, since one has eliminated consciousness and mind as the subject of study. How can then one show this dimension by gross tools of measurement? It implies that the sense of history will also be different, since the past, present and the future becomes an awareness of the NOW, the *bindu* of Now, the Big Bang that is happening Now. The Now, Now, Now is all a Presence! How does one know anything, without taking into account Consciousness or Intelligence, one may ask?

Science is irresistibly coming to the conclusion that there is no separation between the observer and the observed, that matter by itself cannot observe itself. It is awareness — Consciousness — that creates this division. How this mysterious division, this separateness takes place — the drop thinking it is separate from the ocean, forgetting its primary existence — is perhaps the veil of *maya*, or *mahamaya*. The awareness to see this screen created by the ego, which believes it is the supreme entity, is to identify with the Being of a human being. It is to know that the One becomes the many and the many are One. This universal has to be discovered uniquely in each experience, paradoxically, at each moment by a personal-impersonal state, over and over again newly every Now in the Now. That is the game.

As the basal substance of the universe, how can Consciousness cease to be or die? Consciousness, to use an old analogy or even in terms of physics, is an infinite ocean of energy in which matter condenses in many forms without any diminishing of the energy which is prevalent everywhere 'within and without'. It is the boundless ocean, void which is full, dotted with globular icebergs of colossal proportions floating in it, of matter. Our senses know only the tip of the iceberg; they cannot feel the imperceptible oceanic waters of Consciousness which include space, time, etc. At the same time, Consciousness is beyond all of its contents. The Context of all contexts is a limitless, infinite creative energy of a universal order which is beyond even any conceptions of the brilliance of a thousand suns. Normally one sees merely the ice-formations and that, too, conceptually and intellectually; as for the rest, one imagines or believes it, or does not. In a silent state, beyond words or chatter, in a purified mind-state without the 'me', it is possible to catch a glimpse of that state of eternity, the eternal moment of Now or Presence, of *samadhi*, of a union or *yoga* beyond duality or multiplicity. In these states the ice-formations, the tips of gross matter vanish as one knows their superficialness and ephemerality. One knows the boundless energy, the ocean of pure effulgent light. It is now all 'ME', as Shri Krishna says in the *Gita*, either in the pure state, or in its multiple states like seeing light through a prism (the mind-brain complex) which is still the same light — just like the often stated jewel-gold metaphor. Thus is Immanence and Transcendence One, as it always was, and is; it is one in all and all in one, witnessed in mystical experience, in the moments of Now, when the 'me' vanishes — states of ecstasy and bliss knowable in the mundane life, not as something exclusive. It is the 'ME' experiencing itself in all its activities through its creations of the so-called other which is itself, for what is it that it is not?

This is the only conceivable theory of creation one can frame consistent with the latest trends in physics and the mounting evidence posited by the study of extra-sensory perception. Call it soul, spirit, or whatever, it is, and sees its own glory unhampered by the senses of the 'me'. Is this not what the Shaivite, Vedantin, Shakti, Vajrayana Buddhist or Tantra philosophies also say? These *turya* and *turyatitta* states are knowable and experiencable by one and all, we are told, as they are the self-reflection and self-perceptive powers of that which IS. What clouds it all is the dust gathered in the mirror of the mind — the memories of pleasures, pains, regrets, resentments, etc. — which distort that One. It needs cleaning every time, not any different from breathing that must be done every moment afresh; or the dusting of the house that has to be done every day and not once and for all, in order for it to reflect truly. This is the awakening of the mind, created by the mind itself, for a new transformation, a vision of the discovery of the BEING. For this is who one is, always was — not who one thinks one was, or is.

One understands the world in a topsy-turvy manner. The world seen by the senses is taken to be real while that which allows this to happen is seen to be unreal or abstract. But the opposite is true; the world of the senses is governed by a mind-set socially conditioned through concepts and images represented symbolically, and is therefore abstract in fact. This is the commentary which one takes to be real. The action, which is at the experiential level, is indescribable: it is beyond words, even like the taste of water. To know this, one has to wake up from the conditioning. Then one knows that real knowledge is always available, provided one stops clinging and hanging on to the known (Krishnamurti and Bohm 1985).

Such contemplation creates problems since the social system one lives in feels threatened by these manifest expressions and statements, for these go against the old generalisations of mostly nineteenth century notions, ideas to which most of the social sciences and even sciences in many parts of the world, where these are equated to technology and scientism, continue to cling to. Not all of the current state of science perhaps accepts this notion of an ocean of Intelligence, of a universal energy or a unified field. And where it is accepted, it has not penetrated to the larger society of scientists or society at large. This ocean of Intelligence is an attributeless, nameless and formless energy; all name and form fixed in any way will limit it. How does one know it, then? It is like light or electricity which is known by its effect, in a form cognisable as such by our senses. The infinite is present in the finite, albeit often in a diluted form, as it is often clouded and limited but reveals itself when awakened and purified. This body-brain instrument, in its subtler aspects is light and sound vibrations speaking in material terms. The universe is a Play of Consciousness, *Krishna-leela*; it is the clouds that hide the sun which is always there. It is not that it never was: it is.

VI

Science and Consciousness

6.1. *Introduction*

Traditional western thought has consistently modelled world views with ontological gaps that run across the whole domain of existence. For example, human and other organisms, though they share the same cosmic niche, are considered to be worlds apart. This dualism is one of the fundamental, often tacit, tenets of western metaphysics, epistemology and ethics. Dualist conceptions of human beings themselves are rooted in this deep-seated anthropocentrism. This dominant world view was assimilated by evolutionary theory, which historicised this onto-logical gap. All teleological perspectives — religious or secular — construe the variety of life-forms being part of a process leading to the advent of humankind. *Homo sapiens* is not seen as a stage in an indefinite flux of change, but as an end, the glorious result of a history of trial and error. This dichotomy between humans and non-humans was extended to other races, often treated as slaves; and even women were not exactly placed in the same category as evolved humans. This was espe-cially the case with many nineteenth century Darwinians. Social differences within Europe itself were classified in this line of thought (Bouissac 1991). In the context of a discussion on Science, it is important to note the specific historical-philosophical climate of Europe during the sixteenth-seventeenth centuries, within which the Scientific Revolution took place. It is also worth our while to recall some basic presuppositions, essentially western, which dominate our times, summarised as follows:

The Universe

1. A mechanical machine, with no intention or purpose; not an organism having consciousness. In being so, it is indifferent to man — hence it needs to be conquered.

2. It is real to the extent it can be externalised, quantified, measured in terms of mass, dimensions of size, colour, taste, etc., characteristics that are ultimately not real.

3. The internal nature of man is subjective and different from the external, which alone can be objective and true.

4. Matter precedes intelligence; the latter must be explained in terms of the former which may be dead, though subject to purposeless forces.

5. Time is linear, sequential; and space essentially uniform. Energy is basically the same, not gross or subtle — though in quantity it may be more or less. Time, space and energy are only externally real, and are independent at the level of perceiving consciousness.

6. Importance is given to the causal notion in terms of the evolution of complexity and intelligence.

Man

1. Man is essentially a rational cogniser, a body with a mind localised in it or an 'engine with a will' (Descartes and Behaviourism); he is an atomic being, an individual without any transpersonal spirit.

2. There is no essential hierarchy of being or consciousness among men or within man; even if so, it is irrelevant to knowledge and the organisation of society, governments, etc.

3. As he is, man is an imperfect being, yet the measure of all things.

Knowledge-Truth

1. Knowledge is an end in itself, except for the betterment of

the estate of man.

2. There is one truth; it was Christianity once, it is Science now.

3. Subject and object can be completely separated, i.e., without a need for earlier studying oneself.

4. Reason is the only faculty by which knowledge may be obtained. Even experiments are extensions of this faculty. But sensations and feelings are not true perceptions.

5. True knowledge is obtained by proceeding from the parts to the whole.

6. It is important to detach oneself from the subject of study, rather than participate in and experience the object.

7. Reality is a mental construct; knowledge is abstract and general, not a vision or experience of particulars.

8. True knowledge is quantitative, not qualitative. What can be quantified is independent of place and function.

9. True knowledge leads to predictions of what is known, since it is based on external, repeatable perceptions; only that which is externalised is available to true knowledge.

10. The truth and falsity of propositions is self-evident, irrespective of the person who says it.

11. As knowledge has nothing to do with being-ness or consciousness, it is not esoteric, i.e., it requires no moral preparation to be discovered or to be understood.

12. In principle, in the making of actual observations (not in the interpretation of data), the observer can always be replaced by scientific instruments.

13. The dichotomy of faith-knowledge is perhaps more a consequence of the Scientific Revolution rather than a presupposition that truth and knowledge reside in dimensions different from those in which religious considerations about God, etc. reside.

The point of the above summary is to indicate how these concepts, world views and classifications have affected the understanding of the elements, of matter. But these issues do not merely rest at the theoretical level. They have had, and continue to have, pragmatic consequences. For example, the idea of slaves, racial inequalities, ethnic conflicts which one sees all around — even the exploitation of depressed classes — emerge from this higher and lower idea in the rung of the evolutionary ladder; so do the experiments on animals, and humans who are treated as objects because they are known to be driven by blind instinct and hence are dispensable. The exploitation of the environment also follows from this world view, since the non-human world is devoid of an autonomous agency and exhibits only passive resistance. This is due to the use of such meta-phorical categories as mind, matter, conscious and unconscious life, blind instinct and clear-minded intentionality, automatism and free will and objects and subjects. In such a conceptual framework animals are defined negatively as devoid of mind, plants as devoid of mobility, etc. Thus, philosophies and world views are not always abstract models. They are powerful rein-forcers having pragmatic consequences through their authorita-tive legitimisation.

In terms of contemporary science these ideas may seem aberrant. Nevertheless, many of the biases continue, covertly. For example, what is considered universal today usually implies a dominant western world view — in whatever way one may define it — and all other categories have to be subsumed within it in the name of universalism. In this one may include the idea of linear time and progress towards a certain state. But this makes these approaches less flexible as against those cultures which see evolutionary developments in terms of cyclical time, wherein catastrophes are part of nature and reality and, further, encompassed within a larger context. Let us examine some recent ideas for understanding the nature of matter.

6.2. *Physical Whole*

The universe is everything that is, ever was or will be; there can be only one. To speak of many universes is a contradiction.

For if there could be many, they must somehow, in some sense, be mutually related; otherwise they could not be distinguished, or counted, or regarded as many. They must constitute a single complex, within which there may be many distinguishable regions or epochs, but these would not strictly be universes, even if between them no communication of information could pass. If they exist they must have some kind of togetherness. So long as they can be at all conceived and postulated, they will all form part of the all-inclusive universe.

But serious objections can be brought against the notion of an infinite universe, however subdivided. Infinity is a concept that has given cosmologists trouble ever since Newton, and physicists today do all they can to eliminate the infinite from their calculations. Contemporary quantum physicists have invented a method of removing it by what they call 'renormalisation', and Einstein adopted a similar stratagem. Special Relativity establishes an equivalence between matter and energy, and General Relativity identifies fields of force with space curvature. Accordingly, since matter introduces curvature into space and bends it round a hypersphere, Einstein introduced the cosmic constant into his gravitational equation, which eliminates infinity from the resulting model of the universe. The full spatio-temporal extent of the world is now described as finite but unbounded — like the surface of a Euclidean sphere but having three instead of two surfaces.

In thermodynamics, the random activity presumed is that of molecules dashing hither and thither in a volume of gas or liquid. But molecules are highly structured entities, as are also the atoms of which they are composed. Any random movement must presuppose the existence of some such entities (involving their own order) that can be shuffled around. Prior to such order, there is no discoverable chaos. Present-day particle physics discovers no hard, impenetrable granules. The elementary units are quantum entities that are as much waves as particles, and have been called 'wavicles'. They are conceived as wave-packets, superposed waves, at once both energy and matter. Again waves have structure and are periodic, and prior to them there is nothing except time, the metrical field, which itself is an ordered manifold. If it were not ordered it could have no geometry. Where then are we to find the primary bodies that move randomly? But indeterminacy exists only at the particle level, or wave-packets, not at the macroscopic level in which they are embedded. One has therefore to conclude that random activity is always parasitic on some sort of order and cannot have ultimate priority. It is precisely in the primordial form of order that the conditions for the development of life and mind implicitly reside.

The idea of the unity and wholeness of the physical universe has received enthusiastic support from particle physicists in the last decade of this century. At the turn of the century, Planck's discovery of the quantum of action and Einstein's formulation first of Special and then of General Relativity immediately had revolutionary effects. Space and time ceased to be viewed as separable parameters, but were fused together as a single metrical field, and its organising structure provided principles of order governing all physical laws and events; particle and wave became complementary concepts. The energy system, taken as a whole, thus assumed priority over determination of the exact position, or the precise momentum, of particles within it, so that these properties along with others became conjugate. Pauli's Principle of Exclusion, and Heisenberg's Indeterminacy laid the foundations. As Heisenberg said, "The world thus appears as a complicated tissue of events, in which connections of different kinds alternate or overlap or combine and thereby determine the texture of the whole."

Without going into the history of theoretical developments, more recently David Bohm has maintained, by way of discovering a credible interpretation of the Quantum Theory, that the physical substance of the world is a dynamic totality, which he calls 'the holomovement', in which a principle of order is implicated and expresses itself variously in the emergence of phenomena and entities (such as elementary particles), so that, on the analogy of the holograph, the whole is implicit in every part. This is an ontological interpretation of the Quantum Theory, consistent with experimental findings, which conforms to Bell's Theorem and satisfies Schrodinger's equation. In short, the theory is then able to account for the experimental facts, but requires us to regard what is measured and the measuring instrument as a single indivisible complex, within which what is measured comes to be. The theory has not been adopted by many physicists, but it illustrates afresh the contemporary trend of interpreting physical facts holistically in terms of the field.

If dogmatic idealism fails to recognise the dialectical character of the whole immanent in finite experience, it commits the epistemologist to a subjectivism that is as disastrous as dogmatic realism. The first because it leads inevitably to self-contradiction in solipsism; the second because, by confining consciousness to an effect in the brain of an assumed (but ex-hypothesis unknowable) external cause, it excludes from knowledge the very object that the knowledge seeks and claims to embrace. The one feasible resolution of the contradictions involved is in the self-specification of the universal whole as a dialectical scale of forms, manifest in the physical universe and bringing itself to fruition through the organic world in the self-consciousness of intelligent life, as stated in an earlier chapter.

What, then, is to be taken as the criterion of truth? By what standard do we assess the validity of our knowledge of the world? It has to be in terms of the degree of coherent wholeness of the experience, both observation and theory together. When they do not agree, contradiction arises, due to some oversight or omission in one or the other, and corrections are needed, or presuppositions must be changed, in order to restore coherence and systematic wholeness.

6.3. *Artificial Intelligence and Consciousness*

To speak of sentience and consciousness is nowadays anathema to many. A long history of materialism, mechanism, and behaviourism — largely a hangover of the Renaissance world view — has resulted, more recently, in an enthusiasm for artificial intelligence and the opinion that the human brain is some kind of highly complex digital computer or general Turing Machine, to the functioning of which consciousness, if it exists at all, is irrelevant.

To deny the existence of consciousness is self-refuting. It is that, of the existence of which we are directly assured by its very occurrence, and without which we could be assured of nothing. No theory of artificial intelligence, no opinion about the epiphenomenal character of awareness could be entertained without it. The behaviourist, demanding cognisance only of what can be 'publicly observed', disregards the fact that such observation, so far as it is perception — as it must be — is the private experience of the observers, and that they can communicate it only on the assumption that others can become aware of their means of communication. All this, again, presumes the use of the senses and, therefore, the existence and presence of sentient experience. Are we not ourselves consciousness?

A general Turing Machine, the theoretical archetype of all computers, does no more than operate a mathematical algorithm; that is, a procedure in accordance with set rules — howsoever complex and sophisticated. But no algorithm can be devised except by a human mind — no Turing, no machine! So if we try to pretend that the human brain is no more than a complicated computer, we beg the question. Godel's well-known Theorem proves that in any formal system whatsoever, a legitimate proposition can always be formulated that is unprovable in the system; and so it establishes that there is some mathematical thinking that is not formalisable and therefore cannot be computable. This statement seems to be true, because seeing it as true requires insight, which is not the product of this or any algorithm albeit — the brain unconsciously in its operation acts like one for some functions.

That insight involves consciousness must be accepted if we recognise consciousness as the activity of organising sentient presentation. In the first place, such organisation is the establishment and comprehension of relationships within a whole, and the perception of relations precisely is what constitutes insight. In the second place, the relations are established between elements in the sentient field, and nascence is what characterises all consciousness. Thinking, including mathematics, continues this activity at a high level of abstraction, but is never wholly devoid of sentient content.

But how, we may be asked, have we established the existence of sentience itself? The answer is: By the self-certainty of consciousness, the presence of which is undeniable without self-refutation — for one must be conscious to deny it, and could postulate it without having it. And consciousness is nothing other than the awareness of elements in the sentient field. Methods of investigation that ignore the occurrence of sentience and consciousness, or which refuse to make reference to it, may in some circumstances, and for acceptable reasons, be justified. But the pretence that sentience and consciousness do not exist can only be an affectation on the part of those who seek to deny what, by its very nature, is ineluctably manifest to themselves and to all other cognisant beings.

6.4. *Observation and Perception*

Normally sentience has been compared to a camera, in which the entire environment is reflected through a single lens on to a screen within a limited space. But this analogy is limited, as it tells of a clear articulated scene, where sentience is an indiscriminate mass of diverse feelings. It also has further disastrous epistemological results, as it eliminates the viewer from the scene, who sees, recognises, and interprets the reflected objects. We are lured into believing that perceiving is the result of the transmission of physical effects from the outside world, through our sense organs, to create some kind of replica or model in the brain. Even neuro-physiologically this is an unsupportable theory, since it is the mind-set, or subset which is crucially involved in the act of perceiving the external world — that is why the world differs from individual to individual. Maybe to know the true nature of perception, one ought to say what it is not, first, and why.

As stated above, perception is not the end result of a causal chain of physical and physiological processes that is converted into a psychical cognition. First, the causal relation between the object and the percept is excluded from this end result. The percipient is certainly never aware of any such causation. Second, it is usually assumed that the sensation caused from without is an indubitable datum. But perception cannot be such immediate acceptance of data, assumed to be indubitable, or hard. All that is indubitable about any experience is that it occurs when it does. The immediate sense datum, moreover, is not and cannot be apprehended as such, unless it is distinguished from a background and identified as an object, an accomplishment requiring inchoate comparative judgment — some degree of discursive activity. Third, it is said that causal theory requires as its complement the 'idea' — it should be a copy or representation of the external thing taken to be its object. It means some archetype, to which we have no independent access, in order to make the necessary comparison. But if we did know it then we would have no need to apprise ourselves of it.

The sense-datum theories, the building blocks constructed from percepts are erroneous, as unrevisable bases of all knowledge. Yet when we perceive objects, we seem to apprehend them as a whole, beyond mere sense datum. Perhaps, language interferes here, since 'seeing' implies what is seen as an external object either perceived veridically, or 'seen as' what we take it to be. Maybe one can distinguish the two by using the word 'seeing' for the former, and 'looking' for the latter. We need some valid criterion to judge between cases in which we actually see — veridically — and those in which we only think we see. But this again becomes a problem of language and the theory of appearing. We need not go into the whole range of such philosophical discussions available in literature. The point is that whatever we perceive, the object of which we become aware is not what we directly sense. Neurophysiologists and psychologists have demonstrated this for even simple perceptions, which are the products of quite complicated incipient thinking.

Sense-datum theories are the progeny of empiricism, which declares all knowledge to be derivative from sense and is then committed to discovering the sense data on which it is based. But it ignores the fact that all knowledge is organised experience, which is essential to cognition, and without which there can be no perception. This is an analytic-synthetic activity, involving thought, attention, senses and a Gestalt, in accordance with the principles of organisation essential to its nature. Perception is thus the activity of structuring the contents of primitive sentience — from the physical and biological levels, as traced elsewhere. At every stage, from the most elementary to the most complex, it is always the comprehension of a whole.

Cognition begins with perception, when the object is singled out from a whole background, by attention; and, by successive stages, objects are identified and distinguished and relations are established between them. The existence of the organism in the world, its interaction in the world, is registered in sentience. Apprehending mutual relationships, identifying them, and distinguishing them is the thinking activity of the conscious subject thus awakened; each individual act being one of judging, initially implicit but, in the more developed phases, explicit and articulate. Perceiving and thinking can therefore not be separated. Concept without intuition is hollow, and intuition without concepts is blind. Massive experimental evidence shows that the perceived object is formed and conditioned by context, spatial and temporal, and by past experience. No physical thing is presented ever as a whole to the senses, yet it is perceived, when at all, as a whole. But the cognitive result, the implicit judgment, inference, and interpretation — subject to the principle of ordering — arises in relation to the funded knowledge of the experienced world. The realisation, comparatively recently, by scientists and philosophers of science that all observation is theory-laden is therefore hardly surprising.

The experienced life-world, its experience and awareness and perception is a unified one in the ordinary sense also. It is natural for it to be so — an integral whole — even if its intrinsic coherence varies in degree according to the extent to which the experience has developed and is systematised by the thinking activity of the subject. The unity is organic as consciousness. The experience of a structured whole, of subject and object, could only be cognised as related to other presented objects if both or all were held together by the cognisant subject within its own consciousness. It is not as if it is brought from the outside; for the subject is nothing less than the universal principle of wholeness that has been immanent throughout the process of nature, and is intrinsic to the organic unity now come to consciousness through the sentience of the organism, operating throughout nature also. It is the same organising principle that integrates the physical cosmos and unites the biosphere, which unifies conscious experience and ensures the integrity of the experienced world.

In practical terms the belief in the reality of the life-world is immediate and innate; its initial justification is primarily pragmatic. But as stated above, it is the coherence of the experience as a whole that is implicit even in pragmatism. The process of bringing the world to consciousness is, in the first place, the imposition of order and systematic relationships upon the sensory flux. In the life-world — physical and biotic — all are mutually continuous dialectical phases or specific forms in the necessary differentiation of the universal duality. Since the world is a whole it must, of necessity, be complete, both synchronically and diachronically. And as no whole can be complete unless brought to consciousness, the universal principle of structure comes to self-awareness in the consciousness of a cognisant subject, through the natural process that issues in human experience of a perceived world.

In the course of becoming organised, the self is distinguished from the not-self. The spontaneous activity of thinking becomes aware of its own agency as subject concomitantly with its apprehension of its object; and that object is nothing other than its own self in process of generation. Throughout mental life, the object of awareness is always the prior phase of the dialectical process. This generates the perceptual world of spatio-temporal bodies and their properties; but, as accepted in the natural attitude or common sense, the life-world is still far from being fully coherent; so that perceptual consciousness itself becomes an object to a further stage of conscious reflection. Admittedly, we cannot get outside our own consciousness, but consciousness is itself the activity of ordering the contents of sentience; and that is, as we have asserted, a unified whole of feeling which, in the very course of the process of organisation, is revealed as the focused registration of a world external to the sentient body.

The difference between common perception and scientific observation is not one of kind but only of degree of sophistication. Both are active efforts to discern presented objects by a subject framing hypotheses and trying to confirm them by correlating evidence for and against; in the first case the process is largely subconscious, or prejudicial, and in the second it is deliberate and explicit. But it is the paradigm that dictates in scientific advancement, and attention is selective — what guides it is interest, on the one hand, and previous knowledge, on the other. What is perceived is partly what is expected and partly what is sought; it never is simply what is there. A vast amount of material is overlooked, and often in this lack of perception it is not credited as possible. In this sense scientific observation is continuous with common sense, in that it merely raises to a high degree of systematised observation what is already the experience of an ordered world. One may say that it is the same totality throughout, in different phases of self-articulation.

6.5. *Mentality and Sentience*

An organism, as organised being, involves a concept. It is because of this concept that it is a whole constituted by parts that are mutually adapted and are equally adjusted to the overall structure of the whole. To exist at all, such organism must be organised; and organisation can arise only out of what is an already organised being. The very functioning of the parts and processes of the organism involves a concept — a principle of order and relationship. But a concept implies the existence and activity of a cognising mind. The material existence and operation of the organic being, on the other hand, is in space and time, dependent on physical laws and external causes that are antithetical to the purely ideal. This contradiction can be resolved only if, on the one hand, the concept immanent in the material system *qua* organised is somehow objectified or actualised in its practical functioning, and, on the other hand, the organising principle in the organic system is brought to self-consciousness.

Sentience is not only the feeling of the integrated physiological whole of the body; it is also the feeling of all these focused into a single complex whole. Hegel identified sentience with the soul, and Aristotle maintained that the soul was the form of the body. The soul is not a separate 'thing', attached to, or associated with, the body, acting upon it from the outside, or acted upon by it to generate sensation. It is the form of the body, the new quality evinced at a specific, critical threshold of intensity of integrated physiological activity. Feeling, the self-revelation of this new form, is not just something triggered in particulate flashes by special processes in the nervous system. It is basically bodily feeling, the body as felt — the 'lived body'.

From primitive forms to ourselves, the registration of the natural world in sentience is copiously exemplified in the felt response to the experience of seasonal changes, the weather, and climatic conditions. All this is related to the flow of energy into and through the organism from external physical sources, and to the felt needs of its body and the supply through its physiological and behavioural activities. It is believed that primitive sentience must be pre-conscious. But it is the material content of all consciousness and becomes its immediate object. How far down the evolutionary scale sentience occurs, and at what level consciousness proper emerges, is of necessity a matter of speculation and can only be inferred from the behaviour of the organic body. It is hard to believe that the behaviour of paramecium and so on, is not prompted by sensibility to outside influences. How is the response to lack of oxygen possible unless it is somehow sensed? No inorganic reducing substance can migrate to seek an oxygen supply. Yet we may imagine that it is, in some way, sensitive to the presence of oxygen when that is available. Such imputation of sensitivity in physical bodies to physical forces is only metaphorically justifiable, except if one advocates panpsychism. But the hypothesis is not necessary if one regards holism as a matter of degree — a higher degree of wholeness than simple chemical combinations, for instance, or physical cohesion. The relation between sentience and consciousness, at any rate, is one of degree, if only of clarity and articulation. In the evolutionary scale the latter must have emerged out of the former gradually, and probably concomitantly with the development of brain capacity and organisation.

In thus bringing itself to awareness, the universal principle of wholeness remains immanent, as subject, in the experience; and without such immanence the experience could not be true. The immanent universal is what Kant called the transcendental synthetic unity of apperception. It is what constitutes the self, as distinguished within the sentient and conscious whole, a transcendental ego, transcendentally aware both of itself and its other, and cognisant of the whole immanent in its own experience of the world.

6.6. *Attention, Consciousness and Cognition*

Attention selects an element within the felt whole, distinguishes it from the felt background, and creates a figure-and-ground structure within the psychical field, making it an object for consciousness, which in this way is directed upon it. Consciousness thus varies in clarity and definition with the degree of sharpness and articulation of attention. There is no consciousness without an object at which it is intentionally directed. Whereas sentience does not, consciousness does imply the distinction between subject and object. The object is, as it were, projected and held 'before' the subject, which contemplates it as a whole. Consciousness has been compared to a searchlight playing upon successive objects and illuminating the surrounding landscape; it is an activity. While it presents itself as hierarchical structure, it also has the capacity to extricate itself from it all and grasp the whole, the general form; in some way consciousness is also self-transcendent.

Attention, creating the object, by singling it out of the psychical field, is thus initiation of consciousness, the experience described as cognitive when perception is born. Concurrently, the various sense modalities are distinguished. As objects are related to one another and to the body in which sensations are felt, the self becomes opposed to the not-self, and an outer world is built in which the subject is conceived as one member and the organism that it inhabits is placed in its encompassing environment. It is in the virtue of the self-transcendent character of consciousness that the mind reaches the point at which a fresh transition, a further self-enfoldment, takes place; the stage at which self-reflection is achieved.

This is the crucial point at which the self becomes aware of its own identity and knows itself as 'I', at which it makes itself, along with its ideal content, object to itself as subject. Here the mind enters upon the stage of self-reflection — reflection upon the nature of its objects and its own relation to them. This is the dawn of intellect, the birth of wonder, and the awakening of self-criticism and self-appraisal. Reflection is the distinguishing mark of the human. Without it there can be no morality, no civil society, no science, philosophy, art or religion — no materialism, no behaviourism, no scepticism, and no theoretical deconstruction; and the first fruit of reflection is the indefeasible revelation to the self of its own existence. Those who remember the traditional idealistic problematic will no doubt wish to challenge this account of the emergence of knowledge, to ask how, if the life-world is thus constructed from the contents of the sentient field, we can ever know whether anything in the outer world corresponds to our subjective construction. The question is, however, misplaced and misguided. Objective and subjective is a distinction made within the life-world, which experience embraces as a whole. We can in no way get outside our own consciousness. There is no outside, if only because outer and inner is an opposition constituted within experience.

6.7. *On Complementarity*

We have mentioned elsewhere the *Yin-Yang* principle, akin in some ways to the notion of *Shiva-Parvati* or *ardhanareshwara*. In modern scientific terms, the Principle of Complementarity, based mainly on the work done by Niels Bohr, stresses the ancient viewpoint, in essence at least. It states that the seemingly opposites or what one at present calls irreconcilable points of view need not be contradictory. In fact, on deeper analysis these are mutually illuminating, i.e. these are part of the same totality, seen from different perspectives (Kothari 1989). At the social, ethical level, like the Uncertainty Principle mentioned elsewhere, one is allowed the possibility of accommodating widely divergent views and human experience.

From the scientific viewpoint of the educational curricula, this needs to be emphasised. For example, thinking and thought, the way they arise and the way one gets an idea which has existed, go on infinitely; and this infinity is enclosed in an instant, in moving yet not moving thoughts, like Zeno's paradox of an inexplicable contradiction. It is like matter (brain) and consciousness (mind) that are complementarities. This is what Pauli has stated in his Pauli's Extension Principle, the oneness of quality and quantity, matter and mind. Thus scientific principles are applicable to life too: we just have to look at these at the subatomic levels, of which we are made. It is easy to see how scientific knowledge has allowed for the possibility of giving to words meanings that are new and which are unlike those that exist in ordinary language. Even in mathematics, concepts like Infinity or what Godel's theorem tries to prove, lead to contradictions. Thus the ambiguity of ordinary language can further undergo changes to provide insights of greater understanding between the human mind and reality. This aspect, known in Buddhist, Jain and Upanishadic ethics and philosophy, has to be relevant in our times by our own discoveries and perceptions, and in terms of scientific understanding and technological developments. A new vocabulary, a new language, a reinterpretation in terms of contemporary needs and society is essential. Insights (as ancient as these might be) need to be experienced again and gain and restated, afresh. As said earlier, truths have to be said anew for out own purposes, albeit supported perhaps by earlier ideas (or vice versa) which confirm our experiences and insights. Each age and generation has to do it over and over again, afresh. Each one has to stand on its own feet, breathe firsthand and feel for itself whatever it is now; and be a lamp to one's self. This has to be manifested over and over again in its unique yet universal way. In this way there is fresh creation, moment to moment, age after age. In an abstract sense, there is nothing new, unless it is experienced in that perception-action manner, in a timeless yet creative way.

In an abstract sense, pain, hunger, feelings and all that are the same for all humankind. These experiential states are beyond any socio-cultural boundaries. Nevertheless, the universal nature is forgotten by narrow boundaries of conceptual notions; it must also be remembered that each experience is unique even if its cultural manifestation is bound. Thus there are unique and universal states at the same time. Several such paradoxes may be mentioned — being and non-being, I am and I am not, etc. These pairs of the binary systems from the phenomenal world in the Upanishadic sense have been stated by many, and some examples are given as :

1. Noumenon and Phenomenon — one is the other.
2. God and Nature — one is the other.
3. *Sansara* and *Nirvana* — one is the other.
4. *Brahman* and *Maya* — one is the other.
5. Self and Not-self — one is the other.
6. Thought and Time — one is the other.
7. Self and Thought — one is the other.
8. Knower and Known — one is the other.
9. Renunciation and Enjoyment — one is the other.
10. Action and Non-action — one is the other.
11. Being and Becoming — one is the other.
12. *Vidya* and *Avidya* — one is the other.
13. Birth and Non-birth — one is the other.
14. Work and Knowledge — one is the other.
15. Spiritual and Phenomenal Nature — one is the other.
16. Subjective, qualitative and (quantity, language, mathematics, and not communicable) rational, etc. and Objectivity — one is the other.
17. Actor and Spectator — one is the other.
18. Future and Past — one is the other.
19. A and not-A — one is the other.
    And so on.

The problem asked, the questions that arise have within

themselves the answer, since the two levels are not distinct and contradictory except from the purely limited phenomenal viewpoint. How is one to make a jump, a quantum jump which is required from one to the other, since it is a continuous transition, a gradual movement up the ladder? But this is not the way. From the finite self to the infinite self is not possible, through time-thought. If it were, it would have happened again and again in these 5000 years. But it has become worse with repeated attempts. Of course there are complementarities of higher and lower levels when one conceptualises the issue. The simplest and best understood complementarities are those of the wave-particle duality in physics. In ordinary language it means simultaneity, coupling of past and future in every observation, which implies freedom of choice and objectivity, i.e. free will between mutually exclusive alternatives — in a sense a participation in genesis, being actor and the spectator at the same time.

The discoveries of quantum mechanics revealed in the 1920s that the observer and the observed are not two separate entities. It was assumed until then that such objectivity was possible, as the world of matter consisted of discrete entities and man was a distinct entity, at least in principle. But this picture, of the self and the other which are part of the whole, has changed, if one were to project to the human world this sub-atomic reality. At the subatomic level, the interaction is not predictable. The unpredictable nature of things is inherent in their very nature, according also to Plank's constant. Humans are made of not only atoms, but their physics and chemistry as well. We all thus function in a unified system. For anything to happen, everything in the universe has to participate in it. Nothing will happen at any level otherwise. All the suffering one sees around is because one sees one's self as a separate entity unrelated to all else. Things can no longer be explained simply and described forcibly as in physics. This is not to say that all the work done in physics is not objective and scientific;

it provides an insight into the working of all nature, of which man is an essential part.

Thus, scientific truths and ethical truths are not contradictory but complementary. There can be no advancement in science without some measure of ethics in society. Equally, there is not much room for the practice of ethics without science and technology. In other words, the quest is for seeking a unified field in science and in other areas, a unity in nature and man. But it all begins with a personal yearning. Throughout history, in every endeavour, human beings have searched for connections, for ways to make a harmonious whole out of the parts. The Holy Grail of modern physics is the Grand Unified Theory.

The richest and most fundamental of all complementarities is of course that of Matter and Consciousness (mind). Perhaps, Wolfgang Pauli (of the Pauli Exclusion Principle) has stated the matter most clearly and succinctly:

> "To us ... the only acceptable point of view appears to be one that recognised both sides of reality — the quantitative and the qualitative, the physical and the psychical — as compatible with each other, and can embrace them simultaneously.... It would be most satisfactory of all if phusis and psyche (i.e. matter and mind) could be seen as complementary aspects of reality" (Pauli and Jung 1955: 208-10; quoted by Kothari 1986).

The quest for unity has taken on new poignancy in recent years, as the unstoppable sledgehammer of specialisation pounds the world into smaller and smaller pieces, and as humankind grows more estranged from nature. An example is the Gaia hypothesis of Lovelock (1979, 1988; and Myers 1985). Timothy Ferris (1991) is concerned with cosmic unity since he believes that our true connectedness lies far beyond the earth, with the cosmos. Ferris envisions our relationship to the universe as an hour-glass shape. On the bottom side is the inner realm of the mind; at the top is the outer realm of animals, stars, galaxies. Ferris's work encompasses brain studies, astronomy,

physics, mysticism, the 'near death experience', environmental-
ism, information theory and so on; all in the context of the
mind's search for unity and cosmic connection.

We need to ask: is there a unity, in fact, say in the brain or
the interpreter sitting in it, since the unity of thought is an illusion? The brain has a multiplicity of functions and voices that
speak independently. But though the brain is multipartite, it
represents itself to the mind as unified. Were conscious selves
fully unified, we would feel justified in concluding that for all
the disparity of its parts the brain is in truth a fully unified
system. Instead we find that our sense of the personal unity and
command over the brain is something of an illusion.

So, is the idea of unity and its quest a mere assumption?
Does unity really exist? In the world of art this assumption may
depend only on aesthetics but in science, it would seem some
concrete forms have to be taken into account. Lovelock's assumption, for instance, is that there is probably a mechanism
that will reduce the carbon dioxide in the atmosphere when it
is too low for trees; and particle physicists assume a single force
that produces electromagnetic forces, gravitational forces and
nuclear forces. Nature may or may not accommodate these assumptions. Paradoxically, as science digs deeper into nature, it
uncovers alternating layers of unity and variety, simplicity and
complexity. Copernicus's sun-centred cosmos was simpler than
Ptolemy's earth-centred universe, but twentieth-century astrono-
mers found that the sun is merely a resident in the suburbs of
the Milky Way galaxy. The atom was once the indivisible unit of
matter; then hundreds of subatomic particles such as neutrons
and protons were found; then the genealogy of this multitude
was simplified by tracing their lineage to three constituent
particles called quarks; now the number of quarks has grown to
six or more.

Does unity have a reality beyond its conception? Is it that
the mind must impose unity on the inner world of itself? Could
the same be true of the outer world beyond the mind? Could the

unity scientists seek exist mainly in their minds? Perhaps, the unity of science consists alone in its method, not its material, as it is not the facts themselves which form science, but the method in which they are dealt with. Order and reason, beauty and benevolence are characteristics and conceptions which we find solely associated with the mind of man, wrote Karl Pearson (1892), the founder of twentieth-century statistics, in his influential book, *The Grammar of Science*. This is much the same as what Einstein said in the journal of *Science* (1940), "Science is the attempt to make the chaotic diversity of our sense experience correspond to a logically uniform system of thought" (Ferris 1991).

The theory of quantum physics was worked out in the first three decades of the century by Max Planck, Werner Heisenberg, Erwin Schroedinger and Louis de Broglie. The theory has been confirmed with great precision by many experiments, including the double-slit one. But no one understands the meaning of quantum physics. If it has not made the new man of science jump from his chair, it has certainly made him wonder what he was sitting on! We have learned that there is no clear line between the observer and the observed. We are connected to nature. We are part of a whole. The physicist John Archibald Wheeler calls the world as we now understand it a 'participatory universe', i.e. that we shape the properties of the universe by our very observation of it. Not long ago, such a notion would have been dismissed out of hand by every bonafide scientist and many philosophers. We are not mere bystanders who probe electrons to see how they move, or who record the level of carbon dioxide in the air, or who build radio receivers to point up instead of sideways. We are part of the whole process (Ferris ibid.).

Cassidy (1990) writes that at the age of 23 in 1925 Heisenberg laid the foundations of quantum mechanics on which all subsequent generations have built. It abandoned the basic notions of the old classic physics, such as that of electrons moving in orbits, replacing them with a much more abstract description. It is true that a year later Erwin Schroedinger published his theory of wave mechanics, which turned out to be identical in content to Heisenberg's quantum mechanics. But we needed both points of view to develop a real understanding of the physical world.

The Bohm-Sommerfield theory, accepted before Heisenberg's paper, described electrons in the atom as revolving around the nucleus in orbits, like planets around the sun, as in classical mechanics; but only certain selected orbits were allowed. Radiation was emitted when an electron jumped from one orbit to another, and the energy loss of the electron determined the frequency (colour) of the radiation. Heisenberg discarded the concept of orbits which could not in principle be observed — this was made more precise later through his Uncertainty Principle — and he proposed that the physicist should only deal with observable things. This meant concentrating not on single orbits, but on the emitted radiation, which comes from a jump between two orbits, so that he talks of two states of the atom at a time.

Schroedinger's wave mechanics started from a very different approach, but it also gave correct results and appeared at first to be an alternative theory. It soon proved to be the same as Heisenberg's, although expressed in a different language. After a heated discussion the correct view was expressed by Max Born, that the intensity of the waves determines the probability with which the electron will be found at a given point in space. Physics cannot specify the position of a particle; its position is a matter of chance, with only probabilities being the subject of the physicist's description. This conclusion led Heisenberg to his Uncertainty Principle, which has to do with the accuracy with which different attributes of a physical object can be known; the more precisely we want to know the position of a particle, the more uncertain must be its velocity, because the act of observation causes an unknown change in the velocity.

Thus, the twentieth century has exploded a metaphysical bomb, namely, Quantum Physics. It shows that the scientist is inextricably tangled with the objects he observes, as no longer is he a passive observer. It used to be believed earlier that one could observe the pendulum swing without changing its motion; chemists once believed they could measure the rate at which coal burned in air without altering that rate; naturalists believed they could quietly listen to a sparrow without dictating its song; and scientists assumed they could put a box around their subject and peer into that box. Quantum physics has shown that scientists are always inside the box. The answers scientists get to their questions depend on the way they ask the questions. Hence the enigma of whether unity exists outside the mind of the scientist and dissolves in a mist of ambiguity and meaninglessness. A baffling experiment in quantum physics, called the double-slit experiment, demonstrates how 'the observer' finds that he is not really an observer but part of the experiment. Without going into the details of it the baffling part is: How does each electron know in advance whether there are additional detectors behind the openings? How does each electron know whether to remain whole like a golf ball or to subdivide and spread like a ripple on a pond? Somehow, the properties of the electron depend on the mind asking the questions!

6.8. *Physics and Biology*

Ernst Mayr in his *Towards a New Philosophy of Biology* (1990) asks the question, Is evolutionary biology a science? If so, what kind of science is it? His central theme is that the concepts which underlie evolutionary biology make it an autonomous science, and not merely a sub-branch of physics. Not that he does not believe in the unity of science; in particular he believes that the law of physics and chemistry are the same in living and inanimate matter. The claim for autonomy rests on the existence of concepts — for example, natural selection, genetic programme, species — that are needed if we are to understand biology. These concepts are consistent with physical laws but could not be deduced from them.

In distinguishing between physics and biology, Mayr points to the different role of laws in the two sciences. In physics, laws are intended to be universal. Such laws do exist in some branches of biology. For example, the 'central dogma of molecular biology' that information can pass from nucleic acid to protein, but not from protein to nucleic acid, is intended to be such a law, universal as far as life on earth is concerned. As yet, there is no convincing falsifying evidence. The law is important for evolutionary biology, because it provides one explanation for the non-inheritance of acquired characters. In evolution such laws are hard to come by. Even the law that acquired characters are not inherited has exceptions, because not all heredity depends on the sequence of bases in nucleic acids.

The message is that evolution is contingent. It is not the case that, initially, there were a few simple organisms, and that, as time passed, there was a steady increase in diversity and complexity, leading inevitably to the emergence of an intelligent, tool-using, talking animal — ourselves. If there was a replay of it all again, there may not be chance for the same to be repeated since it is a matter of chance which body, phyla, survive; no guarantee or likelihood of the emergence of vertebrates, or mammals. Evolution is not a stately law-governed progression leading inevitably to human intelligence.

Throughout evolution function has preceded the organ through which it is to be exercised; the organ developed in response to a need. So why should the brain be any exception? In other words Intelligence came first, quite able to function in its own realm. Working from such a premise, is it not true that life, intelligence, and consciousness are primal realities? Is it scientific heresy to suggest that biological forms are secondary events, to the primary substratum? It is somewhat ridiculous to maintain the position of a mechanistic, chance creation which insists that thought originates and depends upon the physical brain. For example, with regard to the brain, no special 'box' equivalent to the 'memory' store of the computer has been identified; nor is memory to be found in a particular cell, synapse, or chemical molecule. All experience is not stored in the brain (Lester-Smith 1975). Today, physics and other allied disciplines are clear that there is a non-mechanical reality more like a great thought rather than like a machine — the mind is no longer an accident of matter but the creator and governor in the realm of matter.

Another message is that science is a product of individuals who bring with them, and are influenced by beliefs. Chance events can lead to predictable outcomes. For example, the decay of a single radioactive atom is the paradigm of randomness, but the behaviour of a large lump of radioactive material can be accurately predicted. Hence, the contingency of evolution does not depend merely on the random nature of genetic mutation. It arises because mutations have qualitatively different effects, and because these effects can be amplified. This amplification of quantum events, combined with the unpredictability of the environment, makes it impossible to foretell the long-term future, although it may still be possible to explain evolution in retrospect. There is no stately Victorian notion of inevitable progress toward the Omega point. Empirically, individual lineages do not necessarily progress; they are as likely to lead to tapeworms, or to nothing at all, as to lead to man. There is no such thing as global progress; only a tendency to get better and better at whatever one happens to be doing. Increasing information is transmitted from generation to generation — from RNA molecules duplicating themselves to social animals and animals with language (Mayr 1990).

6.9. *Mysticism and Science*

The movement from a religious metaphor guiding the ancient past to a scientific metaphor of modern times continues to go further ahead, since the latter is increasingly being recognised as incomplete for telling us about the various contemporary issues, the crises such as environmental pollution, ecological imbalances, and so on. The modern movement marked a departure from the old dynamics of life when humankind lived closer to nature, sustained and motivated by an understanding of our higher nature — an understanding that came easily and naturally to them; as against the confidence of the modern era to achieve better living conditions, through progress in terms of the conquest of nature — introducing new parameters, both physical and psychological, which separated man from nature, from the universe. Hence, man was not responsible for an overall harmony by being subservient to the cosmos; he pretending to be the dominant force himself. Being good and bad became mere matters of technical feasibility, since moral, spiritual and other dimensions had little to do with the solid practicality of material comforts. All this is outdated in view of some developments in science, which are ahead of the times, ahead of this reductionistic paradigm which alienated man from the cosmos. It is in this context that scientists are moving in both the inner and outer dimensions — between matter and consciousness — even if physics and chemistry are inadequate to deal with such problems since so far science has no moral dimensions to it (Weber 1986).

Physics has developed wonderfully and become a very important, interesting and useful science. But it is not very self-consistent, and it does not even try to cover the existence of consciousness or life. Also, Quantum Theory and Relativity are not really reconciled with each other; more investigations are necessary. The description of the world and its unity by Quantum Theory is very different from that of oldfashioned physics, that is macroscopic physics, and also that of General Relativity. But contradictions in physics are noticed in a particular theory or system of logic only when we apply it to a new situation and the theory predicts results that are not compatible with the observed phenomena. This may be understood in terms of quantum mechanics that describes probabilities — probability connections between subsequent observations. Sciences thus speak in terms of approximations, which is good since physics deals with inanimate nature. It has not gone into the study of consciousness, just as at one time it did not consider itself ready to study micro-structures, as atoms and molecules. Earlier physics dealt with magnetism, electricity and mechanics, etc.; today, it deals with atoms and molecules. Human beings are more than just that, yet sciences do not consider consciousness to be part of their study — no more than the social sciences and humanities unfortunately do. Perhaps this is because consciousness is considered something non-physical, since the definition of physical is restricted. In similar manner, Newtonian physics considered atomic physics outside physics. Today, even chemistry and physics is incorporated within each other, if not biology or microbiology.

Perhaps a new tool and language is necessary to understand consciousness, just as it was necessary to develop a new tool to understand quantum theory. The questions in this case would be different. Does self-identity demand consciousness, or does the latter create identity, viz., I know that I am I because consciousness tells me so? Is it a product of something, an emergence of evolution more or less accepted by everyone, or is the quantum of consciousness in every living entity the same in its nature or ability? The mechanical nature of each body may be different but consciousness is a state of being. It may be either a transformation of matter or a totally non-material principle. At any rate, in terms of the present science of physics and chemistry, a definition and description of matter will not tell us about consciousness; just as Newton's theory did not describe the emission of energy, heat and light by the sun — may be it was not expected to even — though the sun was always there. Today one speaks of heat and light as transformations of material energy. Maybe the basic ground work of theories will have to be changed to include a study of consciousness — something new has to be introduced, a new art and laboratory of observation. It would mean that consciousness itself becomes a baseline for the art of observation — it is observing itself! It involves a shift from particular entities, atoms and the rest as discrete entities to relational phenomena of events, as Alfred Whitehead suggested. Physics and mathematics is no longer unidirectional in characterising things — these are processes and probabilities. This may be more akin to the processual idea of Buddhists, rather than that of individual *jivas* as living beings as entities, existing separately (Weber 1986).

The unity of things, man and nature, consciousness and matter, inner and outer, subject and object — these can be reconciled not only when there is no separation between one's personal and professional life but also when exploring their unity, and seen as a spiritual odyssey. Thus, there is no separation between creative scientists, artists, humanists and the sufis, saints, sages and mystics. The struggle for harmony, for integration and the search for wholeness is a priority with which nothing else can compare. A coherent vision is possible by searching for deep structures, whether in nature, the area of brain-mind, or mystic realms. It is not possible through contemporary analytical philosophy which has become merely intellectual, ignoring simplicity and unity. The move towards metaphysics from physics, or towards unity, has as yet penetrated only a minority of the researchers in all disciplines. The search for wisdom is suspect, if not ridiculed outrightly. For any search for a holistic perspective, rigorous examination is necessary both in science and the study of consciousness. This is said emphatically since it is erroneously thought that methodology may be dispensed with in this search for wisdom; the objection is to all isms.

Perhaps, one may call science outer empiricism and the inner exploration as inner empiricism. The common ground then is unity, linking the microcosm and the macrocosm, nature

and man, the observer and the observed. Max Planck acknowledged it well: "Science cannot solve the ultimate mystery of
nature ... because in the last analysis we are ourselves part of
nature, and, therefore, part of the mystery that we are trying to
solve." Man himself, is, however, the crucial clue to the mystery.
From time to time some scientists have realised this, and the
relationship between mysticism and science is re-emerging in a
modern form of the ancient relationship between the two approaches. But are these two reconcilable? One is quantitative,
the other qualitative; one's methodology is rigorous
formalisation, the other's meditation; one's mastery is over gross
matter, the other's is over subtle matter (of inner bodies and so
on) which has its own laws, logic, insight and workings analogous to science. Subtle matter has begun to appear in the
theories of the twentieth-century physicist. Science is no longer
value-free even if it is cognitive in nature and understands
phenomena by piecemeal analysis, which is precisely its weakness. The mystic, because his laboratory is an inner one, may
equally be lost in this quest, if he forgets the outer particular
things. There is thus a relationship between simplicity and
multiplicity, the universal and the particular. In chemistry, in a
homogeneous solution chromium stays invisible until it is
coaxed to reveal itself through some appropriate steps; similarly
in the *Svetasvatara Upanishad*, there is the enigmatic metaphor
of creation: "Like butter hidden in cream is the source (pure
consciousness) which pervades all things" (Weber 1986).

In Indian cosmology, the phenomenal world is the solid, the
precipitate which becomes crystallised in space and time by
cosmic consciousness in which it floats. David Bohm speaks of
the Implicate Order cosmology, with its schema of dense and
subtle matter, referring to a single source underlying the universe. Immanence and transcendence become one divinity in
everything in this model where the finite unites with the infinite.
The universe is materialised Brahman. Such a reversible equation recalls Einstein's equivalence of matter and energy, and the

particle and wave identity of quantum mechanics. One may even go to the extent of saying that mysticism is pursuing with ruthless logic the Grand Unified Theory — the one that includes the questioner in its answer; unlike science which wants to leave the scientist outside this search.

Perhaps, the dilemma is that while it is easier to deconstruct nature and the other esoteric stuff by the mind, the latter as ego finds it difficult to deconstruct and reconstruct itself. In both cases of deconstruction an enormous amount of energy is released. It is only the binding power which keeps the atom together, and the ego in another sense, which will reveal that energy and dimensions hitherto undreamt of. Just as there is no ultimate building block, only transformational energy, so there is no fixed entity as the personality, independent and free. Once this becomes clear through different methodologies and techniques, the resultant staggering energy is a channel to limitless universal energy — Cosmic Consciousness. Whether in the deconstruction of matter or of the ego, the immense energy potential in nature and the human realm is unfolded through the substratum, which one was seldom aware of experientially. Whether it is atom splitting or ego splitting, both are arduous paths that cannot be treaded lightly, since both require an attitude of sacredness. In its absence the splitting becomes negative, pathological and destructive, as we all well know by now both in the physical and psychological contexts.

These states of the release of energy are quantum transformational jumps with all kinds of possibilities. The mystic altered states of consciousness harmonise the awareness of the individual, as in some ways his awareness alters the subatomic structure, of which he is made, to the deep structures we referred to above. In this sense, the mystic is a true alchemist since he brings the micro and macro levels together; he lives psychologically in the mode of creation, manifestation, dissolution of every particle of subtle matter and energy. He can let go and die to each moment so that the next moment is afresh and a rebirth. In short, he lives in the timeless present, the NOW — the PRESENCE.

Scientists too talk of beauty, elegance, the good.and true of reality, in this search for Unity. Their search is not merely a mechanical search of an equation, or a single comprehensive law, in a conventional sense, bereft of aesthetics. In this sense their search also is spiritual, since behind the intellectual drive of the great creators of science, a deeper force is at work. One may hesitate to call it consciousness or intelligence, since one is not sure what it is. Yet without this force it is difficult to account for the way scientific genius operates, as behind the multiplicity of appearances lies the unity of an intrinsic reality.

All this is not to devalue science. But science cannot answer such questions as: What happened before the Big Bang? What lies beyond the edge of the universe? What started the universe and why? Mysticism at least points to a direction, that the universe originates in consciousness as subtle matter which gives rise to dense matter, but all matter forms a continuum. The subtler the matter — pure mind — the closer it gets to consciousness and ultimately cannot be distinguishable from it. But neither matter nor consciousness, even if they form one continuum are, according to the mystics, the ultimate. Both have a source in something which is beyond themselves, and cannot become an object of knowledge — not even in non-ordinary states of altered consciousness when there is unity of space, matter and consciousness minus the person, or the ego.

In these ontological-experiential states, the distinctions between inner and outer space, nature and self, consciousness and matter are lost. If science produces pure energy from dense matter, the mystic way transforms the dancer as much as the dance itself. Consciousness is aware of consciousness itself, as is the Zen saying, 'The eye which I see is the very eye which sees me.' The participatory universe, however, demands a dialogue, in terms of the I-Thou experience of Martin Buber. Dialogue reflects the insights of each partner at this moment in time, and does not negate the fact that another moment may call forth another response. In this sense, dialogue is creativity, exchanging energies and insights, adding something afresh to the happenings of the universe in this encounter. Scientists like John Wheeler, Prigogine, Heisenberg, and others support this view and advocate it. Bohm goes even further to state that meaning is a form of being. In the very act of interpreting the universe we are creating the universe. Through our meanings we change nature's being. What the cosmos is doing as dialogue is to change its idea of itself in its questions and answers, its struggling to decipher its own being (Weber 1986).

6.10. *Summary*

Correlating matter with consciousness in science has been a long-standing puzzle. Developments since 1970 in cognitive science have attempted to unravel this puzzle somewhat. Especially the developments of quantum physics and Chaos Theory have shown us that in any strict sense, science cannot predict and control always. Some say that after a certain point in time, in evolution, consciousness, which is qualitatively different from the reductionist causes of science, comes into play. Maybe the all-pervasive energy field of quantum zero-point energy is the all-pervasive field, which Consciousness of the esoteric traditions talks about, too.

Given the above puzzles, researchers are moving into new areas to understand matter and consciousness, unthinkable a couple of decades ago. This requires a restructuring of the approach towards a oneness picture, a Wholeness Science, as some would call it. This is to say, one experiences the world from inside as consciousness, which is the whole also since the outside experienced by the senses is its external manifestation. Evolution is the manifestation of consciousness; it is not just a single track of graded evolution from times immemorial. Consciousness thus becomes an agency. The images and pictures of reality that we desire to create are its relevant data.

This approach implies a sensitisation of the observer. In

knowing, he/she is altered and is willing to be transformed in an ongoing dialogue with the essence of creation — whatever it is; he/she is not bound by any rigid stand of authority, expertise that leads to entropy. This transformation happens for the anthropologist and psychotherapist, and it would happen also to the scientist who wishes to study meditation and altered states of consciousness. Maybe the movement is up and down, as in an hourglass or a spiral. This process of conscious awareness involves unconscious processes, volition, the concept of the self and so on. Depending on the level where one is placed, matter becomes consciousness and consciousness, matter. It all is real or unreal — whatever suits one's terminology.

In the new approach, where it is not bodies that have consciousness but consciousness has bodies, the questions asked will radically change. Thus, how does separateness arise, if all is one? Does the brain act as a filtering and reductive mechanism? No longer will one ask how to integrate the universe but how does it feel separate; how to explain the interconnections — not through linear processes of the big bang; how to seek a unified theory involving many different fields (gravitational, electromagnetic, morphogenetic, string theory, etc.). Following Einstein who took the velocity of light to be basic, consciousness becomes the baseline and different explanations will follow — a quantum jump! This will serve us well in individual and societal development as well. In this scheme, openness to alternative theories, explanations and healthy scepticism is natural. In short, the new approach of scientific research endeavours to include both direct experience of the inner senses and the outer physical ones as a unity of consciousness, and does not exclude any human experience.

There is an urgent need to change the basic paradigm globally from a mechanistic one to a holistic one in the physiopsychic realm. The split-dualistic one is built into the very texture of the scientific study of matter, of thought, in all walks of life. In view of its limitations, we need to look for a unified mode such as is available in particle physics, extra-galactic cosmology, post-Einsteinian physics, and in the dissolution of solid matter into waves of probability by Heisenberg and others. The shift indicates that Consciousness is not an epiphenomenon of matter but the very matrix and the Context of all contexts within which everything functions — it is the way of perception itself.

When one considers the brain-body system to be separate from the external circumstances, one is following the old approach of considering oneself outside the picture, a mere observer. The mental set-up is made up of the socio-cultural world and the individual personality is not a free, independent unit with its own will to play as it wishes. When one tries to solve problems in the implicit belief of the independence of the self, it is like repairing a motor vehicle which is constantly involved in accidents without taking into account that the driver is constantly drunk. If one leaves the brain-body system out of reckoning in the attempt to rectify matters, then the most important variable is left out. But one plods along as if the individual, this unit, the brain is all right and all one has to do is to cure the socio-economic conditions for utopia to materialise.

In this condition the organism, the body-brain mechanism itself, is hard put to understand all the goings on; it is struggling to know this state of affairs of utter conflict and contradiction since in its very depth of being it knows that it is made up of all the elements of the universe. It is, in all of its activities, trying to relate and communicate with its surroundings, the environment. But the conditioning is as a separate self, as an identity, obviously it that it causes agony and alienation. This so-called separate self cannot discover any solid, stable 'me' or an answer to the question: who am I? In normal life, all one does is play the various social roles that are based on a reaction-reaction behaviour within the social system. But the search for one's real identity goes on.

The question may be asked: since the separate self has always been there, why is the turmoil so great today? Perhaps, by and large individuals functioned earlier within certain stable social set-ups that were not governed by rapid changes and one's position in society was relatively stable. This stability extended to one's context of existence in the universe within the given world view. With the beginning of the modern era in the seventeenth century and the rapid growth of industrialisation, urbanisation and the philosophy of crass consumerism that has become the global way of life, all socio-cultural boundaries have been eroded, and there is no certitude even in any world views, unless it is a reversion to fundamentalism as a last-ditch battle. The brain has no time to adjust to changes occurring in all walks of life, not excluding the environmental changes. A new order based on intrinsic equality is a long way off, just as in the case of socio-political and economic equality. The different parts are not coordinated, especially psychologically since thought itself is based, as yet, on hierarchy and domination and subordination principles.

Thus nothing is clear even externally, in this age of transition when even the views of the cosmos are far from clear and the old ones no longer provide adequate answers. Perhaps, these are phase-changes, like what Prigogine (Artigiani 1990) speaks of the time of dissipative structures. One can imagine the state of affairs in the brain, given the enormity of the problem. This is the uncertainty, and the cause of violence and upheavals since every aspect of life is destabilised into several contending problems, their solutions, theories, etc. One may create artificial identities, old or new, but they are not one's natural or spontaneous creations. They are created more out of a sense of insecurity, clinging to a so-called reinterpreted past. These are reactive attempts which do not create security since it is a reaction to the others who also are against it as mutually dependent enemies.

The inner psyche is still looking for 'who am I?', who one is, and no amount of external solutions, in the absence of the overarching umbrella of Consciousness, will bring about any lasting peace or contentment. The organism somehow knows its true nature, or at least that what is given is not its nature. But in the present trance-like conditioning one continues to grope in the hope of 'tomorrow and tomorrow', little realising that mirages continuously recede and will never marterialise. The first sign of the awakening of Consciousness is to be aware of this false image, the false changes, this hope against hope, this untruth. This is the first step towards a new dimension which, without being stated may bring about the radical transformation that is so imperative in bringing about the shift in Global Consciousness, in all walks of life (Malik 1995a, b).

Science has undergone revolutionary changes in its conceptions not only of nature but also of its own workings. It has come a long way not only from a Newtonian universe, but even in terms of Relativity and Quantum Theory with the development of 'Copenhagen Interpretation'. For example, Planck's constant "now renders description of nature inherently stochastic"; and Heisenberg's Principle of Indeterminacy "shows the impossibility of a full and complete mnemonic picture of nature". A combination of both these produces a radically new epistemology in which the scientist participates unavoidably in the picture of nature that he produces. Niels Bohr's Principle of Complementarity recognises the fundamental complexity of nature, "forever repudiating any monolithic reduction of nature to a single level of reality describable in a single language. At the same time, applications of these ideas to chemistry and biology have revealed the importance of non-material realities, like order and structure".

All these new areas in science, or a new science, talk of randomness rather then determinism: complexity replaces simplicity, mind replaces matter, and aesthetic principles replace mechanical impacts. If the old goals of sciences were antithetical to the humanities or for predicting human behaviour, the new scientific canons "respect the same values as do the humanities, while its descriptive laws may make possible an organisational paradigm that will allow history to rise to significant levels of theoretical generalities". One such example is Ilya

Prigogine's thermodynamics, wherein he talks of `dissipative structures', open systems far from any equilibrium states, as thought earlier. Such a model may apply to the study of history and civilisations. Prigogine argues that dissipative structures model the process by which matter organises itself into higher and more complex systems. The self-organisation of matter,

> explains the origin and evolution of living forms and also the emergence and development of the systems in which living forms are organised. The latter is said to include the course of development of eco-systems and even civilisations. The potential of Prigogine's thermo-dynamics for the historian is immense. A science that could track the development of civilisation would give us a model for the organisation of our data, a way to extract meaning from the cacophony of events, and a device for explaining history (Artigiani 1990).

Science has been governed by Newtonian systems and Gallileo's knowledge, i.e. gathering facts to make it a whole which rested on a timeless idealisation. It posited a nature made up entirely of matter and forces, forces which act on matter but do not change it, i.e., it is a static concept that does not allow nature to alter qualitatively. It was a mechanical model (as followed in history and social sciences) of nature that is indifferent to time, where potential and kinetic energy is constant so that any strictly mechanical alteration is wholly reversible. Thus Newtonian forces leave dead matter substantially the same, although the positions may have changed. Newtonian sciences cannot explain the existence of scientists who create it!

Irreversibility is the key to Prigogine's revolution. If nature is irreversible it is not indifferent to time. Time is a fundamental part of nature, not just a device for measuring nature. This means that with time built into it, a historical nature would be one in which new forms of existence could develop as a result of concrete experiences. These new forms, in turn, could constitute wholly new levels of phenomena, dependent in their antecedents but not reducible to them. Dynamics would then become profound, for movement would result in qualitative change leading to increased complexity and new laws of behaviour. This is like a science of systematics theory, for it would be the very evolution of a structure over time through experiences that defined the structure. The structure would be self-referential, like a work of art. Science thus absorbs the epistemology of history, for it describes nature existentially as the narrative sum of its experiences. This, in short, is Prigogine's science, rejecting monolithic idealisation of nature, but embracing Bohr's Complementarity and developing different languages to describe nature in its several stages (Artigiani 1990).

Dissipative structures thus are often systems exchanging matter and energy with the environment. Because it can draw upon environmental resources it can maintain its internal order even though that order is far from equilibrium. Therefore it is open to variations in environmental inputs. A dissipative structure is always vulnerable to evolutionary developments. Thus structures follow function and are dependent on environmental fluctuations. In summary, dissipative structures combine freedom with order, stability with change, internal with external factors. Their self-consciously Aristotelian character describes a nature in which dynamics is significant, for now nature not only moves, it also changes. Change, growth, and development are now fundamental to nature like time. But change takes place through a process of evolution punctuated by non-linear departures occurring when a system is driven through a stage of complexity which exceeds its organisational capacities. This leads to bifurcation points — catastrophes endured. Continuity and discontinuity, order and transition succeed each other in ways which can never be predicted. All structures are the result of wholly random occurrences, but structures once in existence are far from a state of equilibrium, as these can govern their internal behaviour and thereby sustain themselves. All these laws could be applicable to the study of history and social sciences. Prigogine's science is about what matter thinks about itself, once matter gets complex enough to think, in the sense of what history has not done in the very narration of it!

Prigogine's Bernard instability, of replication, all at the molecular level, suggests that the emergence of civilisation, like a phase change, is a wholly unpredictable event caused by free and creative people as they react to environmental factors. In other words, it suggests that a new civilisational structure would demand greater environmental resources than the simpler organisation preceding it. In open systems many variables are involved; in this way boundary-structures are defined by the system itself, to be defined into higher forms or be crystallised. Details of such aspects will have to be worked out. It is a mind-effected, mind-affected world — a snake-eating-its-tail symbol. When mind transforms matter, it may leave behind a template that reconstructs the creating mind in any succeeding intelligence encountering it. Works of art are obvious examples of how the artist effects his work, the medium, the latter affecting the artist too and the viewer as well. One could say, in a similar way, how technology has affected humankind albeit it was created by it, e.g. cars taking over man's organisation.

In this way a physical record of historical experience survives to programme future actions, in a manner quite like the DNA molecule which is also a system of organisation. In the case of humanity, it is its capacity to record and communicate experience symbolically that most affects behaviour. Recent social theorists have developed the idea of a cognitive map to explain the process by which environments and experience are encoded to orient behaviour. The cognitive map is a set of symbols held in the mind that represents the environment and preserves the record of ancestral experiences to deal with environmental challenges — a data bank and programme constituting the cultural complex relating to one another and their world. The maps are meant to match the environment, and like a thermostat maintains homeostasis. Often the map is clumsy and seldom recognised and or noticed; people are unconscious of it, of how to use it and read it. It is only when systems of values in it are most important like the hexagons of Bernard's instability, that transformations become possible. In other words, when knowledge and experience fuse into values they undergo phase change. If this does not happen, civilisation is unable to match internal changes, and environmental changes, then enters catastrophe phases. One can play the game conscious of these processes, or be overcome by reactions and chain of events including ways of explaining one's self. There is no meaning of history; there is meaning in history, the meaning people give to their own experiences when they map and thereby order it. History is not deterministic but self-referential for the purpose of testing their validity. To create non-linear departures or psychologically quantum jumps, civilisation requires, at this crucial juncture both historically and in terms of evolutionary goals, that we learn how to fuse knowledge and experience into values. This may be done by self-organisation, self-definition, and redefinition of cultural values that are not antithetical to nature. This would bring about the that revolution humankind today urgently needs (Artigiani 1990).

> Om
> That is Whole
> This is Whole
> From Wholeness emerges Wholeness
> Wholeness coming from Wholeness
> Wholeness still remains.

VII

Violence-Nonviolence: A Binary System

The present century is marked by violence, both visible and hidden. A heritage of all the previous centuries, it haunts us increasingly in tandem with the rapid onslaught of urban-industrial civilisation. No region of the world, or culture, is free from it.

How is one to conceptualise violence in order to understand it? Will it not helpful one were to broaden the notion to include not only the occasions and threats of physical harm but also other forms of diminution of personal integrity and autonomy? The phenomenologist may see violence as a rejection of powerlessness; others may see its manifestations in a society in terms of their fundamental conceptions of human nature. Whatever the conceptions, the role of the media in escalating violence cannot be by passed. This it does by highlighting out of proportion terrorism, warfare and all the ugly incidents, often transforming real societies into theatrical spectacles. In extreme situations participants are very keen to dominate the coverage as part of 'live' dramatic effects, even if it means to kill or be killed. There is also the historical aspect of tracing violence regionally, and attributing it to one community or another. Violence in the home, work place, and so on, though these areas are not classified as criminal areas, is indicative of serious psychological disorders which are widespread and yet have not drawn much attention. While the study of the external manifestations of violence is no doubt necessary, it is the even more dark hidden chambers within the psyche, where this violence is primarily generated that require close study. These inner dimensions are not restricted to those available to modern psychological analysis of the West. This chapter lays emphasis on the experiential dimension within the framework of consciousness, and sees violence-nonviolence as a binary system.

Violence is universal both in its practice and its condemnation. People are terrified by it and yet are fascinated by it. They seek it out in films, videocassettes, literature and newspapers, as if violence in real life is not enough. From times immemorial violence is part of tradition, social institutions and religion. People's ambivalent attitude to violence may be because violence and power go together. Etymologically, violence means 'to carry force towards' something. This can have endless meanings; maybe all human action in the normal sense wherever the ego is involved, implies violence. Even otherwise, it is clear that violence is related to physical force, injury or harm to another or even to one's self with some intensity. Its psychological complementarity is vigorous psychological abuse. This is meant to disempower the other, to exploit in many other, often subtle devastating ways, within the 'domination versus subordination' paradigm of survival. The harm or injury to be caused is intended, pre-medidated and foreseen, although there are various dimensions to this statement. We need to consider the viewpoint of perpetrators of violence, and that of its victims. The perpetrator of violence may not see himself as violating another person because of his dominant position; he may see his action as quite 'natural'. Moreover, we need also to consider the context within which we are discussing the issue of violence, its purpose and the specific situation.

Violence has physical and psychological aspects, as also personal and institutional aspects. There are personal violations of the body, and of groups — slavery, racism, communal attacks, ethnic cleansing, war, terrorism, riots and so on. In all cases one is trying to coerce the decisions of one's adversary, physically or otherwise with regard to his right to determine his life. It may not always to possible to determine where fundamentally such violations take place. But we can certainly take into account the diverse ways of human behaviour, physical and moral, in the context of violence and its definitional range. At the same time, one cannot help reflecting that human interaction involves, concomitantly, a whole range of cooperative effort in cultural traditions. Without it, one would not survive in the institutional framework of social structures, knowledge, language, arts, etc. There is the aspect of altruism also, within any given cultural context and also that of love and compassion, empathy, sympathy and other non-violent dimensions.

In the twentieth century, the power to act, to interact in bodily and decision-making ways, has been curtailed on a largescale, by someone or the other. In other words, growing disempowerment of persons has taken place over a long period of time. This process has spread in all conceivable directions, to threaten the very fabric of society and culture, disturbing the identities of individuals and communities — the way they see themselves both at the cultural and psychological levels. Violations have reached gigantic proportions, becoming self-destructive for humankind and even the planet itself as a consequence.

Power at one level arises for reasons of survival, in terms of basic needs — food, shelter and sex. Today, yesterday's novelties have become necessities; so that the range of basic needs is related to consumerism, which is an endless game. But more importantly, power is related to domination of one kind or an other. This is a central fact not only at the political level, but in many other areas, say, in interpersonal relations in the family. What is paradoxical is that the same political or religious leadership continues to emphasis or spread the message of peaceful interaction, altruism, non-violence, and peace and harmony. There is also greater consciousness of human rights in decision-making processes. Nevertheless, perhaps, because power is related to desire and the latter is in modern societies insatiable, despite all statements to the contrary, violence is inevitable. The point is that desire, power, violence, domination, control, competition and so on are interlinked at all levels.

There are then certain self-defeating characteristics, actions which have collateral effects mainly on civilised life since all areas — agriculture, transport, housing, arts, literature, knowledge and what have you — are run by this basic paradigmatic system. Civilised life requires cooperation, consideration, altruism, and a symphony — like intermeshing of interactions at various areas of life. If every member is at odds, there will be no harmony; this is especially true since modern society also lacks any holistic worldview as the motivating force, which traditional societies had as a guiding force in all their interactions. All earlier creative interactions, which have produced agriculture, language and literature, arts and crafts and so on meant acting in concert, to coordinate the vast spectrum of cultural phenomena; it was not to impoverish others but to enhance the quality of life, not defined in terms of quantity, allowing each one to express the essential human capacities. In the absence of a holistic world view in both public and private lives, controlling authorities are employing more and more of physical control, which in the long run has had disastrous effects — since it is imposed and is not self-sustaining in any way. Self-restraint must come from within. There is power in the positive sense of empowering people, and in the negative sense of disempowerment — it is the latter that has overtaken modern existence.

Words not only have different meanings, but give different meanings to the world around us. They are the medium through which we structure our experience, make our world, so to speak. This kind of plasticity allows us to redescribe the world or make adequate conceptualisations of it. There are however negative aspects to language. Elsewhere we have noted that the world in actuality is mixed up with the symbols and languaging we use to describe it — it is taken to be the reality. Language thus obscures significant distinctions, causing confusion that can

lead us into fallacious lines of reasoning. The expanding connotation of the word 'violence' may be one such case. The dictionary gives seven different meanings to the word, ranging from
interpersonal, social and political violence. The additional
meaning attached to the word as psychological violations and
attacks on personal rights may involve a whole range of meanings and conceptualisations. There are thus overt and covert
areas of violence. The former may be at the social and political
levels; covert violence may be at the institutional, say at the
school level, to ensure order and obedience to rules and regulations. A distinction also may be made between the use of
force, and violence. When we describe a phenomenon as violence, we imply a moral judgment against the use of force. The
word is emotively charged and has a prescriptive function. It
also implies that one has some notions of a non-violent ethics
in mind, which may not quite be spelled out except in a sense
of not causing harm to anyone, verbally, physically — passively
or actively — and so on. In spite of using the word 'violence',
however, we may be without any guidelines of behaviour in
specific situations.

The commonest form of violence in the modern context
may be seen and defined as gratuitous, impulsive, excessive,
unreasonable or immoderate aggression. It is irrational, blind,
immoderate. It bespeaks the impatience of desire that refuses to
postpone pleasure and that refuses half-measures and compromises demanded by reality and the law. Psychologically, it reveals accumulated resentment of all the frustrated desires of the
past. It involves narcissistic exaltation of the ego, which is
achieved through the illusion of having sloughed off all constraints. If a whole community is involved, the illusion is shared
and becomes real for everybody. It means a new mythology.

* * * * * *

Whatever the definitions of violence, the modern world is

deeply involved in active mental and physical violence. Concomitantly, there is the opposite yearing, for a state of non-violence. The wish, individual and collective, is somehow to overcome violence in order to bring about a non-violent and peaceful state of existence. At least 230 million people have been killed, premeditatively and systematically, in so many 'big' and 'small' wars in the present century. This is besides deaths due to man-made epidemics, 'natural disasters', famines, accidents and so on. Why has the situation worsened, despite all attempts to overcome violence?

All the violence seen around us is a direct consequence of several unexamined assumptions which form the framework of reference for the contemporary world. One such deeply entrenched guiding force is the binary system of confrontation dualities. For example, violence versus non-violence, domination versus subordination, man versus nature, you versus me. In the early evolution of man these notions may have served humankind best for the purposes of survival, against predators. But this paradigm continues rigidly long after its functional utility is over, to the detriment of humankind. These and the other dualistic paradigms are cases of overspecialisation, that has led to disastrous results. We are all not only witnesses to it but participants in it. Of course, the elite — the haves — who lay claim to responsible action for the transformation of humankind into a peaceful society share a greater burden of guilt than those at the receiving end of the socio-economic-political hierarchy since the latter do not have a 'holier than thou' attitude.

Thought processes cannot but function within the binary system of duality. Undoubtedly, this phenomenon brought about in Early Man a rapid growth of mental operations, especially with the ability to form symbolic and linguistic structures. This power of abstraction, through memory, allowed Man to project a future event from the experience and abstraction of a past event. This intellectual growth increased exponentially, especially with the beginning of writing about five millennia ago. From now on, thought processes were to dominate human activities. Thought was no longer aimed at the sheer physical survival of the species. Instead, the game of survival was at the level of ideas, language and symbols. The binary paradigm became predominant with the onset of what is labelled as the modern era beginning with the seventeenth century, when 'man versus nature' paradigm gave man tremendous powers. At this time there was also a separation between the secular and the sacred order. The latter was no longer considered necessary in the context of this-worldly life. Perhaps, this is what brought about a rapid growth of scientific, industrial and technological developments. It also, concurrently, brought alienation all around. Nevertheless, despite their obvious disastrous consequences, almost all of humankind continues to function on the basis of confrontation dualities. In all probability, the functioning of humankind is located in the old mammalian-reptilian 10 per cent of the brain. The rest of the brain continues to be dysfunctional by and large, except in rare moments, and more so within rare individuals. In this evolutionary sense, the human brain as such is in disorder. Humankind continues to function within its myopic view even though the post-modernist findings suggest that man is not the sole creator and destroyer of the universe. Also, as yet there is no substantial and effective deity — except in a ritual sense — which may be propitiated and meditated upon beyond the body-brain material self of the persona in which the brain predominates.

The nature of thought is to create dualities and to fragment reality. This also forms the baseline of our times, with the domination of the rational-analytical left brain where linguistic structures are formed and located. Language itself is causally structured in the paradigm of conflict, in 'either/or' statements (day versus night, light versus darkness). Today, the findings of relativity and quantum mechanics, biological sciences, chemistry, medicine, and so on tell us otherwise of a continuum, of a unified field. It is the holistic right-brain world view that suggests complementarity, simultaneity and interrelatedness. Such was the world view in most traditional societies also. Thus, *yin* and *yang*, refers to the same idea as *purusha* and *prakriti*. It refers to a world where there is a 'you and me', 'individual and society', 'man and nature', 'man and the cosmos', and so on. The linear and either/or paradigm is included within the larger context. Linguistic structures are meaningful in this world view within the context of a continuum, a spectrum with varying shades of grey in between the extremes of black and white. Here, all operational functions and variables involve interlocking relational processes within the totality that is knowable by the right non-verbal brain, in harmony with the left one. Nevertheless, in any understanding human behaviour — whether through philosophy, psychology, social or human sciences, most attempts continue to be governed by the modernistic — Newtonian-Cartesian — principles and paradigms. This may be why no headway is being made.

Unprecedented violence is taking place in the twentieth century at the same time that non-violence, peace, harmony, love, compassion, sanity and balance — as moral values — are vociferously being preached on many platforms — religious, political and social. The pendulum of thought swings between the binary system of 'violence-nonviolence'. Thought notices violence and states that it is bad — an evaluative statement — followed by another judgmental statement that one must move to the opposite ideal, non-violence. It is in the nature of thought — whatever example one may take — to swing perpetually like a pendulum, between what was and what ought to be. Thought thus becomes a pretence for actual action, since this movement is really from an abstracted past to an abstracted future. Living in abstractions, taking the food to be the menu, all symbolic-linguistic images that are comparative and evaluative are taken to be real. Any statement about an experience obviously is not the experience itself. But one is so thoroughly conditioned, socially, that one believes that the abstract commentary is reality.

For example, when there is violence, physical or mental, it is a fact; yet it is judged as bad since it causes discomfort or pain. This thought is followed by another that violence has to be replaced with non-violence which is good, since it is the ideal goal, not an actuality existentially. Of course, making a statement about the latter does not bring it into existence except as an escape away from 'being with it' with violence, an actual existential state. In this subtle way thought, as ego and as linear time, maintains its control, staying away from the *now*, the present. Since the latter remains elusive, the organism lives in contradictions and is deprived of its ability to live fully.

This living in abstraction, away from Be-ingness, is itself violence. In evolutionary terms, all overspecialisation leads to extinction of the species. Thought as applied to the understanding of violence is an example of this. Thought wants to get rid of it — push it away — in the belief that pontificating about non-violence, the opposite, will enable us to achieve the goal. But contradiction is inherent in trying to achieve a relative if not perfect state of non-violent society wherein peace and harmony will prevail. It may be noted that in all these pious statements it is the same linear-time framework that governs all 'action', especially so in all of modern life, i.e. from an imperfect state to an ideal perfect state, both being abstractions. This psychological attitude is widely pervasive, from personal relationships to social goals, towards which one is striving to reach, or achieve 'one day'. Similar is the hope of peace on earth, when one day, plenty will be available, with long life and no sickness, and when love and compassion will come forth spontaneously. These are commonplace statements made today. It is little realised that the root of the crisis of modern civilization lies at this 'one day' philosophy, simply stated.

Included in the linear paradigm is the causal notion which dominates modern times, of some kind of logical connection between event A and B, especially at the psychological level. This causal connection may not really be there except in terms of a social agreement to provide an explanation within a specific context. This is especially true of violence-nonviolence, which is a psychological issue. By seeing a causal connection between the two, one hopes to get at the roots in order to get rid of violence. The solutions, however, continue to be dictated by external signs and symptoms which are in fact conceptual metaphors of the abstracted movement of thought. This overall process creates a powerful mirage, which does not provide any actual solutions of reality. Living in abstractions it does not allow one to experience the 'here and now' of one's existential experiential states. The absence of the latter causes agony to the body-brain organism which, as a psycho-biological system, demands a sensitivity of being alive moment to moment. This need is no different from wanting to breathe moment to moment, since there is no such thing as breathing in the past or wanting to breathe in the future.

The movement of thought disallows the experiencing of the 'what is'. To illustrate, one may be angry, violent, in conflict, in pain and so on — all these states being an actuality at the given moment. But thought as the commentator, immediately passes a judgment — which is socially conditioned in us — that it is a state to be avoided, overcome or replaced. Obviously, one says, who wants to be in these uncomfortable states which are the cause of such anguish? The commentary further states that there are certain practices to be followed as given by various systems and authorities, which if followed will eliminate the undesired state and create the desired state. This, however, implies that an action is required by the one who is in this state of discomfort. Or, rather, first there is the thought about a state of discomfort — the word itself is evaluative — followed by another thought which states that 'discomfort' must be overcome immediately. In this way, one avoids, unconsciously, experiencing any state, especially any so-called uncomfortable state. It is the nature of thought to avoid being actually sensitive to experiencing. The self-conscious 'me' in this way is governed by the stimulus-response mechanism, which is impulsive and reactive, giving the appearance of a great deal of action taking place. This statement needs to be elaborated further.

For operational purposes, in a sequential linear sense, there is in the knowing process the following sequence. There is first perception; second experiencing which is stored; third memory as encoded knowledge which forms thought; and fourth scanning through itself as 'me' or 'I' which suggests action — the thinker here being thought itself. Of course, one has split the 'reality' of one continuous movement for purposes of analysis. This is the limitation of a left-brain understanding, which one must be aware of. In any 'true' knowing, it is all one simultaneous process, this true 'understanding' or 'knowing. All the talking about breathing does not bring it into existence — it being a normal process which happens by itself when all the functional variables take place in consonance and in coordination. The universe functions optimally at the same time if one human being is to breathe. However, while functioning through thought as thinker, ego, and time, to simplify further, there is a gap between perception and action. For instance, when there is perception and experiencing, then as social conditioning, looking into memory of the known stored symbolically, it is thought that suggests the next step of action. But while this is taking place, there is a time gap since by now existentially the universe has already altered its state. Thought does not allow perception itself to be action, since this minimises its role as the controller. This process is true of any instance when there is a thought — a languaging symbolic statement — about any event for which any action is undertaken in one's life. Every moment, during this gap, the dynamic universe has already come into another state. There is another aspect worth pondering over: it is the same thought which states that it is angry, it itself wants to overcome anger; also, is not the thought of anger itself yet another thought? Is this not an endless regression or solipsism? Is it therefore possible for thought to take any action in the true sense of the word? Thought may, for instance, make a statement about wanting to swim or cycle but can one actually do so with mere words? All this requires an action of 'doing it', which happens itself, suddenly like an 'aha' experience.

The significance of this argument is that the disturbance and frustration in this violent-nonviolent movement is because of the inability to actually experience the 'what is, the now'. Thought, which is an operational vehicle, nevertheless finds it more convenient to operate by creating false images, so that it can continue to dominate. It is comfortable for it to escape the present. Thus, when one's thought becomes one's identity, all of it at the psychological level, existence becomes one continuous state of resistance to any existential-experiential states. In this way, it is experience turned to memory, stored symbolically and codified as in a computer, which forms the self-conscious 'I'. It also acts as a self-referential, self-generative movement, where time, ego and thought are one. It continues to build itself up in a binary system where it is both self-glorifying and self-effacing, in a mirage-like structure. In the binary system of the self-and-the-other, of 'this-and-that', of a separate thought structured self operating in dualities expressed symbolically, the experiencing moments of 'now' happen less and less, though one may not be aware of it. At the same time, thought continues to make statements that it is longing for such thoughtless free states of happiness, if not of ecstasy. Thus once again it continues with its binary game — the game this time being about going from one state to another, even if it implies eliminating itself. The ego cannot possibly eliminate itself since the me and not-me are not two actual separate entities. Can one lift one's self by one's boot straps? No two separate thoughts are autonomous, albeit it appears to be so since thought moves very fast; and the self-conscious self, an entity created by thought itself — since the thinker himself is thought — cannot grasp this process, busy as it is creating a debate and dialogue with its self, within the closed system. The debate is to the effect that there is one thought and another and a third one of the me or self which appears real and claims operational or functional superiority as the controller. In the process, the self little realises that it is really a part of the split-up whole; the controller being the controlled.

The anguish *per se* is due to anger itself or any other state of discomfort. The discomfort does exist, and one is conditioned from childhood to re-cognise it. But the frustration that leads to violence is the inability to reach the ideal state, which one is told one ought to be in. It is a conflict between the dualities created by thought, which creates resistance of 'liking-and-dis-liking', of what could have been and what should be, and so on. This is the source of violence — the resistance of thought to experience sensitively (be with it) any emotion or feeling with-out labelling it, be it violence or pain. It is the inability to accept the 'what is' that causes violence. It makes one feel incapable and handicapped, this inability to merge the head and the heart. It causes a feeling and emotions of incompleteness, of being socio-psychologically inferior within. In the socialising process in the modern achievement-oriented world, one feels left out in any case, so that one is always looking forward to that one day, to be complete in some mirage-like future. This process goes on all of one's life at all levels, most of all in one's head as a dialogue. This process itself does violence to the organism — brain and the body — which demands a sensitivity and vulner-ability to the moment of Now; it demands that all the senses function purely and fully in the totality of life wherein thought as an abstraction is subservient to this wholeness.

Unfortunately, the senses do not function fully and purely, to experience the fulness of life. Instead, the 'I' as thought, in linear time, and the achievement-oriented one-day philosophy — even if it is to achieve *moksha* — dominates one's daily functions. This overspecialisation of a partial area of the brain has already caused the rest of the brain to be in abeyance. Even if the other areas of the brain are functioning there is no in-terchange of information between the left brain and right brain activities, which might bring about a balancing, a harmony within the organism. Instead, there is the neurotic, almost schizophrenic, behaviour of humankind because of this discordant functioning of the two areas. This split movement itself does violence to the brain-body mechanism. For example, in deep sleep one is not aware of one's body, thoughts, emotions and the rest of it. One refers to this state as a very peaceful, refreshing, undisturbed state. But the moment one wakes up from this sleep, thoughts flood in, as the chatter of the 'I', which states that it has to do this, that and the other, or reminisce about the past or dream of the future, etc. In short, all the addictions begin all over again. In all these activities — desires, wants and so on — one is seldom conscious of them because one so totally identifies with all of this paraphernalia. Paradoxically, at the same time there is a strong urge — very soon during the day — to end this incessant movement or chatter appearing as major problems of everyday life; and to wish for a quiet head, a moment of peace, a longing for silence. People seek to do it in terms of altering circumstances, such as by changing things, going away somewhere, starting new relationships, as also by changing the intake of stimulants, all of which they hope will accelerate the pace of bringing about this moment of peace. This moment does appear, but much too briefly, when one obtains the desired object. It is very fleeting since it is in the very nature of the mind to chase 'what is not'. In this process, it soon wants to move on to a better object, repeating the old pattern that itself amounts to a secondhand experience, being an abstraction. One is seldom aware of this movement of thought, which forever wants more and more, always a better and better 'tomorrow and tomorrow'. All this is built into the framework once again of this 'one-day' philosophy.

Thus there are two movements going on simultaneously, one that enhances the ego and the other which is trying to get rid of it. The same thought characterises itself as the thief, and at the same acts itself as a policeman. It is almost like one leg going in one direction and the other in the opposite direction, thereby causing extreme pain and suffering. The organism and instrument of functioning in the world is thus doing violence to itself. One is speaking here not of any personal brain but that of the brain of humankind itself. This state of affairs gives one an inkling into the disorder and entropy that man has entered into; and this is where the roots of violence maybe found.

Why does thought behave in this particular mode? Those moments which are completely experienced — whether of pain or pleasure — seldom become the basis of residual thought that recurs again and again. For example, in everyday life one speaks of pain and anxiety situations and all of the other negativities, almost as stimulus-response reactive systems, and seldom of the happy complete moments. But because unhappy moments are part of the unexperienced experience — the stimulus-response reactive process — these are to be avoided and replaced. In this way thought is repeated, since it has become the accumulated unconscious storage system of symbols and images. These are the thought processes which, through associations, are activated repeatedly in various forms and garbs. This is what sets up chain reactions of the movement of thought. Out of the manifold characteristics, not only learnt in this life time but also inherited genetically in the evolutionary process, a few form the core of the persona. This is the ego, of dependent origination, not an enduring entity by itself or independent. It is like a shadow which is subject to change within the universe of a reaction-reaction, 'being-at-effect', system. Because wanting to remain incomplete is inherent in the very nature of the thought system, the ego sets itself up so that it can perpetuate itself indefinitely, by wanting to be complete. Its illusionary nature, however, causes the feeling of loneliness and isolation, since one is not aware of the shadow or the illusionary nature. In this way the self wants continuously — or pretends to want — completion and interrelatedness with the world around itself, which it considers also to be consisting of discrete entities like itself.

But how can shadow become the substance? Can a mirage become the real thing? The personality is like a bucket with a hole. It is constantly trying to fulfil itself as also attempting to measure the ocean. It would take aeons for the bucket to do this, even if there was no hole in it, then too, it would not give one any idea of the vastness and immensity of the ocean or the universe. But addicted to its blind belief, the ego must remain incomplete; the incompleteness in fact is a necessity for the survival of the ego. This it does either through repeatedly wanting pain or pleasure or in the pretence of erasing itself. The wanting more and more is a need for this pretence of wanting fulfilment, satisfaction, and so on which one believes in this externalised social conditioning to be outside oneself, albeit both the self and the outside (and inside, external and internal) are really conceptual abstractions. These shadows can do nothing, even to become one with the world. But this game becomes an addiction, a world of make-believe, where one is chasing one's own tail. The self is naturally in agony, violent, because the separation from the holonomic order — the separation of the self from the other which was created for operational-functional reasons, as a psycho-social-biological entity — itself is violence. Also, since it is not aware of itself as an operational entity and takes itself to be real, the 'I' is by its very nature violent. In other words, the becoming without the being is negative and destructive. When the becoming is a subset of being, then the operational part works smoothly and in consonance with the universe by being the universe itself. Thus it is the 'who I think I am' that is the problem, not 'who I am' since that am I in any case.

Given this upside down understanding of the universe in the context of a hypothetical entity, the metaphor of a shadow trying to become the substance or the wave believing itself to be separate from the ocean, violence is built into this self, though it sincerely wishes to be non-violent.

This is true even of the ego wanting to erase itself, to merge with god, the eternal and so on. This movement is, to repeat, by its very nature disturbing an original state. In sheer ignorance one is therefore creating violence in the very broad perspective of psychologically getting to the roots, not merely restricting one's analysis to external violence. All acts begin in the mind as mental phenomena. They are very powerful because their movement is imbued with energy — which one sees operating in everyday life at the physio-psychological level, in the stream of consciousness, be it negative or positive. Thought is matter coded into it and it is thereby also technology since it acts as a medium or vehicle of transmission of communication and allows one to relate at a very mundane level within one's universe or to the world.

In short, all duality beginning with thought as a movement of a binary system is violent since it is constantly striving, and is achievement-oriented in order to become something other than what it is — itself. It is this non-acceptance of 'what is' at the mental level — happened in the unconscious paradigm of linear time, one is socially conditioned in the relative world of comparisons to believe one's self always to be one step behind or ahead, more or less than an other, who may be real or ideally imagined. It is this non-acceptance of 'what is' at the mental level that begins the anguish of all the fears and anxieties associated with being not up to the mark in this world of reward and punishment, which one creates for one's self. If one is sitting on a chair and does not wish to acknowledge the fact, it becomes impossible to get out of the chair despite all efforts. If one gets out of the chair in ordinary life quite easily and effortlessly, it is because there is a tacit acknowledgment of the chair. It is only after this acknowledgment of what is, that one may go elsewhere if one so desires, and not otherwise.

The sitting in the chair — or any other similar example — is experientially acknowledged and not in any supposed mental statement. The latter is possible for purposes of hypothetical discussion, but it will not allow the actual action to take place when it comes to jumping out of the chair if there is a fire in the room. In this manner the two domains, that is, the domain of action and the domain of commentary or chatter on the action — say differentiating between the menu and the food — are mixed up and not kept apart. The chatter about food is not the same thing as food. We all think we know this but seldom act accordingly. Humankind has in this very specialised and fragmented manner lost itself in the maze of words that seem so real, in an 'as if' food reality. The ceaseless use of thought does not allow one to be present in the Now of an experiential moment where all the senses function sensitively. It allows one to be agitated and disturbed, not to be one's self. Rather, one's beingness is limited to the little 'I' of the persona that is not in touch with the larger context which is bigger than itself. This is the root cause of violence. There is no escape from it since in trying to extricate itself the agitated self creates further violence by getting caught in the web of its own creation.

One may question the statement that one does not experience the eating of food or any such other 'experiential' action. One may counter and say that we all seem to be doing so all the time — feeling, sensing, having emotions — that we go around seeking emotional sustenance and fulfilment which seems to be goal of all desires and wants. We need to examine this counter argument deeply from our own lives. Take the example of food.

When one desires or wants any kind of food it seems like real pangs of hunger, because the ability of the specific dish to satisfy one's self arises from a previous memory. (One's wanting food at the appointed hour of lunch or dinner itself is conditioned by the cultural context and Pavlovian conditioning). The need for the morning tea maybe felt as an empty feeling in the stomach or it may be just a matter of habit. In either case, it is an empty feeling commented upon by the mind, which states the need for tea by searching its memory bank. This is to say, one seeks the satisfaction in terms of a previous experience which one has learnt psychologically in the culture. This may not have been the case the first time one experienced something, at one's own initiative, or because one was told to do so in one's childhood. But the act was recorded as pleasurable, or painful, and it was repeated or avoided because the mental phenomenon of the 'I' seeks its continuity by wanting to repeat itself. This is because once some situation or act is labelled as uncomfortable or painful, it is to be avoided. All labelling in the cultural conditioning tells one evaluatively what is good for one and what is not, and the game becomes one of avoidance or attraction. In modern society the emphasis is more on avoidance of pain and discomfort, to put oneself in a mental shell, isolated and lonely. This alienation is common in the urbanised modern world. While externally it may appear as if people are very gregarious, one fails to experience true participation unless one is willing to give up this mental isolation. But the anguish for togetherness, to avoid the loneliness yet give reality to the separate self simultaneously, which Einstein called an optical illusion, is built into this seek-pleasure-avoid-pain reactive principle.

Once something has been tasted, the second time it is a repetition of the first experience and not an original experience. It is the encoded memory which recreates the sensations of experience as triggered off by the encoded mental statement. Words are powerful, being physiological matter itself. They come with many associations of sensations and feelings that make one believe that one is experiencing afresh the feeling of hunger, or thirst or whatever else. One is also comparing the drinking of tea with the previous recorded evaluative judgment — this is good, bad or better, etc. — and this absorption in the commentary avoids the actual experiencing. The experience is hence not a firsthand one but a repetitive secondhand one. This is a simple example of how in everyday life one believes that one is experiencing life moment to moment when in fact one is not. In many ways, living unconsciously in the structure of culture, one's life was over the moment one was born — if not in the womb already — since one comes already loaded with some preconceptions, potentialities and predilections. In many ways one's life is already fixed and programmed by inheritance, both physiological and cultural — by one's *sanskaras*. Acting unconsciously one is under the dictates of the *sanskaras*, which condition may be altered any time provided one is awake or conscious of one's true nature. Any idea of one experiencing life, normally speaking, is a myth because all one does it to repeat.

The chain of repetitive actions which seem to arise from this lazy self which claims to be very active, causes fatigue and entropy since the freshness of life is missing. The accumulation of this vast amount of unexperienced experience burdens the mind or the organism with garbage, or it clouds the freshness of the brain cells or the mirror of the mind and thus does not allow one to see life afresh moment to moment. The mirage of the self as a mental phenomenon deliberately makes sure that the cleaning up process does not take place since that means its demise, albeit it continues to pretend to want to get to that state. The game is very subtle for this self-referential self, to even notice it, covered as it is with so much dust gathered over the aeons.

What has all this to do with the problem of violence and non-violence? Is one to live with violence since this is a fact and is determined; and even cannot be eliminated since that is another thought? It ought to be clear that if the programmer itself is the programme, this state of affairs itself or even the asking of the question of eliminating violence is couched in the same old paradigm. This is the same old double-bind situation that avoids the 'what is'. This avoidance itself is the cause of doing violence to one's self or the organism. In such a state the instrument needs to be cleaned up before any action is taken at any level.

It may again be asked: in this impasse what is one to do? If one is asked to do nothing, that is impossible, for apparently it is to ask that violence be accepted. Also, how is one to eliminate thought, me, etc.? One may indicate certain directions in this process which lie beyond words, and beyond the hypothetical entity of the little self which itself must realise its limitation and helplessness, whether at the intellectual level or verbal level. The initial step is to be awake, conscious and attentively aware of the fact of seeing a mirage and not be carried away by it. Once one knows that what one is seeing is a mirage, this itself is a beginning in directions totally different from what one has been following. One is talking of a vertical take off, as reptiles did into the air leaving not a trace behind, and when in the air harboured no trace of yesterdays that were discernible in their smooth flight.

In short, there is nothing really that the 'I' or me, a shadow — a hypothetical entity considering itself as a separate entity — can do despite all its planning and pious intentions. All that shadow can do is only to pretend and assume or subsume the role of a creator and maker. It is like the clown in the circus who pretends to be doing everything and yet makes the children laugh because they know where the real action is. But as adults we take the clown, the ego, seriously as if it is the real actor. There are of course roles which one plays socially in the larger cultural context as part of one's conditioning. Within that framework matters seem to work well and one even gets the false feeling of freedom. But this is because one is not conscious of the fetters within which one is working. This is well illustrated by the fact that often the underprivileged take their position for granted and are not even aware of their bondage until someone, or some book, makes them conscious of their state of misery.

Many things happen often despite one's intentions — at a personal level — as millions of variables, nay, the entire universe operates simultaneously to bring about an event. It is a chain of multi-layered processes in which everything is linked to everything. But if one positions one's self as a separate and independent entity, it causes immense suffering and alienation since its linkages with the universe, with be-ingness, are broken. It is like a swimmer attempting to go upstream to reach the source; continues to struggle, hardly making any progress and yet continues to hope that 'one day' he will make it. Little does he know that if he flowed down the river he would make it to the ocean without effort. That is how it is with life. If one flowed along with it, all the variables would support one's effort without allowing one to bang into the rocks of suffering.

A piece of woven cloth, which is formed by the five major elements, via the seed of the tree, has come to be present in the shop through a whole chain of events. An electric lamp, likewise, needs wiring, plugs, switches and of course electricity; all these units must function as a unit if the lamp is to give light. The light will not burn if any unit insists on its separateness and works in isolation. The clearing of the false notion of a separate self is the first step towards understanding violence since this notion is based on the perpetuation of duality, conflict, strife and the underlying factor of desire of movement.

The categorisations of the modern world are within the binary system of 'avoid-pain and have-pleasure' that misses out the 'what is' and the actual of life in general. And what one does not observe choicelessly or does not experience fully becomes a residue of further thought stored in the unconscious for future linkages, which have their own logic of mere associations, whether at the dream level or at the waking level. All forms of resistance, both pain and pleasure being a part of this, are potential thought formations remaining symbolically as abstractions for revival and recall, whether immediately or thirty years hence. That is why the same pain or pleasure events recur over and over again without one's wanting it, as psychological associations forming one's personality. Simply put, 'what one resists, persists'.

The idea of avoidance is how the 'I' has learnt to survive through the ages. Obviously it has worked so well, including the idea that it will be free one day. But this is the subtle unconscious fooling, the mirage, the illusion, *maya* which keeps each one entrapped in the game. The crucial issue is to be aware of all the processes, of thought, of the emotions of anger, pain and the other uncomfortable feelings within the framework of the binary system operating within the paradigm of survival. This awareness itself brings about an experiencing of 'what is', be it pain or any other discomfort with which then one is 'with it'. In this sense there is no me or self or 'I' experiencing; there is an impersonal-personal kind of experiencing through the energy of consciousness which allows this choiceless watching, observing of a moment to moment living. There is no ideal state to be achieved. About anger or violence, for example, one does not follow the conditioning of the commentary or thought which states that one should be nonviolent or stop being angry, etc. The commentary is not the actuality; and this being away from the actual moment to moment experiencing is itself the cause of violence to 'what is'. It is not violence *per se*, which is manifested externally and symbolically, and which one labels constantly, that is to be eradicated. Living in the commentary is to live mostly in abstraction, at conceptual levels whereby the living of life is almost completely eliminated. For the *yogi*, one who is awakened from the slumber of this unconscious functioning, the impersonal-person, the day of normal people is night and night is day. No longer does he live off the menu of words and concepts.

The experiencing of the 'now' moment breaks the binary system of duality; it makes for one singularity, an integral wholeness where conflict, fragmentation, divisions and the like are non-existent. These are eternal moments of completeness, of be-ingness that leave no marks or residues which will form the basis of thought as matter, and as concepts. This experiencing is like a tape which erases all of yesterdays and tomorrows, in these moments of total action, experiencing. The information is still stored, but no longer in the form of a 'reaction-reaction' stimulus-response system. The information system is now in the files — memory bank — which may be consulted whenever desired at will. It is no more out of control, coming up reactively and at whose controlling end one was a pawn. Earlier, one was affected by people, opinions, circumstances, etc.; one was not the cause in the matter, one was not responsible for the universe of one's life. At the new level, one is the creator in one's universe which includes all that is around one at any given moment of 'now'. It is a clean and pure mirror, the instrument, which reflects truly. Nevertheless, since the mirror has a tendency to collect the dust of memory, of experience, it needs to be cleaned in the same way that one does one's body, house and the like. It is like breathing moment to moment which is a must if one is to stay alive, for there is no such thing in actuality whereby one breathes in the future or the past.

The 'I' has nothing to do in this cleaning process; for if it has then one is back to square one. The process is through an impersonal choiceless observation where there is no identity as such that intervenes to judge, to evaluate. The separate self now merges into that which it was originally, which it was in any case. But through a false perception it gave itself the nature of a permanent entity, like the bubbles and the waves on the surface of the ocean considering themselves as separate entities with separate existences. Conceptually one may make these differentiations; but the totality of all of it being the ocean cannot be minimised or eliminated. The smaller units are to be perceived in the larger context — the subset cannot be understood without the major set. It is the absence of the latter that is the cause of the endless frustration and alienation, attributed to various 'causes'.

The awareness of all this watching and witnessing, as consciousness, in the context of violence, the nature of violence, etc. is all tied together as one package deal, where there is no self and the other actually, since it is all Self or Consciousness. This state is not describable. It is ineffable as the mystics tell us, and yet it is known and experienced by every human be-ing. But it is not given much attention since one is caught up in secondhand descriptions of it that form one's goals and ideals as images of one's self and others; and this is what takes one away from the authenticity of one's be-ingness. This awakening and shift of perception is a first step towards that transformation which will make one's understanding topsy-turvy, since that which one calls reality becomes unreal and that which one formerly called unreal and ungraspable now becomes real. There no denying it, though is no adequate way to represent it in the phenomenal 'normal' world.

So what is one to do except sit and watch and do nothing? What is happening in the universe is already given as happen-ing. The fact of being a man or woman, or anger coming up is already there; any denial of it does not alter the fact of its givenness and no amount of analysis and the seeking of causes will alter it. The givenness in that experiencing is a re-creation of what is in a self-aware consciousness. In this process of creating what has already appeared, by choosing what is there in the experiencing, that which is disappears and gives way to the next moment. Mentally it is the re-creation of anger, of violence, pain and so on that allows the state to disappear and in turn creates space for love as there is no 'I' in this experi-encing, no striving of a separate self.

Each of us is aware of these thoughtless moments, espe-cially any aesthetic experience when there is a no-mind state, so to speak; such as when one is listening to music, watching a painting, in mathematics, gardening, in all creative activity be it scientific or otherwise. These are the moments when one seeks peace and silence, or receives it in communion and harmony that is beyond duality. The organism desires such states for its fulfilling and satisfying original state, and is no longer caught up with the addiction of the commentary. From now on it is a discovery from moment to moment that each one has to find out without repetition from one's self or from any other information. In this sense it is the mentally experiencing of violence (not the physical action) which is equally a state of ecstasy when one is in touch with the self, or away from the non-self which is the root cause of it all!.

VIII

Integral Listening as Communication

8.1. *Introduction*

A pre-eminent component of human and animal identity is language. There can be no social interaction and behaviour without it. Language is also a part of cultural life styles since it allows for both communication and identification.

Human language is not static; it changes along with other variables. It is at the centre of human societies because language reflects patterns of thought, it being the output of the social and cultural conditioning fossilised as symbols and images. It provides cohesiveness of any life style, creating a cultural identity with its norms of behaviour to which members of a group can respond and identify. This, in turn, creates a sense of confidence. The cultural frame of reference of language is intangible to most of its participants under normal conditions; but it becomes evident — with disastrous results — in times of trouble, when various outside impacts threaten this linguistic-cultural identity. Obviously, language is crucial for one's style of life, as an expression of originality, of our uniqueness as individuals, as a part of the larger society and even of the species.

This would be commonly agreed. The emphasis in this chapter is, however, on the area of communication and integral listening, the silence which forms the background of true human communication. The context of this discussion is the beginning of the modern era with the seventeenth century. This period is also important in an evolutionary sense, since it is during this period that language along with all other associations begins to dominate human behaviour, reflecting an overspecialisation of a distinctive area of the brain. The positive advantages have thus become detrimental to the further evolution of the human species.

In this context, the functioning of the cerebrum, in the brain, which consists of two distinct halves needs to be noted. Each half of the cerebrum functions autonomously in sorting out information received. The left side is more logical, rational and involved with the use of language; the right being more intuitive and syncretic. This is part of the evolutionary growth of bilateralism in this integral development of the nervous system, which gives success and survival advantage to the species, to get around — for animal species in general and man especially. But when the two halves, it has been studied, do not exchange information and get severed for one reason or another, then a dualistic, or split personality is formed. Man today is in this oppositional duality psychologically, the neurotic, schizoid life of saying one thing and doing another. This psychological state has something to do with the unidimensional use of language, the left brain, which simply stated is the cause of the alienation and agony of humankind.

One of the most conspicuous indications of this functional asymmetry, or laterism, is the phenomenon of 'handedness' (right or left). Dramatic evidence has come through the observation of the effect of damage to the respective hemispheres. If a part of the left hemisphere is affected by accident or disease it can seriously impair certain higher intellectual faculties, such as speech, in a way that seems not to happen if the damage is sustained in the corresponding part of the right side. Today it is recognised that both hemispheres are involved in higher cognitive functioning, but that there is a division of labour and fundamental modal differences between the two sides. The two hemispheres process information differently, and are organised differently. It is not surprising, in view of the fact that they are separate entities, that they should have differing views of the world.

In spite of their marked differences there is a modal complementarity in the functions of the separate hemispheres. One could generalise and say that the left tends to think in words, and the right in images, but the division and specialisation of their respective talents go much further than this. For example, the left side is associated with logical, verbal, rational, analytical, convergent, sequential and linear order of thinking; the right with intuitive, emotional, non-verbal, syncretic and divergent, simultaneous and spatial behaviour. There are fairly obvious risks attached to a brain that operates on a double-plan system, the gravest being that the two separate mental domains might vie with each other for control over the organism. The most important bridge to avert this is the massive bundles of nerve fibres that establish reciprocal connections between corresponding centres in each hemisphere — this is the corpus callosum that carries something like 200 million lines of cables analogous with a telecommunication system. The combination of the two systems in any time far more effective than one on its own. Just as even if one may see with one eye our stereoscopic vision is essential, so also is stereo-cognition necessary to function fully, in harmony and creativity. Thus alone may one respond but to a universe and nature which is similarly organised but which may never be revealed except in its own style of dynamic functioning — in all its various dimensions.

Every individual brain is subtly organised in different ways, its psychic configurations creating unique patterns of ability and personality. Each individual psyche makes its own response to the inherent dualism of the mind/brain just as it responds in its unique way to the cultural dualisms that are a feature of all social structures. In general these responses are made as unconsciously as those of the left/right dominance determining reflex itself: we are quite 'naturally' of an artistic or scientific cast of mind, or, for that matter, political orientation. The divide between the East and West may also be seen, beginning with the seventeenth century, to be the dominance of the left-brain activities as against the non-verbal, non-logical and 'fluid' methods of eastern philosophies; or as available in traditional small-scale communities, the likes of which have disappeared in western thought but are, surprisingly perhaps, making a return via the new vision of science itself. At any rate, the tendency of the left brain to control the whole brain, which psychologists have noticed, is worth mentioning. It has been noted that the left brain has a distinct tendency to 'take over' and feel itself responsible for all the actions of an individual, even to the extent of rationalising those decisions made by its right partner that it has played little or no part in making. There is surely an analogy in the functioning of modern society, of rulers, political and other authority — the experts and their systems — who over-bearingly claim to know what is best for society. One of the philosophical problems thrown up by the confirmation of the dual mechanism of the brain concerns the nature of consciousness. If modern science — Relativity and Quantum Theory — has cast doubts on the nature of space, time, matter and energy which are no longer tangible, solid 'things', then what is the self, if neither of the hemispheres is the separate self that it pretends to be — nor can it be the corpus callosum — then what is it, this Self and Consciousness?

This brief introductory background is necessary in the context of the dominance of the western mode of communication prevalent all over the modern world. The stress is on the holistic functioning of an integral human being, where both silence and language are necessary.

8.2. *Language and Communication*

Contemporary man, within the context of the modern era has consistently endowed the power of communication to expressive language. Due importance has not been given to the negative dimensions of this fact, which is easily seen in the domination of the media — whether newspapers or audio-video means. The latter often act both as the judge and the jury in all modernised cultures where there is a chase for name and fame — this need to be splashed in the headlines. This has led to a social behaviour which reduces the unspeaking, non-expressive other to a void, a negation. In many earlier non-industrial small societies, the power of the unsaid was of equal crucial importance. A large part of communication was carried out taking into account this aspect of the functioning of the brain which now has been lost in the use of mere expressive language, this constant internal and external chatter.

The overspecialisation of cerebration restricted to the reptilian-mammalian areas of the brain is the source of a great deal of anguish and sorrow for humankind. This is obvious from the tremendous need that so many feel to take to drugs, alcohol, sleeping pills, tranquillisers and so on. It is a clear indication of the urge to stop this incessant restlessness and agitation further provoked by a consumeristic overkill advertisement. All external remedies of the serious crisis are, however, futile, as we see from the self-evident destruction which is going on in the world despite all the good intentions. The fundamental issue is an internal — psychic — one. It may be called psychological or spiritual, but is closely linked to the development of language and the framework of philosophies governing it.

8.3. *Speaking and Listening*

Modern man and his philosophies are grounded in only half a language. Within any discourse, the strength of listening is ignored. What one takes to be a genuine dialogue, is a mere speaking without listening. There is no authentic listening taking place. Fiumara, who synthesises in her works the insights of Wittgenstein, Heidegger and Gadamer, among many others, called it 'warring monologues' (Fiumara 1990). Her vast project covers the domain of linguistic philosophy and especially the area of encounter between analytic philosophy and hermeneutics. It opens up areas for an integral understanding of western logic, and unifying reasons for the philosophy of life and psychology itself — a rare combination. We may summarise some of these ideas, in support of the statements made in another chapter about space, time and knowledge, and about language, in an attempt to elucidate the nature of dialogue and true communication.

Among the widespread meanings of the Greek term *logos* there do not appear to be recognisable references to the notion and capacity of listening. By and large, generally in western thought the system of knowledge ignores listening processes, the simple reason being that it is not relevant in the realm of the so-called practical activity. Here, too, the word that can be associated with 'doing' (action), is the verb *legein*. While it was identified with relational propensities it seems to have disappeared entirely historically (Fiumara 1990). The verb l*egein* has many meanings, such as shelter, gather, keep, receive, which would surely be more conducive to a cognitive attitude based on 'proper hearing', i.e. there is no saying without hearing, no speaking which is not also an integral part of listening, no speech which is not somehow received.

The important point to note is this: an individual can speak only if he is listened to, rather than there being something he might say that one would subsequently attend to 'by means of listening'. In the modern world *logos* has gained worldwide acceptance and *legein* has been disregarded, with its semantic richness. Since this one-half context of *logos* has been elevated to an essential principle, its ruling set of meanings appears to control and shape all of one's rational pursuits. It is easily seen how the mechanism of 'saying without listening' has multiplied and spread, to finally constitute itself as a generalised form of domination and control, ignoring ways of life capable of 'letting-lie-together-before'. If any semblance of an integral being has to arise once again, the vital need to be listened to must coexist, not as a subordinate but as an equal, with the derivatives of an increasingly arrogant *logos*, which is ready even to ignore anything that does not properly fit in with a logocentric system of knowledge.

To illustrate, language already resounds with worrisome expressions such as 'ozone layer', 'greenhouse effect', 'acid rain' - all sad news coming across from nature. One seldom hears this news until these things begin to affect one personally, and not when it only damages the planet we inhabit. This is the deaf logic which dominates modern times, since today listening is thought to be the mere activation of the body's audio equipment, this hearing proper. Hearing basically implies harkening and heeding, and in this way listening is supposed to be a transportation of hearing proper into the realm of the spiritual. Obviously, in this sense it is not relished by a materialistic world. It is precisely this aspect of our culture that rationality has largely neglected (Fiumara 1990).

Modern culture is interested in the monotony of comparing and contrasting the so-called theoretical contrasts which perhaps only represent an archaic warlike strategy transposed into the realm of epistemology. It most of all manages to express itself in the deployment of controversies and invectives. It is an aggressive and assertive culture intoxicated by the effectiveness of its own 'saying', and increasingly incapable of paying 'heed'. In order to survive one has to develop acumen in all such areas of life that no longer bridge the various chasms. It is no longer important to experience the 'thou' truly as a "thou", i.e. not to overlook his/her claim and listen to what he /she has to say to us. To this end, openness is necessary. But this openness exists ultimately not only for the person to whom one listens. Rather, anyone who listens is fundamentally open, and shows concern spontaneously. Without this kind of openness to one another there is no genuine human relationship, this belonging together.

8.4. *Non-listening*

This non-listening has given rise to two types of conceit, one of nations and the other of scholars who believe that what they know is as old as the world. The tacit, ubiquitous belief that recent Western logic represents the most reliable cognitive standpoint appears to characterise worldwide culture. Has not listening, as ancient art, been gradually lost in the noisy inflation of discourse and by the infestation of pseudo-symbolic language? Or, conversely, could it be that the vital, eco-logical rationality has exhausted itself in its overwhelming production of talking and since it is more interested in hunting than in cultivation? Has this intellectual heritage not caused the conceptual connections of other traditions to disappear? Has it not given rise to an idea of truth which befits the vacuum it has produced?

Today, intellectuals appear to be comfortably intent on a logic that has little interest in diverse logical paths. At the same time, there are countless voices which continue to propound wise and rational arguments, arousing in us a desire to appear as equally rational, and holistic in approach. Paradoxically, these voices give assent only to the idea of competing in the same old style. While they are a major theoretical trend in search of the capacity for listening, their claims of being rigorous knowledge systems are only a demand to be listened to. The need is so impelling that even double-edged means are adopted by the adherents of these systems to ensure that they are heard and accepted. Not being sufficiently conversant with the attitude of openness, they confuse acceptance with indoctrination and consider the standards of success and popularity to be the conditions best suited to guarantee knowledge claims. If the quest of seeking 'totality' or wholeness is to be interpreted as a 'togetherness' of our ecosystem, then the listening approach, in its concern for letting-lie-together, becomes important in clearing the blind-spots which have arisen in the social and human sciences because of the dominance of this halved logic.

8.5. *Language, Science and Power*

Disciplines dealing with the study of man, governed so long by a very powerful and long-lasting paradigm, must come to terms with all kinds of abysmal irrationality. In the scientific domain, on the other hand, there is a growing concern for the unfolding proliferation of context-less achievements; namely 'local scientific successes which precede even the remotest notion of how to deal with them ethically or how to integrate them into the needs of the totality'. There is a whole world yet to be discovered, not of unsolved issues but of relationships among things we know, of ways in which they might fit together. The tribal god of intellectuals, called objectivity, has to be replaced with one that sees whole, thinks whole and hears as a whole, effortlessly.

If one is asked how a philosophy of listening can 'coexist' with the multitude of languages that speak the language of the west, the only language spoken on the earth, one could reply as follows: the point at issue is probably the attempt to perform an exercise whereby we can develop a capacity for genuine listening, that is, an attitude which occupies no space but which in a paradoxical sense creates ever new spaces in the very 'place' in which it is carried out. This is what will open up the possibility of a philosophical activity that is no less rigorous than the logocentric tradition which tends to scoff benevolently at the magical as the absurd. This new philosophy does not oppose the tradition of western logos nor excommunicate anything that 'normal' rationality is unable to grasp or systematise (Fiumara 1990).

Western knowledge, in this excessiveness of rationality and logocentricity, leaves no room for listening. In fact there is one voice only as the accredited source of knowledge — the celebrated science-power equation revealed in the coincidence of technological development and social-political hegemony. The games of power are, however, seen simply at the superficial levels and not at the deeper philosophical levels — say language as power. But whenever one defines the effects of such power in terms of control and repression, one draws upon a formal notion merely understood as a function that is carried out through the acts of forbidding, restricting and distinguishing — the definition is not empowering. Knowledge is also information technology, saturated with both scientific and intellectual discourses constantly reaching out to inform, permeate and mould. In all this the process of listening becomes nothing more than a minimal philosophical aspiration or the concern of a minority. This is why unless listening, a part of this holistic approach, comes to be seen as a radical and valid point of departure, the biosphere will become uninhabitable. This is why a radical turnabout is essential, and a change of route is worth the attempt at the level of world views and philosophic foundations.

There is a risk of being 'turned to stone' by constantly fitting our experiences into the old mould, of the known, and asking within the old paradigm, the predetermined reality, of too many whys which prevents one from seeing and listening. The path rooted in listening constantly locates the various linguistic games, based on the class of meta-languages, that are being played, in order that one can express and correlate the results of a variety of disciplines, where they are more deeply rooted and possibly in the interactive categories which rule our primal experience of the world.

At the moment all research attempts seem to be just copies of an ideal prototype, basically being an aversion — almost — towards listening to the rich multiplicity of 'reality'. This approach seems to be linked with a background of profound fears and the resulting defensive postures that express themselves in a tendency to reduce knowledge in general to a set of principles from which nothing can escape. A relentless battle is waged as an attempt is made to organise everything in that light, or shadow, of the best principles of knowledge; a chronic struggle of territorial conquest where 'territory' now is a set of notions and principles for constructing reality. It is this predatory aspect of knowledge, which we know from the results, that is dangerous, since it is under this rubric that all considerations are carried out. This is not generative listening. It is not creative and it is not empowering because it is linked to an underlying strategy — first do and then justify — that has even been transposed into an epistemic level.

This meta-structure of the modern world's scientific-philosophical discourse has really taken possession of its own cultural territory, and has established rules of legislative power of what is correct thinking, especially as it is correlated to forms of productivity. It does not allow any questioning outside its system of speaking, *logos,* and no listening is allowed. There are thus 'executives' and 'administrators' of thought and concepts. Unfortunately, this is the cognitive attitude in the pursuit by intellectuals, of language as language, well suited to their habitat rather than to any actual human beings they come across. There is, despite a high level of cognitive awareness, little familiarity with what it means to listen, and one is too involved in speaking, moulding and informing. And, when a chance to listen arises, there is always a suspicion that one might be submitting to a 'warlike' phenomenon of benumbment or of violence, in which 'listening' becomes an anti-philosophical acceptance of an invasive message. In practice one becomes incapable of listening, because there is no time to waste listening to those stories that do not form part of one's own history or, paradoxically, of one's own dialectical overturning. The already known continues to be consolidated by the increasing hegemony of information processing which must be accepted, as enunciations of knowledge. This kind of distortion, the reality-normative blindness which ignores the being and symbols, predetermines the end.

As Prigogine and Stengers (1980) also point out, the dialogues conducted with nature by modern science are similarly codified by the experimental method, which is the basis of the originality of our science and, at the same time, of its specificity and limits. When nature is questioned through experiment it becomes simplified, prepared in a specific way and occasionally even mutilated according to pre-existing hypotheses; and nature will always answer in the frame of the theoretical language in which it is being addressed. The issue is whether there should be only one language, namely that of the questioner!

8.6. *Language, Culture and Communication*

In this more or less shared hegemonic cultural structure, the problem is that of creating sufficient silence to be able at least to hear the incessant rumbling, chatter of a cultural machinery — thought — that seems to have lost its original vitality as a result of its enormous success. Because we are no longer able to hear the noise thought makes, there is alienation and a sense of desolation because of this logocentric dominant orientation which denies that the earlier, the minor or unsuccessful traditions ever existed, or maintains that they have become totally irrelevant. No real dialogue is possible in this blindness. But the same holds true if there is an over-valuation of other traditions, leading to cultural games and presentation of the real, or even imaginary cognitive values of those traditions. This approach is framed within the same game, with its debates which are yes and no games within the dichotomies of rational and irrational, and coherent and absurd. One negates life itself by being dogmatic about this kind of yes-no states. The question is not of making every tradition equal, or allowing everyone access to the highest knowledge; it is about the domination of one form of knowing, the tenet of the single-way-only, about the absence of the balancing of *Yin-Yang*.

The problem that one faces is to be open to the logical structure of openness to one another, to this listening without which there is no genuine human relationship. There has of course to be a fundamental aspect of questioning, but the inability to distinguish between the vital capacity to listen and hearing as such is seldom noticed. The illusion that one can speak to others without being able to listen is, perhaps, one that we all share. The problem of listening might thus be considered the shadow dimension of the epochal development of our culture. One is too busy, for example, with textual analysis as an innovation intended to explore the possibility of 'collaboration' between the text and the reader. The problem of letting a text relate to one may seem rather circumscribed when compared to the vaster and more generalised problem of listening. The written word is important to those who, in the Gutenberg galaxy, are the consumers of printed culture, unlike consumers of the oral ways of the transmission of culture which was widely prevalent in all traditional societies. In the latter case, listening is not restricted in terms of time or space; this is elaborated a little later below.

Where language is concerned, knowing how to listen does not represent a 'further stage' that must be attained. Listening belongs to the very 'essence' of language. Human beings are ever trying to put into words whatever they believe is hidden or absent in the culture. At the same time they are attempting, as never before, to give voice to that which is inexpressible or blocked in their inner world. The 'attentive willingness' to listen is even perceived as an eminently 'futile' stance that need not even surface in modern culture. Humans are perhaps no more unhappy now than in the past, even though one aspect of their condition does seem to be emerging; and that is, people are no longer prepared to accept in resigned 'silence' the many problems that living and surviving involve. A state of dumb resignation no longer seems suited to human beings, and when they are unable to express themselves effectively they feel cheated of something that is rightfully theirs.

> Western thought, and as it has covered the entire globe, has failed to grasp the need to begin to understand and abide by the listening process, as a primary and indispensable requirement for coexistence. In a language which pays such homage to speech one arrives at the point of concealing any culture of listening that might possibly be wedded to it. It is presumed that there is a

stupidity of the person who is listening — who is silent
and does not speak — and might be a tribute to a
logocentric culture that artfully decrees the 'poverty' of
the listener (Fiumara 1990).

8.7. *Monologue and Dialogue*

As stated elsewhere, the way the problem is expressed, the
questioning itself, not the contents or the phenomenon which is
probed, ultimately constitutes a most salient element in the research. The development of the humanities and sciences is
usually characterised, therefore, more by the formulation of
essential questions than by the solutions that are elaborated in
answer to them. Although it is certainly true that the answers are
the material from which the edifice is built, the structure of the
edifice is determined by the type of questions that are asked —
in the sense that the answer collaborates with the question and
produces everything that is demanded of it, and nothing else.
The possibility, however, that the answer eludes the restrictive
nature of the question remains. It might be helpful for one to get
rid of the habit of only hearing what one already understands.
The authentic attitude of thinking is not putting of questions —
rather it is a listening, the promise of what is to be put in the
question. To perceive a clue, one must first be listening ahead
into the sphere from which the clue comes.

By its very nature, a non-listening language sustains the tendency to institutionalise mutual suspicion between areas of research (not to mention between persons or at other social levels), an attitude possibly conducive to an increasingly rigid and
drastic subdivision of responsibilities. Furthermore, in accordance with such an 'urge' to subdivide into categories, all sense
of responsibility with the life of, and on, the earth ends up by
being banned. If this process of 'fragmentation' is continued,
any sense of overall responsibility cannot help but recede indefinitely until it loses all meaning. The insurmountable bulk-
heads between different areas of knowledge are perhaps one of

the most obvious consequences of an underlying rationality that is able to induce cognitive advancements even when it is hardly capable of generating forms of mutual listening among different disciplines. A perspective of reciprocal listening would, in fact, allow for the cultivation of a knowledge in which techniques and types of discourse might fertilise one another to the point at which a philosophical space might emerge without hierarchies based upon peaks of observation that encourage the breaking up process (Fiumara 1990).

When one still does not sufficiently know one's own personal and social weaknesses one becomes incapable of understanding those specific instances that determine the development of different cultures. One may persistently continue to believe in a scientific or ideological fetish and, with satisfaction in one's heroic sacrifice, remain enchanted by it to the bitter end. Proximity to the listening approach may release a faculty for breaking up with respect to 'closed' discourses and an ability to reorganise the most rigidly constituted symbolic circuits.

Authentic dialogue is undermined not only by modes of thought considered as forms of cognitive or ideological violence, but even by standpoints that appear to be absolutely non-partisan, neutral, antithetical to any kind of intrusion. Part of such thinking is its cruelty, aside from its content. It is the process itself that is cruel, the process of detachment from everything else. The halved *logos* underlying the power of culture can be expressed through both assertive and critical means. In both cases an essentially colonising thought, and one that is rarely conducive to coexistence, seems to be the result. One could even say that the *logos* that knows how to speak but not how to listen represents the model of power in its primordial form. If technological and scientific development represents the goal vouched for by the logic of modern culture, and if no other power capable of counterpoising technological advancement exists, one is forced into believing that a technical civilisation is the way in which the non-listening language dominates unopposed (Fiumara 1990).

The producers of the body of knowledge, like its users, almost seem committed to discovering ever more ways of translating into languages that can be exported into everything that is invented by accredited managers of responsibility. A conviction arises that the users will perpetuate their need to learn such ratiocination to avoid the danger of falling outside the dominant language. And any discourse initiated outside the dominant body of knowledge turns out to be so very difficult to think and articulate that it almost seems unheard of, simply because it is unhearable; something only suitable for lapsing into madness or irrelevance.

What one calls 'agreement' and 'consensus' remain major philosophical problems. Productive power represents, effectively, the noetic apogee of the west. But this is not surprising if only one considers that 'productive forces' represent the conclusion and the culmination of the dominant ways of thinking in western tradition. Today, language embodied in vast theoretical systems, in scientific power of producing and eliminating with ever increasing ease, 'competes with the gods'. It confronts the creative power of the 'divine word' and that, in any case, one does not need to listen. It is indeed a language rooted in a delusion of omnipotence and such that it inevitably creates the risk of detonations or Babel-like conditions (Fiumara Ibid.).

8.8. *Knowledge: Importance of Oral Traditions*

The avid assimilation of western philosophical tradition often seems to be aimed at a better articulation of how one has arrived at current knowledge claims, that is, the sort of knowledge which now permits the technological control of both the animate and inanimate world. If one listens to the cultural history of the modern world, the errors may change their appearance and even help us escape from the narrow path of the dominant cognitive system. By listening patiently, humans in the process of becoming fuller persons are able to tell us how their specifically human physiognomy is established. Now, the most archaic images rise to a symbolic level in order to gain some familiarity with the personal and group archetypes that tell us of restoration, mutation and awareness. Something can 'speak' if it is listened to, rather than there being something it might say, that one would subsequently attend to 'by means of listening'. As is well known, mythological and exegetic disciplines agree in suggesting that myths actually celebrate the reinterpretation of an earlier story. It is the capacity to pay heed to a story that allows the unfolding of its meaning; the narrative does 'exist' because it is listened to and thus its sense may reach across and develop into further myths. A propensity to listen thus appears as the condition for all accounts. An account of connected events, in the order of happening, depends on the maturation of a dialogic disposition. The refusal of the history of something is tantamount to refusing that thing altogether. Here lies the importance of cultures dominated by oral traditions. This may be elaborated a little further, with reference to India.

In the understanding of Indian civilisation the transmission of cultural traditions, of both continuity and change, may be seen within the totality of a communication system. Within this system a crucial subsystem is the oral means as expressed, for instance, in the performance of myths, songs, dance, stories, folk tales and similar audio-visual — verbal — forms, all unwritten modes of human communication. In the history of human civilisation it was only about 6,000 years ago or so that the written word became an ingredient for the growth of culture. With the onslaught of urban-industrial civilisation, however, the dynamics of oral traditions which have played a major role in India, as elsewhere, were generally ignored. In recent years disciplines like literature, history, folklore, anthropology and others have recognised the significance of these areas beyond the written word, viz., performance, memory, emotions, artistic actions, linguistic and other literary unwritten texts. This is an area of interest also to oral historians for constructing historical fact, and to others to seek psychological and social constructions of past societies.

Obviously there are problems of definitions, concepts and theoretical models which need to be evolved with regard to notions about oral traditions — taking into account the controversies involved, not to mention the social science debate. At any rate, oral traditions cover a major area of human life, the whole of culture especially as it is tied up intricately with the written word, linguistics and the like in Indian civilisation. The approach to knowing Indian civilisation therefore cannot be restricted to the written word, and this is true since Harappan times (Malik 1968a). Our objective has to be an integral one, a holistic view of the totality of cultural transmission. This is important in terms of current developments when the focus moves away from 'high written forms' in history, anthropology, philosophy and literature. It is a movement beyond normative, prescriptive and ethnographic description of written forms. The importance of global cross-cultural framework — this may be true for this subcontinent also — is clearly seen today. This has happened because of increasing power shifts, and expanding cultural links in a worldwide perspective. In short, it is no longer possible to work within old dichotomous boundaries, viz. primitive/civilised, industrial/non-industrial, tradition/modernity, written/oral and so on.

In other words, no longer may one regard the traditional (oral) forms of less academic and real interest than classical culture in the western sense. The oral and written interaction is part of a whole network of human communication system in which a number of different media and processes are involved. The notion of pure forms is practically or theoretically no longer true. In this process, new terms are emerging, such as 'discourse', 'text', 'narrative', 'performance', 'folk', etc. in order chiefly to bridge the old divide which made it difficult, by and large, to understand the long continuity of a civilisation like the Indian. This allows one to focus attention on comparative questions about historical and culture-specific approaches to cultures, local, regional and all-India ones. The emphasis is thus on the multi-layered nature of the transmission of human expression — especially on audio-visual, verbal, artistic and literary forms. The entire approach also points to the equalisation of human beings — beyond socio-economic and political status — and of ethics. Obviously, it involves a deep discussion of the nature and definition of tradition, say, which is to be seen as a process happening in the present, where verbal/written/oral divisions no longer stand in isolation in terms of some simple generalised concepts but represent a multiplicity of interpretative approaches that are not fixed within binary divides (Finnegan 1992).

Related to this topic of oral traditions, a brief example may highlight the manner in which there exists one of the ways to classify cultural transmission of tradition in India, different from that given in Greek, Latin or Hebrew models of the west. There are three such levels, viz., *sruti, smriti,* and *adi.* While the first two cover the highly intellectualised order of memory transmission of cultural tradition, the third, identified with technical oral literature, consists of oral traditions of the so-called folk and tribal cultures who have no writing but a great sense of creativity at the audio-visual and verbal dimensions. (Are these divisions not related to the left and right hand hemispheres of the brain activity mentioned above?) These divisions in India are to be seen as an organic whole, indicating interconnectedness, interdependence and multilayeredness which may be studied not in isolation as historical, anthropological or philosophical enquiry but necessarily as interdisciplinary and multidisciplinary studies. Further work is required in India, for instance, to see what relationship exists between written and oral in the context of pilgrimage centres, artistic manifestations, and ritual texts; how does the recitation of Vedic texts differ from other forms of chants and mantric incantations? Can one adopt an epistemology of oral traditions, in the field of literature, social history, arts and aesthetics, healing practices, indigenous sciences, separate from the written traditions?

Some of the general critical questions which may be raised in the context of oral traditions (Finnegan 1992) are as follows:

1. What are the concepts and definitions of orality traditions (Is there a time limit of tradition?), verbal, audio-visual texts?

2. What is patterned communication in tradition, in myth, ritual, oral history and literature? Is there such a thing as a neutral text?

3. What are the problems related to collection of data, observation, equipment used, analysis of data, and other ethical and social issues involved during field work?

4. In this seamless area of speech, idea, action and performance that make up living — where there is no clear-cut 'object of study' — how do cultures express their ideas, emotions and actions both in terms of formalised and oral ways? Should not both ways, empirical and theoretical, western and eastern, verbal and non-verbal, be taken into account? Is there any universal category applicable throughout Indian civilisation, or elsewhere?

5. Is orality transmitted by word of mouth alone, or does it also refer to non-verbal media — artistic performance, paintings on rock, monuments, sacred places, etc. — as opposed to literacy defined in the modern sense? In this sense, is not oral tradition an 'open' system compared to the literate one since it is not restricted and receives knowledge from many other senses and sensibilities?

6. Does not this means of communication refer to group identity since the process of handing down is related to a common memory bank — with methods of recall — of particular cultural groups vis-a-vis another group in terms of some generalised tradition of context, myths, genre and so on?

7. Who or what group and for whom does it transmit tradi-

tions, and is there a power group involved (rituals, etc.)?

8. Is not oral literature literature even if it is not written? (Here, can one make a distinction between speech and song, prose and poetry, art and non-art, etc.?) Is it not a contradiction to say that it is not literature since the oral has a literary form? Where would poetry, folk arts, other verbal art forms and artistry fit in this all too generalised label to cover folklore and does it not include items of 'material' culture?

9. Do current definitions seem true, and is the term 'folk' to be restricted to rural, traditional non-literate people, in contrast to modern urban populations who themselves have no verbal arts worth studying and are gradually becoming illiterate through the media of movies, television, etc. without becoming creative as they are passive receivers only?

10. What is the information base of specific cultures characterised by oral traditions? What, in this context, is the theory about memory — *sruti* or *smriti* — is it automotive, is there mere recall or does it involve change by individuals, both in terms of culture-specifics and the brain itself in terms of scientific laws, and what is remembering both as rote and creative and reorganisational recall? Is there a stream of verbatim recall in terms of style, content, or form; and who in a culture is trained to do this memory transmission? Is there not an ideology, and process involved in the preservation of records of memories? Who are the experts and specialists involved in this process, and can these be identified?

Thus, it is not simply a question of 'hunting' for more cogent, imposing truths in the deep waters of the historic past. One will be disappointed if one's 'knowledge' were to be restricted to a familiarity with sets of debatable opinions that are hierarchised into a conglomerate under the pretext of a universalising 'scientific' value. As a result of this one might be tempted into presuming that one can be free of one's tradition; and, thus run the risk of forgetting, losing one's bearings and foundering. There is a need, therefore, to make also an attempt to create a communion that 'springs from the depths of our life'. Hunting out a thinker's exact doctrine eventually seems to end in a constrictive and predatory procedure that lies outside the fertile labours of a listening-based communication.

8.9. *Communion and Listening*

When one adopts the kind of listening mentioned above, it is no longer guaranteed or bound by a guiding thread of linear causality. It is an all-encompassing way of receiving ideas that emerge from universal human traditions. The prevailing ways of approaching cultures do not allow for this to happen since the concern is reduced to a game based on the reckoning and recomposition of philosophical findings. But a listening horizon may reawaken something which is not easily reached through the exercises one performs within the domain of current, normal disciplines (see the chapter on rock art). If the enigma and peculiarity of human nature are rooted in an unutterable crossing of innumerable horizons, an intellectual approach that favours a predominantly 'spiritual' or 'biological' horizon, segmentation may end up by usurping and disfiguring a depth that can barely make itself heard and which, ultimately, deprives one of its generative contribution.

The pursuit of listening cannot be associated with one or an other philosophical orientation. It is a form of rationality that can be thought of as underlying, going along with or reaching beyond, but not as being in opposition to anything. It is an effort that tends to free the movements of consciousness from those meta-paradigms that predetermine it. If it is not seen in this light, any creative need for innovation might relapse into the aims intended for it by the assumptions of dominant ratiocination. One can 'think' about knowledge because one has been told authoritatively about its basic structure. It almost seems as though every irrepressible endeavour to 'transcend' standards has to flow back into the ways of our salient criteria. This refers to a consciousness that is imitative, reflecting, rather than 'false', inasmuch as one is dealing with limits imposed by culture itself and not only by a class or dominant group. Living under the influence of this mirroring and complacent consciousness is not the same as living with an openness to life. It involves constantly assuming and construing the 'format' of life, searching for it beyond our reflecting state. And how could one begin to learn about genuine listening? First of all by eliminating all grossly misleading meanings of what listening is. Among the most deceptive of these is the idea that listening is something imposed by the holders of standard rationality upon those who cannot or should not speak. A large part of the linguistic interaction that underlies human coexistence is certainly not listening so much as endurance or forced feeding, hypnotic induction or epistemic violence; a linguistic game that one would prefer to stop playing as it is ultimately futile and fatuous. When a codified 'inner' life and the normative science of this epoch no longer has much to say, one may finally try to transform the setting and include a life-enhancing awareness of death. When 'life' and 'reason' are isolated in too artificial a manner from 'death' and 'madness' by excessive power of dominant rationality (beyond which nothing can be legitimately envisaged) the complexity of living and thinking becomes relegated to epistemological illegitimacy; as a result they become unheard and unseen, even though they are interwoven with culture itself (Fiumara 1990).

If one communicates in this silent dialogue, one might frame the hypothesis that an orientation towards discourse, rather than towards listening, provokes far more a sense of cognitive security and far fewer demands. While a non-listening speech tends to favour 'simple' mechanisms that divide and extinguish, listening requires a laborious attitude more consistent with problems of integration and living. And the gathering that allows these qualities to unfold is not so much concentrated on a single point to the exclusion of others; it is a silent acceptance that tends to unite through the attitude of integrating and letting live. The communion stemming from this gathering perhaps simplifies without reducing and overcomes without winning; it re-creates time and space as a depth that may become inhabitable by every language. In this way, one may be able to exercise one's listening potential and reveal features emerging in the modes of western language — before they hide. In other words, one should be able to listen amidst the din. The vector that moves away from the word as mere sign discloses levels of inner life the existence, or survival of which is dependent upon listening to those numerous levels. As a result of this silent attention, threads of mental life are granted which make coexistential resonance, or recognition possible. This allows an incipient structure to be inserted into the life of thinking, rather than rejecting or else reducing what we hear to the most elementary semiotic mechanisms.

8.10. *Evolution and Listening*

From an evolutionary viewpoint the ability to listen authentically (as distinct from simply receiving a signal) arose not so much in terms of perfecting linguistic capacities that had been attained, but rather as a kind of unutterable rupture, as silence that indicates a crisis beyond healing. The evolution of the higher primates probably cannot be accurately conceptualised as a process in which existing semiotic faculties are pushed to their absolute limit, but as a 'hole of memory', a fissure in earlier habits. It is a new reality, equivalent to something that did not exist earlier — not a discovery of what was already there. It is almost like a failure in memory, a sudden silence in the routine of survival, a cognitive support that disappears and leaves one dumbfounded.

If language represents a specifically human way of 'transcending' biology in order to arrive at the level of culture, one may nevertheless see that the patterns and archetypes of that transcendence call for a 'dialectical' procedure which contrasts these archetypes with their own 'opposites'. If, however, authentic dialogue needs to have time for the silence of listening, a system of dialectical opposites does not seem to have any room for a listening silence. The force of silence is as deep as the 'infinite' of one's inner world. As long as one remains firmly attached to one's capacity for creating silence the 'external world' will not be able to completely reabsorb one by aggravating the danger of an illusory monism that excludes the serious problem of relationships: either everything is within one, without the world, or everything is outside one, in the world. Every undeserved (arbitrary) exclusion of a voice entails the paradoxical effect of producing more noise. For as long as the function of silence is somehow respected one does not run the risk of getting lost in the meanderings of one's own verbalisation or, conversely, of losing one's self 'centrifugally'. To illustrate, the question of environmental degradation in terms of the excess of something and the extinction of something else, is hardly addressed with regard to the world of language; even the linguistic domain could be irremediably damaged by an unmonitored saturation of written or spoken words and by a concomitant lack of silence. A sufficient 'degree' of silence could be regarded as a medium suited to enhancing the linguistic life of the symbolic animal and to averting irreversible deteriorations. The enormous evolutionary impetus that is gained by the experience of being listened to and, therefore, of being able to express oneself, constitutes a phenomenon that cannot legitimately be undervalued in a dialogic context (Fiumara 1990).

The highest function of silence is revealed in the creation of a coexistential space which permits dialogue to come along. But to keep silent does not mean to be dumb. A dumb man still has a tendency to 'speak'. He who never says anything cannot keep silent at any given moment. Keeping silent authentically is possible only in genuine discoursing. Silence is an isolator but, simultaneously, the most efficient conductor. 'Silence' on something in fact prevents that something from gaining access to any categorisation. In its creative function, silence basically represents a way of being with the interlocutor. Contrary to the general notion of silence as something opposed to dialogue or as the expression of a desire to keep one's thought inside a well-defended fortress, is a very fertile way of relating, aimed at the inner integration and deepening of dialogue.

The creation of an empty space, or distance, within a dialogic relation might be the only way of letting the deeper meanings and implications of that relationship emerge. The nature of silence is as a gap or distance in which germinal meanings can be developed. (The hollow of the drum, the spokes of the wheel around no-thing). This no-thing, this emptiness, can be compared to silence and is probably called 'no-thing' because it is not manifest or immediately perceptible; it is not a question of thoughts or emotionally tangible events but, possibly, only of that which organises them from within and allows their springing to life. Silence is not an interval but one that unites sound (Malik 1989a).

In general, modern man is constantly doing something — speaking, thinking or dreaming. This continuous involvement with language might be considered an automatic, repetitive defence against the separation anxieties that silence can represent. These discourses may not always be justified in terms of the relationships in which they occur. Silence, therefore, when regarded as an 'opposite' situation to speech, must not be considered necessarily as a defensive of an offensive stance. On the other hand, it may indicate a healthy desire to set aside certain automatic defences that are only intended to fill emotional vacuums. This silence may also represent a desire to abandon quasi-symbolic or pseudo-symbolic expressions that are only fictitiously oriented towards the stipulation of truth conditions. It is also a willingness to seek the origin of a more mature capacity for recognising and tolerating the gap, distance, or hiatus between the self and the others, between language and reality.

Perhaps, transformations that are required for coping with life may only be attained if one becomes capable of abandoning something, say a basic assumption — an explicatory Gestalt — for which one has developed cognitive 'addiction'. What one really needs is the detachment from a hypothesis that is constantly and unconsciously introduced into the way in which we confront a problem and which, itself, makes the solution of that problem impossible. In this case dialogical relationships can degenerate into exercises of impossible logical seductions in which one does not even hope to be convincing, since one is attempting to gain the other person's interest through pseudo-revelations, in any case. When the 'exploration' of inner life is undertaken in this manner, it is deformed into an involuntary parody of the 'life of the mind'. This is why, in this so-called idea of progress, increasingly it is said — especially by modernised Indians — that pursuing this inner life is hardly worth taking seriously, as though the journey towards interiority were only capable of revealing emptiness and noise.

8.11. *Listening; Humanities and Sciences*

In the humanities and the sciences there is an enormous attraction for explicatory theories. Increasing emphasis in contemporary thinking is placed upon the need to clarify issues, giving rise to numerous explicatory 'mythologies'— a stance that insists upon investigating until an 'explanation' is found. This attraction for explicatory theories prevails so often that it hastily declines into a blind prejudice in favour of a particular type of explanation. In other words, at the very moment in which we 'arm' ourselves with a cognitive model we are, paradoxically, justified in losing interest in the object. We no longer consider it as enigmatic since it is our turn to speak to it — the object no longer has very much to say to us. Obviously these considerations subtract nothing from the enormous value of scientific research and theories since one is not so much interested in theories as in the 'relational' spaces between theories and the object of one's knowledge.

In the twentieth century, human culture is moulded by the advancement of the humanities and the sciences. But it seems to be immersed in a kind of multifaceted understanding that exempts it from stopping to listen. Not only does this attitude 'guarantee' the identity of the person who controls understanding, but it also establishes a one-directional, pseudo-dialogical circulation in which the only 'virtue' that is revealed is that possessed by the researcher, the adult, the analyst, the teacher and so on. Aware of the partiality and provisional nature of cognitive models, one could moderate these assumptions and consider all explicatory ventures merely as a set of instruments to be used for reference — leading to a more authentic orientation towards the object. Attempting to understand the multiplicity of models and the difficulties involved in their integration could also have the effect of a salutary demythification that would provide enough silence to live with, and let the other speak.

Clearly, a knowledge, and therefore a culture, sustained by the indifference of a non-listening rationality is being massively produced. Hostility, in contrast, appears to be an intense, acute, and tiring emotion that is only experienced with difficulty. The indifference of non-listening is incomparably more extensive and less demanding. It extends in time and space without losing anything; it abandons itself to its inertial course, drawn by the mechanisms of a conventional, noisy language that impedes the inner silence of the individual. Perhaps, from a remote perspective, humans might be seen as a species that moves in waves formed of masses, as though the vestiges of the reptilian brain operation in each of us (however disciplined it might be by more evolved structures) did not function so much in the individual as in the extended groups; the mass to which there is the risk of returning with the powerful excuse of the great pseudo-philosophical ideals of this age.

'Objective' knowledge provides one with defence mechanisms that cannot be underestimated inasmuch as we become inclined to an idea of cognition rooted in the illusive belief that it is neutral and that it will protect us from any involvement with the repercussions of the cognitive event. Such knowledge may entail the presumption and the illusion that it does not share in the event it produces and in the problems that it generates; as a consequence knowledge-makers would be exempted from participation in such problems. 'Real knowledge' may claim to be neutral in the sense of being 'intellectually healthy', aseptic, uncontaminated by subjective or traditional obscurities. It is not a question of adhering to one of the anti-scientific fluctuations punctuating cultural fashion and opposing the triumphs of rationality, just as one may follow with enchantment the advances of scientific knowledge. The point at issue is the capacity to create enough distance from a Cartesian, rationalistic stance — all too lonely and secluded — which presumes itself capable of summoning and repelling deceiving demons. The language of knowledge can degenerate to the point at which it arrogantly excludes all proper hearing; it might be a question of holding back such an attitude that increasingly involves not simply individuals but the entire species. The myth of Narcissus, who sees nothing but himself, might indicate the extreme opposite of an open dialogic field that unites the human race (Fiumara 1990).

In the modern world, the output of knowledge tends to be expressed in an endless series of sophisticated informatics, so specialised that they induce an incapacity for mutual exchange between discourses which then become increasingly fragmented and specific, or even seem to purport opposing theses. The problem of listening may then appear as an issue that should not even be touched upon; as something totally inappropriate or futile. Listening may, in fact, seem a worthless concern until it is capable of considering as a whole the myriad of subtly opposing accounts that culture constantly produces, and consequently tries to impose with western 'rigour' and 'elegance'.

While one is presented daily with the possibility of choice — as with products — or of casting a vote, one does not have the 'opportunity' — or freedom — to envisage and theorise the grid-like nature of the vast cultural output that constantly shrouds one. Superficially this search for greater awareness might seem to be a generic exhortation to tolerance. When one examines the problem of listening more closely, however, one is also confronted by the crisis of modern culture tormented by splitting mechanisms, and perhaps so lacking in methods of reconnecting that the most disquieting of questions — such as linking branches of knowledge — are forced into silence since they cannot even be adequately articulated.

8.12. *Listening and Development*

If the world community persists with its current pattern of development, perhaps the planet at the beginning of the next millennium will be more crowded, more ecologically unbalanced and more 'spiritually' vulnerable than it is today. Acknowledgments of such possible crises, however, are not so much 'forecasts' of what may happen, as the expression of an attempt to delineate the conditions of human coexistence as it might develop in the absence of adequate transformations. Obviously, there is something profoundly lacking in the rationality that underlies a scientific culture with which planetary trends are inextricably interwoven. The present way of 'listening', aims not at viewing but at attaining a kind of predictability of the other's moves. This way of paying attention is not an authentic listening experience. It is a kind of self-interested and manipulative 'eavesdropping'. A good part of dialogic communication is based on the possibility of at least one of the two interlocutors being able to understand. This only means reproducing the paradigm of a rational power emanating from one mind that encompasses, grasps and contains another subject who is not equally skilled at understanding. But listening is not simply an activity of applied thinking in which, with a minimal amount of personal involvement, one occupies oneself with an object of study; it is, on the contrary, a procedure the authentic advancement of which depends upon one's ability to re-enter one's own self (Fiumara 1990).

There is a general tendency to remain within the framework of linear causality, that is, within an explicative description of reality which implies a string of simple causal relations between events. But such an abstraction neglects a vast array of factors at this simple level of elementary explicative forms. Isolating a relationship of simple causality from the apparent chaos of innumerable connections sometimes offers us a partial explanation of reality and, thus, a criterion for creating some degree of order. At a certain point in the development of a science it is no longer simply causal relationships that provide the key to the explanations, but the connections that one may gather between them. In this epistemology, one comes up so frequently against links of reciprocity in causal relationships that one begins to wonder if they are not a general rule. Simple causality establishes a subordinate relationship, whereby each event in class A produces and determines an event in class A'. But as research continues one finds with increasing frequency that even though one has discovered the causal relationship A-A' at a certain time and under certain conditions, there are circumstances in which one discovers phenomena that correspond to the relationship A'-A. The simplest case is that of reversible causality, A-A'-A, with the result that linear causality is broken and cyclic paths are introduced. This type of relationship is generally known as circular causality, raising the method to a higher level (Fiumara ibid).

One is thus aware of the incompleteness of a culture founded upon discourse rather than upon a capacity for heeding and corresponding. To undergo an experience with something — be it a thing, or a person — means that this something befalls one, strikes one, comes over one, overwhelms and transforms one. And when the event tells, beyond any shadow of doubt, that one does not know how to listen, some kind of homeostatic tendency inevitably comes into play which repairs the event, annuls its consequences and prevents it from 'existing' any longer; that reality does not correspond at all to the 'well-founded' accounts and that it is, on the contrary, something quite different. At that moment something happens to one, howsoever reasonably secure one is with one's beliefs and habits, one's 'reality'. And, above all, the event tells one unequivocally that the only reality that functions at the moment is the reality of the event in which one is involved. In other words, the authentic attitude of thinking is a listening experience which could come across like a storm and overwhelm one — silently — distancing one from the constant din of the discourses that saturate modern culture, ready at all times to convey on the market the most sophisticated 'philosophical' devices against the storm. Listening involves the renunciation of a predominantly moulding and ordering activity; a giving up sustained by the expectation of a new and different quality of relationship. But this giving up is not a loss, sadness — rather it is a learning, joyful and in harmony a positive experience that humans can have 'directly' by being' with it'. This is when language also touches one with its essential being. In meeting the unknown, the unspeakable, the other, one must let it talk. When that is no longer possible for one, then death has begun. Conversely, one could then justifiably say that until one is capable of getting something unknown to talk to one, one has not yet begun to live and interact. The accepted event impinges vividly upon one's cognitive organisation in such an abrupt manner that any kind of discursive reasoning is deflected. In this sense it takes one back to one's innerness, leading one back to silence. The event perhaps might be seen to function as a sort of 'nemesis' of a reality that has been shrouded by this kind of conceptualisations. Every now and then this reality sends signals, warnings to which one is virtually deaf since one has been moulded by, and for, a culture in which listening does not pay.

In this cognitive insatiability and in this constant search for novelty, one does not, however, have any desire at all that innovative events be produced. However afflicted by boredom, one does want nothing to be announced, even though the deepest philosophical aspiration is rooted in the desire to be one to whom something happens — the protagonist of the event (Fiumara 1990).

> Researching into the philosophy of listening represents a path that is unattractive and troubled in the sense that one risks fragmenting the protective devices in one's reappropriations of inner layers which are ill-adapted to levels of awareness. It is easier to try to recognise people who are no longer with us and at the same time, and continue to ignore the people around us. Even the flourishing state of the anthropological sciences can end up in the production of 'studies of anthropology' primarily meant for the academic market. A cognitive dedication to the word of the other demands a philosophical methodology that involves the person entirely, since it demands a kind of inner abnegation. Without this inner renunciation the individual can only hold a dialogue with himself. One is not in fact dealing with epistemological concepts unrelated to the knowing person; one is an instrument of knowledge that must transform oneself in order to know, rather deform objects in order to recognise oneself in one's own illusory immobility. When a word says something, it discloses something not only of its entities, but of Be-ing (Fiumara ibid).

In the modern world there is a serious split in our inner world, which impedes us from listening to ourselves; it even prevents us from distinguishing between those options that aggravate our condition and those that might alleviate it. Not heeding to ourselves in totality induces also a radical philosophical distortion in terms of damage to the human potential. One tends to believe erroneously in having reached a cognitive, or even a social liberation, thus precluding the mutations that are needed to maintain oneself at the level of or above the technical and logical achievements that humans have created. In the absence of inner listening, the individual gets lost in the manifold advances of rationality that slip ever more out of his control. At every level the modern world is experiencing an inner vacuum, the sensation of a fragile identity and the terror that in the depths of the self there is nothing — no one can insulate himself.

The lack of inner listening emanates from an educational policy that preaches linguistic 'altruism', or the surrender of one's 'philosophical' living space, as if there is nothing like an 'inner voice' to which one should pay heed; whereas in fact it is a question of the preliminary development of a capacity for listening to one's own self. No message is received precisely because one ignores the philosophical, Socratic, art of listening to oneself and to others. Today, one has mastered the capacity for picking up external social codes and to censure one's limited capacity for tuning into the dominant wavelengths. This restricts the possibility of a self-awareness capable of listening to itself. The handicap is reinforced by a developmental history that teaches from infancy how to grasp and take into account the powerful and incisive messages from those who are in control of established rationality; it is up to the individual, as he develops into a fuller person, to know how to comprehend and recompose these messages. In both phylogenetic and ontogenetic perspective, practical advantages for survival depend specifically upon being able to manage relations with 'parental figures' in the broadest sense. Inasmuch as one is capable of understanding the rules of the game one is guaranteed greater chances of social survival (Fiumara 1990).

8.13. *Finally*

One may well begin to recognise, by listening, that one is dealing with 'positions' that are phylogenetically archaic and ontogenetically precocious and which, nevertheless, determine our deep vicissitudes. It is imperative to balance the external messages with the inner ones, which might bring the preliminary stage of clarification so badly needed in today's state of void and alienation. Possibly the apex in the trajectory of western thought, modern culture does in fact tend to ignore this voice, the only concern of which is for the 'health of the soul'. And thus the most credible voice is ultimately represented as the most negligible.

The inner voice, rather than being merely a guide to the single individual, is an essential part of the nature of a great teacher. It safeguards the quality of education, preventing it from degrading into a purely argumentative pursuit and secures a connection with that element of mystery. The current search for personal identity actually seems to coincide with the heeding of one's own inner expression; it is a contact anchored to listening rather than to logical interrogation. One does not proceed towards it: one should simply let oneself be approached. It is not a question of combining different elements, but bringing about the ability to recognise what is common to many of the mythical symbols. These symbols had a vital sense in the ancient world, and were probably derived from a listening attitude that had not yet been overwhelmed by the uncontested triumph of a rationality that concedes 'civil rights' to the weak Eros which exudes everywhere, but has no space for the strong Eros that is linked intimately to Socratic inner listening. To say that such 'symbols' do not exist and never have existed, that they do not speak or that they no longer speak, testifies to a sort of schizo-paranoid approach — 'If I see nothing it is because there is nothing to be seen', in the language of the prevailing metaphor. Paying attention to our inner inspiration can be articulated in different ways and can be seen from different angles. In the 'scientific' urgency of establishing whether one is dealing with a myth, a symbol, a concept or a figure of speech one might lose sight of the relevant fact that at the dawn of our rational tradition inner listening had a creative and salient function. A listening argument gathers and allows for life (Fiumara 1990).

It seems that civilised humans are no longer capable of a cognitive propensity for inner time as they are constantly suffering either from boredom or from haste. Much of the total yield of 'cultural' messages seems to be an antidote to the ever more serious problem of boredom in the sense that we are now inextricably tied to media of all kinds, everything becomes a performance intended for a show. It even becomes 'necessary' to change things into a show so that humans can have some diversion and thus de-flect attention from themselves, turning centrifugally toward external stimuli of any sort. Technological advances, for example, are geared to develop instruments designed to make everything faster — growth, exchange, elimination — and thus to 'save' time or delusionally even 'produce' it (Fiumara ibid).

The technology of informatics and the achievement of 'real time' constitutes precisely the annulment of the time spent in waiting. In this way one moves even further away from biological time, undeniably contained within the limits of birth and death time and scanned by such rhythms as sleeping and waking, diastole and systole. Modern 'time' of rationality has lost all rhythmical flow and only speeds up in a planar, uniform and unhalting way. It is a notion of time that can be integrated more easily with a technology of treatment than with the prevention of pathological states. In a practice that is incapable of abbreviating, economising or annulling time, the listening approach comes across with even greater relevance in the context of temporality. A listening dialogue is fertile inasmuch as it is willing to ignore time measures; the maieutic word can only be expressed at just the right moment and with a philosophical patience that makes for a renunciation to bargain on matters of precedence. In the absence of such an approach, the cultural constraint does not allow creative thinking, and the human being can no longer really live his own awareness of time; the experience of death inevitably assumes the stereotypical appearance of an absurd. Thus the knowing subject is reluctant to let himself 'die', even when cognitive 'death' is equivalent to relinquishing familiar models in order to be able to seek models elsewhere, in a creative knowledge rather than in the mirroring of standard rationality. We palm off 'having' for 'being' (Fiumara 1990).

> A purely academic or limiting investigation may ultimately induce circles that spin emptily; vicious circles in which the great voices come and go out of fashion; and even more 'vicious' circles in which debate simply delineates territorial areas of cognitive control. Being aware of finiteness, however, human beings do not fear the extinction of life as much as that of personal significance. And if the 'meaning of life' is considered of primary importance, humans want to know that their lives have value, in the sense that they make a significant mark. Speaking, in this sense, is presented to us above all as an instrument for living and surviving. In the phylogenetic 'moment' we become symbolic animals. In this sense, writing possibly represents a particularly incisive way of speaking — the specific way which is supposed to leave a lasting mark, as creative listening (Fiumara ibid).

Creative endeavours obviously do not follow circuits of articulation traced by standard use but only through a heeding language, a language able to accept a temporality that reconnects the inner events of birth and death. As presumably the only living beings capable of awareness of time and of our own end, in the absence of inner listening we must pretend not to know, then feign to pretend, and so on. Humans would thus produce a mind with the capacity to be with 'what is'. The creative process in fact appears to be dependent upon the ability to mobilise attitudes that are simultaneously contrasting and reciprocal — activity and passivity, orientation and confusion, 'springing forth and surging back'. One might say that creativity may be linked to that paradoxical ability to know how to use one's cognitive coordinates and, at the same time, how to abandon one's rational ground by not using it. The guideline of inner listening can allow one to drop, or arrive, beyond the circumscribed spaces of that which is knowable in order to let something new come forth. As Rilke said, "If you want to make a tree grow, surround it with the interior space which you have in your self... Only in your own renunciation can it take form and become truly a tree" (Fiumara 1990).

One of the most important aspects of listening is discernible when cognitive frontiers are opened up without any 'frontal' attack, but only in relation to one's availability to listen rigorously — the disposition which gives life to a 'listening event'. Being open, without even knowing any clear direction, gives one the readiness to listen, and opens the way for the birth of authentic thought. In the readiness to understand there is precisely an effort to follow up the inner consequentiality of someone's expression; the thing experienced itself becomes capable of utterance, providing a strength of thought springing to life in the other, free from the cognitive claims provided by his own interpretative parameters. In this way one moves beyond apparent fragmentation, and the fragments of one's own inner world organise themselves; this represents thinking in the process of its formation. It is an activity which begins to distinguish itself from a flow of effects and which at the same time expresses itself as genuine thinking, because it is not passively interjected from external sources of utterance. In the absence of such maieutic listening, listening situations are experienced as a collision, or insult. A listener can only 'enter' in a way which is at once paradoxical and committing: 'by taking leave', by standing aside and making room (Fiumara 1990).

One is often tempted to maintain that the 'richness' of one's inner world possesses a guarantee of existence in itself, and that the 'problem' merely consists in knowing how to select the words which are best suited to expressing and representing it in a context of consensus. But the organisation of this innerness seems to exist on condition that it is heard, brought out. It is not just a matter of entities lying there, waiting to be linguistically seized and organised in the most diversified expressions. Thus, if one envisages the practice of listening as a process aiming at the birth of thinking and interaction, one may recognise that maieutics is an indispensable preliminary for any authentic form of ethos. Maieutic listening increasingly appears to be an essential condition in both a phylogenetic and ontogenetic perspective. Says Heidegger, "Being with others develops in listening to one another." The challenge of the listening process is distinct from the construction of reality by means of a language which organises and shapes. But the opposition between speaking and listening does not exclude a meaningful resemblance. What warrants this affinity is always the creative function of symbolisation. And while this function attains open expression in language, in listening it is pursued in 'secret' (Fiumara ibid).

The person who recognises a maieutical listener in his interlocutor in fact is posing this tacit request: 'I don't ask you to believe what I say, but I ask you to think it, to make it the object of your interior world of thought; then my thoughts will enable you to recognise their own message of truth.' In this way there seems to emerge the indication of a preliminary methodological feature which may be summed up in the need for an attention, without reserve and without preconceptions, to the revelations of life interactions in general. When one cannot find the names or the words to describe the treasures which one has in hand, these are not transformed into the cultural values of this cultural 'land', or era. One has no clear idea of the nature of the jewel, too. It cannot become a treasure of our land even though it is 'rich' and 'frail'. Clearly, it is not only words that we have in hand. The search is of that treasure, undescribed and undescribable, an asset, a revelation of something 'rich and frail', which cannot yet become a 'treasure of our land' or a 'negotiable currency' of our culture. One may recognise, first, that at times one is tempted to ignore the inner depths of humans. In the wake of pseudosymbolic linguistic degradation, 'nonexistent things' can be represented by words more easily and elegantly than unavoidable realities. In genuine symbolic life, on the other hand, a contrary propensity is developed. In fact, nothing escapes so easily from representation by the use of proper words as what is pretended or simulated. And yet, the greatest necessity of symbolic life is just that of bringing out into cultural life — letting unfold — certain 'things' the existence of which is initially neither demonstrable nor necessary. In a non-listening culture, one may be rewarded without being understood, satisfied without being heard, and well cared for without nurturing. But a philosophy of listening cannot, for seeking philosophical theses, be rendered 'normal' as an alternative to other perspectives; it should be conceived rather as a theoretical development which one is allowed to try out. In this commitment to listening and in the effort to distinguish it from the productivity of thinking-as-power, there can hardly be any deceptive longing for, or risk of, relapsing into a sort of pre-logic golden age. It is not a question of favouring one polarity or the other (the universal or the particular, reasoning or emotion), but rather of resisting the temptation to perpetrate exclusions and thus draw boundaries which cannot be redefined. It is not the rejection or criticism of the prevailing and accredited forms of cognitive conduct (Fiumara 1990).

The method of listening cannot strictly be learned. For listening is a way of relating that can function only on condition that the learning is continuous, uninterrupted; one is dealing with a concern which is not conducive to an ultimate 'grasp', or mastery of the issue. The whole question, therefore, lies in the constant renewal of one's approach to language; in learning and relearning how to listen to it. Unless one is prepared to become, in some way, different from what one is now, listening cannot be understood properly. The maieutic method is not comparable to the learning of a set of intellectual axioms, theses or paradigms; it is an experience — unattainable unless we are to some degree ready, receptive and vulnerable. The 'advantages' of a concern for listening are obviously not linked to a 'Why?' Understood in one of the logical or causal senses; they may as well be associated with an ironical 'Why not?'. Moreover, listening can be a support to the hermeneutic effort whereby one seeks to establish a relationship between this world and a different 'world', between one's own attitude and a different attitude which seems to be pursuing 'unthinkable' aims and using an untranslatable language (Fiumara ibid).

Adopting a dialogic outlook on language one may be able to discern the levels of discourse that are expressed in it and try to identify — beyond a genuinely 'symbolic' type of language — two other kinds of expression, viz., concrete or pseudosymbolic. Concrete expressions are intent upon eliminating inner events which cannot be contained. The purpose of pseudosymbolic expressions, on the other hand, is actually to

pervert language by reducing it to an instrument of non-com-
munication; thus a language that is neither sym-bolic, nor metabolic but rather dia-bolic. True symbolic discourse is one that is
oriented toward communication, constructive symbolic games
and the deepening of self-awareness. In the area of this expressive style, verbal and non-verbal communications function as
vehicles for the derivatives of rational processes, as well as of
affective and imaginative dynamics, in a form that allows them
to be interpreted with reference to symbolic language itself.
Invoking the hypothesis of a dialogic field we can also make
use of a conceptual space suitable for distinguishing whether
the prevalent motivation of a message lies within a single interlocutor or whether it is determined by a collusive interaction. It
is a question of understanding whether what a speaker says
represents primarily the expression of his inner world or primarily a response to the other's message. Methodological attention
to the interactive field of listening thus involves a tension toward otherness, since all communicative levels inevitably allude
to both the 'I' and the 'thou' of the situation, as Buber often
states (Friedman et al. 1994).

> The eminently philosophical quality of integral listening
> becomes evident when one juxtaposes it in a degraded
> way of being interested in something, which today
> borders on questions of boredom, and indifference. In
> a culture determined by the technology of information
> the human condition is ever more scrutinised and ex-
> posed, as if the dominant tendency were to seek out
> ever more 'interesting' material, with the result that one
> is increasingly immunised through exposure to human
> suffering as it is passed to one by the media. On the
> other hand, in the process of heeding symbolic dis-
> course one begins to draw upon the unusual, without
> aspiring to consume it as 'interesting'; and, through the
> same concern, one familiarises oneself ever more with
> that which is ordinary until it actually becomes discon-

certing. And so one finds one's self committed to the posture of reciprocal listening which alone is capable of generating genuine intellectual wonder. Normally one wants interesting things; one does not want to listen, patiently waiting for wonder to be born. The activity of listening in fact has nothing cogent about it but simply indicates an opportunity for cooperative creativity. It does not arise from a psychoanalytic tradition of empathy, containment and interpretation originating from a person who is 'superior' by definition. A symbolic discourse that has been sufficient, reveals in fact an abundance of meaning that would otherwise be squandered and extinguished. A word that is 'heard' is not truly able to speak to one to the extent that it is lacerated by one's premature questioning or mutilated by one's deafness (Fiumara 1990).

The corroboration of a listening propensity could act as an antidote to this 'poison'; and yet a culture, that in some respects has rendered itself torpid, can generate a vast 'philosophical' production concerning expression and, comparatively, very little work on the process of authentic listening. But this should not surprise one if one is capable only of regarding one's self as producer-consumer of a stupefying and benumbing culture that is unaware of any 'poison', a culture in which one 'interest' is replaced by another in an alternation that is merely apparent since it is determined by an underlying stasis. Where authentic listening is absent, it is not uncommon to discover for fear of a terror of listening due to the imbalances and damages that some heeded expression can cause. But it is obvious that the pursuit of a dialogic event, sufficient awareness of the extremely exacting nature of the interaction in prospect is greater than ever today. To the extent that one is able to cultivate an awareness of belonging to the biological history of the planet one might be able to develop the sort of openness that allows one to reconnect the biological and dialogical dimensions. Whenever the phylogenetic depth is not taken into account as an inseparable aspect of the human condition one is restricted to an 'abstract' sort of philosophical knowledge that fails to measure up to the task of encompassing one's biological nature.

Looking back at the stratified and archaic 'components' of the inner world, one may no longer perceive them as fossilised vestiges, but as functioning structures that somehow contribute to determining the present moment of hominisation. The propensity that allows one to recognise the involvement with phylogenetic history can, in the same way, be conducive to a constructive openness toward man's future. In an evolutionary outlook involving the awareness of this historical and biological depth, one might regard the practice of listening as a progressive self-acceptance that in fact makes it possible to acknowledge ourselves as rational animals. But this 'rationality' often tends to split us off from our biological history (Fiumara 1990).

One cannot possibly deny that one is also an animal; and recognising this 'animalness' is the first step toward overcoming the animal condition. Those processes of self-awareness that include the phylogenetic history of the species can also be seen in terms of cultivating the most rigorous forms of philosophical endeavour. Such potential awareness seems to be inseparable from a listening propensity. To surpass some of the archaic mechanisms, say the reptilian ones, one ought to pay sufficient attention to them; disavowed, they might dominate the whole cultural scene. Whereas in many way human activity adapts to the standards of its own culture, in several other aspects — even cognitive processes — it reprocesses the behavioural engrams of cerebral structures dating back millions of years.

In evolutionary relevance, a complete maturation of language stands out clearly in the processes of hominisation. In an evolutionary approach the world of culture is essentially a world of storage. The development of capacities to receive, keep and remember appears to be motivated by an underlying potential for listening; and it is possible that evolving humans tend to speak out at their best because they are listened to — and not vice versa. In authentically philosophical moments a part of one's mind seems to remain suspended, 'passively' waiting for whatever expression might originate from a source that seems to be playing a more 'active' role. Today, certain cultural structures appear as excessively outmoded paradigms. At this point, being aware, the opportunity is offered for becoming aware that the compulsion to win is due less to the intrinsic difficulty of the situation than to inhibitions induced by a non-listening language that prevents one from seeing that which would otherwise be clear. For those of us who are to live through this challenging philosophical moment it is a question of understanding the passage that is drawing near, and of glimpsing its evolutionary potential (Fiumara 1990).

IX

EPILOGUE

The imperative is clear that certain new paradigms, which are already being stated within various scientific disciplines, need to be integrated within the development of the social and human sciences. The implications of science in the New Age are particularly crucial for the growth of anthropology, history and archaeology, which are disciplines attempting to visualise patterns of evolution in various civilisations both in their universalistic and particularistic aspects. Also, there is no gainsaying the need for a radical departure from the present consumeristic paradigm to alternative futures. Humankind has to shift its ways — style of life — drastically if the disaster that awaits us all is to be avoided (in terms of the oft-stated ecological, social, economic and psychological — spiritual — crisis).

The focus of this book in a sense reflects an anthropologist's attempt to clear his own head, by looking into various ideas from a number of disciplines, without necessarily following a linear-sequential order. The sustained argument in the book, however, is about the role of Consciousness, which the sciences and the humanities have unfortunately neglected. This forms the basis of each topic in the various chapters, in different contexts. In a sense, each chapter is self-contained. The basic proposition of the book is that humankind must emerge, so to speak, from the caterpillar to the butterfly stage if it and the planet is to survive; and this breakthrough in the crisis can come about only through an understanding of the Self or Consciousness both at the individual and universal level.

The origins of anthropology — in the modern sense — may

be traced back to the seventeenth century, Age of Enlightenment, when science came on the scene. It was a time when
Darwin's evolution played an important role. In its wake came
social evolution, in terms of superior-inferior ladders of developmental scales, based on physiological factors largely on the
basis of phenotypes. This paradigm of understanding human
civilisation was to have diabolical consequences both within
Europe and those civilisations and peoples who came into contact with it. In effect, the simple way of classifying Mankind into
the scale of primitive, savage, barbaric and so on led to unheard
of barbarities. All this is too well known. These same aims,
however, persist under different cultural and economic garbs,
disclaimers not withstanding. Until the basic paradigm is radically transformed, the old pattern of thinking (you versus me,
domination versus subordination, and so on), which leads one
into false hope and belief of a better world, will continue to
haunt and produce unparalleled pain and suffering for most of
humankind. In all walks of life the fragmentary and partial approach to the study of man continues; such as biological man,
traditional man, sacred and secular man — religion versus science, village versus urban areas — not to speak of all the racial
and other biases that have surfaced in terms of seeking 'ethnic'
identities of various orders. The study of humanity continues to
be restricted by the fragmentary approach. In addition, in the
developing nations the indigenous variety of colonial policies
dominates planning and orientation for seeking alternate futures.

Even at the and of the twentieth century, the dominant paradigm governing the study of human behaviour is that of dichotomous confrontational dualities, and thus of one-
upmanship motivations. It is like applying a bullock cart understanding to the workings of — computer — technology. Science, and following it social science, continues, despite contrary
findings by a few, to seek singular explanations — a unified
coherent theory which will explain everything — even if within

it there are differences of opinion. The new science, however, contradicts the older objective, in the sense that the notion of certainty, and predictability has given way to principles of uncertainty and probability; for example, the changing forms of wave-particle as expression of energy, the interrelationship of the observer and the observed, the subjective-objective division not being valid, and so on. The notion of opposites does not appear to be as irreconcilable as it was earlier thought to be, and is not paradoxical.

Reality is thus, what one may term, an all-inclusive universe in which there is a balancing of different forces, a shifting of harmony at various integral levels wherein symmetry-asymmetry, order-disorder, light-darkness, rationality-intuition, and so on continue to manifest as complementarities, rather than as opposing energies, in various ways. The dualism — science and religion, rationalism and mysticism, form and energy, mind and spirit — which formed a part of the either/or paradigm no longer holds true. The complementarity principle — the this-and-that framework — spoken of by the ancients in Asian speculative thought and meditational traditions, was never paradoxical. It has now begun to emerge through scientific studies that the two poles — at any level and in any context — form the centre of all there is potentially and actually within the range of creation. They belong to a dynamic universe of innumerable possibilities, ever changing, moving and playful in its own creation.

We need to learn from current scientific studies to arrive at a balance, even in evolutionary terms, between the study of man — anthropology and allied disciplines — and the sciences, forming a totality — a comprehensive, holistic world view. Any other viewpoints need not be left out. All that we need to perceive is that there are various viewpoints of reality; that all these are subsets of a comprehensive whole, within this all-inclusive universe, not in any way contradictory. When the either/or paradigm gives way to an 'and' paradigm, it will make room for an open-ended system, which is how the universe is.

One way of attaining this would be to emphasise the common framework of science, humanities and social sciences within the overarching all-encompassing cover of Consciousness, without recourse to ancient scriptures to show parallels. A convergence does exist between contemporary science and ancient speculative — meditative — thought about the nature of the universe. The way and method of ancient thought, however, is totally different from that of modern science. The former speaks of a sacredness directly; the latter is supposedly secular, and yet many sciences ultimately end up in metaphysics, poetry, music and dance — probing deeply into the 'mind', Universal Mind. One has thus to speak afresh in terms of Universal Science, Universal Man and a Universal Science of Integral Man.

In short, the humanities and the sciences need to shed the old skin, the Newtonian-Cartesian assumptions and consequent epistemologies. These have been surpassed by the sciences themselves moving into metaphysical realms undreamt of hitherto, especially in the fields of chemistry, physics, biology, medicine and astronomy. The common reference point emerging in all these disciplines is Consciousness, a Global Consciousness in which we all are enmeshed. At the subatomic level the ungraspable fundamental energy translates itself quite smoothly into metaphysics and philosophy of the mystics. The evidence of the latter is in terms of existential experience of the Now, which is not easily put in words. But the evidence from various cultures through time speaks of states that are equally comparable and verifiable as in any scientific methodology.

The evidence is especially clear in experiential meditative and contemplative disciplines which are related to the total life style of that culture, such as poetry, painting, music, sculpture. Even in arts, it is being realised that the definition of a separate area of the arts in terms of modernity is no longer true, since it refers to an isolated fragmentary phenomenon. It is being realised by a few that authentic expressions in these areas, as probably in all areas of creativity, emerge from a totality or wholeness of Life. There are no barriers here between the sacred and the secular, between aesthetics, art and spirituality or between any this-worldly and other-worldly life. Further these states are communicable beyond the verbal and symbolic level. Although symbolic behaviour is essential as codified or encoded keys to open up dimensions not available otherwise, symbolic behaviour in the modern world becomes a mere mechanical ritual in most walks of life. These states, in contrast, are known by even the uninitiated by the resonance and empowerment that they create all around, the sense of communion.

Hence, to speak about human behaviour at any level without taking into account Consciousness — not as in traditional systems of knowledge but as contemporary scientific knowledge conceives it — is to be misled into faulty generalisations. When these generalisations are used by those who direct the destinies of societies and nation-states to make policies, the result is much too obvious in terms of the havoc and destruction caused in this century. Less obviously, they have drowned the humanistic attitudes in the extensively consumeristic and object-oriented modern world. The damage that has been done to the psyche of man is so extensive that no amount of analysis of external social conditions, howsoever sophisticated, will yield any results in terms of bringing about a peaceful and humane society. Neither will joining the bandwagon of holism, since the problem is psychologically deep rooted. It is a problem that requires total attention by at least a critical mass of people if not a vast majority of humankind.

What does the new science speak of? In brief, it speaks of interconnectedness, interdependence within a coherent evolutionary world view that indicates the emergence of a global consciousness essential for man as a self-referential system linked entirely to the holistic ecological perception of reality. This is not to deny the ancient wisdom of all kinds of societies, even those who are today somewhat untouched by the urban-industrial influences — though how these will escape the onslaught of destructive forces is a moot point. But the new hope for harmony and integration has to emerge in a rediscovery and recreation by individuals and collectivity that is manifested all on its own in contemporary terms and idioms. This approach requires not only a conceptual or paradigmatic shift but also one at the experiential level in each being; i.e., it is a package deal of unity, mutuality and harmony where perception itself is action. Contemporary knowledge has generated quantitative and qualitative data that point towards a harmonic convergence of different dimensions of human existence.

It is urgent for the humanities and the sciences to rethink and re-examine their explorations in the above light since in everyday life it is these findings that are used by decision-makers. External remedies will not dilute the biological, nuclear and ecological disasters that are upon us already, not merely imminent. We are all aware of how the manipulation of material phenomena has produced suicidal results, as is apparent in the sale and production of armaments. The control of scientific and technological power is in the hands of small men with no vision or statesmanship, and most policies are based on adhocism and selfish interests — not universal or global — howsoever altruistic these may sound. But the sense of responsibility is not merely to emerge with the bureaucrat, technocrat and scientist. The obligation to change lies squarely with the social scientist who has changed little in incorporating the latest 'thinking', that is, if there is any authentic thinking done at all. In fact, it is this non-thinking of fundamentals — this forgotten ability to 'stand and stare' for a while — that is at the root of the crisis.

The breakthroughs in biology, physics and so on seem to have had little impact on anthropology and allied disciplines, which continue to dismally follow in the footsteps of the colonial nineteenth century approaches, while claiming to know and understand human communities and thereby to suggest some predictability of human behaviour. But none of this research on communities has taken note of any of the challenges facing humankind as a result of thoughtlessly following notions of progress and development. Because matter and consciousness converge, the application of the Newtonian world view to human societies must cease if world civilisation is to get back on the rails. This is what one learns from the Theory of Relativity, Quantum Mechanics, Heisenberg's Principle of Uncertainty, Bohr's Law of Complementarity, Schroedinger's resolution of Particle/Wave Paradox, Prigogine's Dissipative Structures based on self-organising and self-transcendent systems and Roger Sperry's right and left implications of hemispheric brain processes, etc. It all leads one to contemplate on the physico-physiological and psychic processes which reflect the unity of energy consciousness within which the researcher himself functions. Mystical insights of yore, such as the oneness of Brahman, the divine, and so on are also being correlated to the discoveries of science, which states that matter in some way is a graded manifestation of consciousness. This is being recognised as more accurately expressing the 'real' structure of the universe than classical theories of science. The overlap of mind over matter is also upon us (Gandhi 1990).

There are thus available radically revolutionary alternatives for the emergence of a new human social and moral order. The direction is clearly in understanding the psychological malaise, the crossing of the wires in the brain. Once the fault in the circuit is clearly understood, new channels, which have been lying dormant in the brain for eons in the evolutionary process will open up. But to be able to break through the old barriers that continue to run everyday life, causing contradictions and conflict psychologically, these new directions must have an urgency for the humanities and the sciences. The task is to incorporate these contemporary and ancient insights into new formulations within the social and human sciences, so that the new epistemology and ontology they bring about can help mould some new social and moral order. If not done through man's conscious choice and volition, this change is in any case bound to come about through some haphazard law of the jungle, so to speak.

Each age and each generation needs to discover and evolve experientially, its own expressions. The urgency for it is all the greater in an age when man considers himself to be the main actor and director rather than owing allegiance to some higher deity. Not only human civilisation but life on the planet itself is in danger despite the apparent glamour about the 'brave new world'. The danger, however, is ultimately a symptom of the deadly psychological disorder in the human brain itself.

This book is not a scientific treatise, and I have no qualification to attempt any such thing. All the scientific material presented here is borrowed from the writings of those who are competent to pronounce on such matters. Many others have also stated these ideas earlier, in different fields, and I claim no newness in this. It is, however, important to note the implications of twentieth-century scientific findings for traditional speculative thought. Scientists themselves have noted this; and, if many do not do so as yet, it may be because they still have to come out of the long and exclusive influence of the Logical Positivism that prevailed in the late 1930s. Logical Positivism prevented thinkers from addressing themselves to metaphysical questions; and its dominance of modern education has been such that it has prevented many gifted minds from noticing the powerful trends in the physical sciences. Perhaps not all scientific theories relevant to the issue are well established, yet these are of interest in their stages of development. Being a specialist, the scientist may not be able to appreciate non-scientific disciplines, and may view any kind of speculation cynically since it often sounds superficial. Active rapprochement between different polarities, however, is essential, so that fresh perspectives emerge for the turbulent contemporary world.

* * * * * *

Finally, a clear awareness is necessary to see that development and progress of modern civilisation is linked with the illusion of 'tomorrow and tomorrow', even though it may appear as if technologically giant steps have been taken. But the giant step has to be a great leap from what went before — a breakthrough from the past, a discontinuity since creativity is of that order. When reptiles flew for the first time, it was, in a sense a clean break from this earth; it was a sudden new development, without a conscious clinging to the old. This is what man has to psychologically do. Einstein did so, whereby our perspective of the universe radically changed. Revolution is creation in this sense, a newness; the chick has to break the shell to come into its own, the butterfly has to emerge from the larval stage to become so. Are the stages connected? — yes and no!

Is Reality a paradox? From our limited perspective it is, yet not by itself. At any given moment it contains all the possibilities present in the universe. It has always been so, except when we walk about in our pigeonholes, with blinkers on. Like electricity, it is always available, except when it was suddenly discovered. There never was a time when it was not. The time has come in all walks of life to create a breakthrough; and this can come out of uncertainty and insecurity alone, for uncertainty alone demands a new creation every time. The dynamics of the universe and nature demands this, not to be certain with one single notion of reality, say of the past. This creation is not out of the past; it energes from the past as if by standing on it and yet is not an effect of it. The need is to transcend duality, to a dimension which is unthinkable so to speak, for that is the unknown. It is to make life a mystery once more, for that is what quality of life means.

Life is living it, not thinking about it. Thinking about it is only one part of it. Thinking, feeling and experiencing are one process which we may classify separately but which are subsumed under a larger whole of Being. The falseness of the triad of known, knower and knowing needs correction. The constant need to be secure comes from not knowing Be-ingness, of the Self, of some inner unnameable core of existence, an ineffable experience which every one of us has experienced even if for a moment. These moments of aliveness, when that 'I' is not — this is what one seeks to repeat, but which is not repeatable. The moment, when it comes, is a discovery of one's self only. This is the Oneness of the universe, Alone — all one. It is without a second, and has to be discovered at each moment, anew, like breathing afresh every time; that is, knowing-living moment to moment.

The feeling of pain, happiness, sunset, a child being born, of love, it has existed, always. Yet when it happens to oneself there is a thrill, a sense of discovery of daffodils, as if 'I', 'you', is the first to discover it on this earth; and in that joy one wants to share the experience of this ecstasy — because it is Oneness that is sharable, because one wishes each one of us to have it, because each one of us wants to truly make a contribution and difference in the world towards peace and harmony. But one goes about it the wrong way, mechanically, going through the motions, the rituals, the repetitions; and by wanting to achieve, to score over others, to get ahead. This game of reward and punishment — this becoming — is what ignores Being. It is time to make the shift of the paradigm from an either/or one to a you-and-me world since 'you' and 'me' are fundamentally the same.

The quarrel is with the externals which reflect us, which think us — we seem to become the paradigm rather than come from it. One's viewpoint becomes one's identity, and its separateness seems very real. It is this seeming separateness that one wants to unite, not knowing that the Oneness is real and the separateness unreal. One forgets that life is larger than its content, it is not simply its content put together. It is this forgetfulness, this shallow thinking that is the cause of all the incessant problems. That also is why all the desire to create peace brings nothing but more wars, killings and violence. Nothing changes, because at bottom the thinking itself is wrong. It is like trying to earn love through carrying out the conditions of love. There is no mechanical way of knowing love; it just happens. And when love happens, one is loving. Love is then manifested as feeling and knowing, and is transformed into action instantly and spontaneously. No one can know peace, love and harmony through doing, having, achieving these. They create themselves in the inner Being only by being known deeply, and, contemplated without duality. This is because both body and mind have their own intelligence. The universal 'I' is intelligently manifested in the body, it is the holograph of the brain.

It is not limited human thinking, where each one of us is seen as a island, that is going to create peace and love. The islands may become enlarged to become the globe, but they still remain islands: the same 'ego', the same notion of separateness, not considering the other as one's self still prevails. It is an illusory state, because the 'me' is in fact only a social, psychobiological functional and operational entity without any stable reality, albeit each one is different in presenting different viewpoints of the same reality. In a sphere there are several viewpoints; but there is no fixed centre, and any point can become the centre in terms of the appropriate situation.

In the study of history, culture and civilisation, which continue to be dominated by the empiricism and theoretical models of western philosophy also, the old paradigm of duality needs to give way. The Indian academia continue to be governed by the notion of subjective-objective dichotomy concepts, a product of the Cartesian mind-body duality. Because the duality is taken to be real on *apriori* grounds, it is assumed to be true; hence arises the notion of 'I versus you'. All these need to be examined. For example, it is commonly believed that the world is out there to be examined, objectively and clearly, without taking into account the 'me', my group identity which is viewing it! Today even the sciences speak of the object being influenced by the subject — by the latter's sheer viewing of it (Dossey 1982). If this is true for particle physics, how much truer it must

for us, humans, whose lives are so much more complicated
(Bohm 1980). Without going into deep epistemological issues of
scientific endeavours, it is clear that certain basic assumptions
need to be reviewed and taken into account afresh. While it is
true that knowledge at a given time is in terms of the notions of
reality accepted by a social group, we need to consider who this
group, this 'we' is, that speaks of culture, emphasising one or
another dimension of it. This emphasis, or shall we say bias and
prejudice, is legitimate; yet it needs logical arguments and justifications that are clearly worked out. Often it is the dominant
groups that are the 'we'. These too must have some norms of
verifiability, canons of acceptability; again dependent upon
some tacit agreement within what we may call 'normal' for that
period. At the moment, it is imperative that knowledge be
viewed within the context of consciousness. For as the *Vedas*
say, "Knowledge is structured in Consciousness"; or as Aldous
Huxley said, "Knowledge is a function of Being" — meaning
thereby, it is time one went behind, beyond, or transcended
conceptual reality which is taken to be the only reality today in
this search for so-called truth.

Unless this is done, we shall continue to reinforce pre-existing notions, within the framework of the survival paradigm that
dominates our psychological make-up. It continues to dominate
despite all attempts at change, since we function within the old
paradigm 'box' which one becomes. All attempts to refine,
elaborate, modify are therefore mere superficial movements,
governed by the underlying and hidden rules, say those of linear hierarchy and other notions which form the main focus of
the reptilian-mammalian brain that is interested only in its survival or its notion of survival. It is this conditioning which governs all research goals, leave aside what must be happening at
the levels of politics and economics not withstanding all the
good intentions to create a benevolent, peaceful and harmonious society. For example, if a study of Indian civilisation has to
contribute through archaeology, history and culture, it must

change its direction by means of the holistic approach on which contemporary science and the indigenous insights of our ancient land have been speculating by means that are of a different order than known to the western world.

In this quest for a radical transformation, knowing one's self, one's psychological make-up becomes important; to be conscious of one's judgments, evaluations, prejudices, biases and the viewpoints - not trying to get rid of them, to overcome them. Each discipline, of course, has to follow its norms, laws, canons of acceptability and logical verifiability by a group of people, academic or otherwise. We all believe we are in search of 'truth', without being conscious of our conditioning since in its absence one is only reconfirming or reasserting past knowledge into new bottles. Without being aware that reality is conceptual, and therefore relative, we constantly reinforce only those assumed notions which have been dominating the modern world for the last two centuries or more. Thus one muddles through life, going through the motions, refining conceptual formulations, modifications of the same old hidden notions — the unthought of unconscious notions that actually run one's life, contrary to what one believes. The paradigm of survival, inheritance of the biological ancestral notions of survival, of scarcity with which we began in our evolution at some point of time, is what haunts us today. That the reptilian and mammalian brain, which forms a small fraction of the human brain — not yours or mine individually — is still what dominates our thinking even though this is no longer necessary for a large part of humankind. And since the older notions are deeply culturally entrapped within the framework of the same hidden reality, nothing radically different, a breakthrough, a mutation takes place. The search for 'freedom' — that is what every one is pursuing, each one in his/her own way, not ultimate moksha but a liberation of sorts in order to contribute to life, to make a difference — therefore remains a dream.

Why does nothing whatever happen? Because the ultimate

'urge', 'source' has been forgotten, because all this is not considered 'rational', 'reasonable'. But creation is out of no-thing, not something; peace and love come from such a creation, not by having it or doing it. It is evident that we are in the grip of an enormous crisis, which governments analyse in terms of superficial symptoms and spurious remedies. The crisis is one of authenticity, if the quality of life is to emerge globally. Western science and technology need neither be glorified nor decried. What is important, for instance, for India, is to stop copying. We have become good innovators, but no longer creators. The borrowed technological overlay has inhibited the indigenous creative activity existing in the Indian psyche. This is not to say that spiritual and material science are mutually exclusive. Creativity will emerge once again if we are in tune with the creative Self or Universal Consciousness, which is the true path to Cosmic Revelation.

The crisis which faces humankind cannot be identified with backwardness of computerisation or lack of funds, or one or the other dysfunction at social and cultural levels. We have to stop functioning derivatively, both individually and collectively especially from other civilisations. Derivations can bring about only a limited change in the social fabric and living pattern of a people. Copying is a condition of evolutionary fatigue, a regression. But when innovations and creations arise out of the indigenous human spirit, they have a profound impact on society, since they have an organic relation to the life of the society. Organic innovations are like avalanches, and their ripples go on far into time and space. The correction for copying lies in looking at the experiential dimension or the wellsprings of one's Be-ing, so that an authentic quality of life may come into existence.

In the final analysis, in the broadest meaning, colonial goals continue in all walks of life — it is a psychological issue tied to political and economic goals and interests that are covered by cultural programmes and policies camouflaged by ideological subtleties. All these arise out of a notion of knowledge which is governed by heavy conditioning. In this feedback mechanism, the old notions are not rethought. Thus, say, while power groups might change the hierarchy stays in this colonial viewpoint; and nothing radical or revolutionary takes place, as a break from the past.

The pursuit of 'freedom' is at the back of all research — search — of intellectuals, and others as well. It is a hunt for the mysteries of the universe, for finding a meaning to life and the desire to relate the self to the group around, human and non-human. Without this context, of liberation of sorts, the goals of creating a better understanding, to evolve a new world order, get jeopardised. This is because psychologically none of us feels free and none of us feels as if he is making a difference in the quality of life — no matter that humankind has been doing so for thousands of years, to contribute to life around. The same problems in different garbs keep cropping up, because the thinking continues unchanged. One does not know who one is — not who one thinks one is — since the ultimate source and 'urge' has been forgotten, restricting one's self in the phenomenal world, ignoring the experiential noumenon dimension. We forget that it is not in the doing, or having, that one gets to the Being nature of one's self; it is from Being that the doing and having need to emerge. It is from no-thing that creation takes place, not out of something.

References

ARTIGIANI, ROBERT. 1990. "Thermodynamics and History". In Kishore Gandhi(ed.), 1990a.

BADEN-POWELL, H.BADEN. 1892. *Land System of British India.* London.

———. 1953 (reprint). *Indian Village Community.* New Haven.

BATESON, GREGORY. 1984. *Mind and Nature — A Necessary Unity.* London.

BHATTACHARYA, S. 1971. "Indian Philosophy and Religion". In Malik(ed.).

BISWAS, GOUTAM. 1995. *Art as Dialogue — Essays in Phenomenology of Aesthetic Experience .* New Delhi: IGNCA, D.K. Printworld.

BOHM, DAVID. 1980. *Wholeness and the Implicate Order.* London.

———. **J. KRISHNAMURTI.** 1985. *The Ending of Time.* New York.

BOUISSAC, PAUL. 1990. "Semiotics and the Gaia Hypothesis: Towards the Restructuring of Western Thought". In *Philosophy and the Future of Humanity,* 1-2: 168-84.

CASSIDY, DAVID C. 1990. *Uncertainty: The Life and Science of Werner Heisenberg.* W. Freeman.

de CHARDIN, TEILHARD, P. 1959. *The Phenomenon of Man.* New York.

CHILDE, V. GORDON. 1954. *What Happened in History.* London.

COHN, BERNARD. S. 1968. "Notes on the History of the Study of Indian Society and Culture". In Singer and Cohn(ed.), pp. 3-28.

——. 1971, *India: The Social Anthropology of a Civilization*. New Jersey.

COWELL, F.R. 1952. *History, Civilization and Culture (An Introduction to the Historical and Social Philosophy of Pitrim A. Sorokin)*. London.

DIRAC, P.A.M. 1958. *The Principle of Quantum Mechanics*. Oxford University Press.

DOSSEY, LARRY. 1982. *Space, Time and Medicine*. London.

DUBE, S.C. 1971. *Explanation and Management of Change*. Bombay.

EISENSTADT, S.N. 1973. *Intellectuals and Traditions*. Chicago.

FERRIS, TIMOTHY. 1991. *The Mind's Sky: Human Intelligence in a Cosmic Context*. Bantam.

Finnegan, Ruth. 1992. Oral Traditions and the Verbal Arts. London.

FIUMARA, GEMMA CORRADI. 1990. *The Other Side of Language — A Philosophy of Listening*. London: Routledge.

FRIEDMAN, MAURICE, S.C. MALIK, and PAT BONI. 1995. *Maurice Friedman at IGNCA — An Intercultural Dialogue, and the Human Image.* New Delhi: IGNCA, D.K. Printworld.

GANDHI, K.(ed.). 1990a. *The Odyssey of Science, Culture and Consciousness*. New Delhi: Abhinav.

——. 1990b. "The Synchronization of Science, Culture and Consciousness: The Quest for New Epistemology", in ibid.

HARRIS, ERROL E.1991. *Cosmos and Anthropos — A Philosophical Interpretation of the Anthropic Cosmological Principle:* New Jersey.

HEISENBERG, WERNER. 1959. *Physics and Philosophy (Clifford Lectures).* London: George Allen and Unwin.

HSU, FRANCIS L.K. 1969. *The Study of Literate Civilizations*. New York.

KANDINSKY, WASSILY. 1977. *Concerning the Spiritual in Art*. Dover.

KOTHARI, D.S. 1986. "Science, Culture, and Values" (mimeo).

——. 1989. "Complementarity Principles: Physics and Beyond". *N.R.L. Technical Bulletin,* (special issue). New Delhi.

——. 1990 "The Perception of Truth in Science and Philosophy", in Gandhi(ed.).

KROEBER, ALFRED. 1963a. *Style and Civilizations.* Berkeley.

——. 1963b. *An Anthropologist Looks at History.* Berkeley.

KUHN, THOMAS. 1970. *The Structure of Scientific Revolution.* Chicago.

LANNOY, RICHARD et al. 1978. *Extracts from the Upanishads.* London.

LESTER-SMITH, E. 1975. *Intelligence Came First.* Illinois.

LOVELOCK, J. 1979. *Gaia: A New Look at Life on Earth.* Oxford.

——. 1988. *The Ages of Gaia.* London.

MALIK, S.C. 1968a. *Indian Civilization: the Formative Period — A study of Archaeology as Anthropology.* Simla: IIAS, Reprinted 1987, Delhi: Motilal Banarsidas.

——. 1968b. "Archaeology as a Source in Writing Sociocultural and Socio-economic History". *Eastern Anthropologist.* Lucknow.

——. 1969. "Culture Areas, Ecology and Regionalism". In *Language, Culture and Society.* Simla: IIAS.

—— (ed.). 1971. *Indian Civilization: The First Phase — Problems of a Source book.* Simla: IIAS.

——. 1972. "Human Evolution: Some Reflections on its Philosophy". *Eastern Anthropologist.* Lucknow.

——. 1973. "Models and Social Relevance of Indian Archaeology". In D.P. Agrawal(ed.), *Radio-Carbon and Indian Archaeology* Bombay: TIFR.

——. Malik, S.C. 1975a. *Understanding Indian Civiliza-*

tion — A Framework of Enquiry. IIAS Simla: IIAS

———. 1975b. "Prehistory as a Social Science". *Man in India.* Lucknow.

———. 1976. "India: C. 1000 B.C.-1000 A.D.: Interpreting Economic Patterns in a Civilizational Framework". *Eastern Anthropologist.* Lucknow.

———. (ed.). 1977. *Dissent, Protest and Reform in Indian Civilization.* Simla: IIAS and Motilal Banarsidas.

——— (ed.). 1978. *Indian Movements: Some Aspects of Dissent, Protest and Reform.* Simla: IIAS

———. 1979. "Changing Perspectives of Archaeology and Interpreting Harappan Society". In Agrawal and Chakrabarti(ed.), *Essays in Indian Protohistory.* New Delhi.

———. (ed.). 1986. *Determinants of Social Status in India.* Simla: IIAS.

———. 1987. "Dual Nature of Thought". *Vishwabharati Quarterly,* Santiniketan.

———. .1989a. *Modern Civilization — A Crisis of Fragmentation.* New Delhi: Abhinav.

———. 1989b. "Intellectuals, Traditions and Ethnographic Studies — Some Basic Questions". *Man in India.* Ranchi.

———. 1990a. "Towards a Psychological Transformation of Man, in *The Odyssey of Science, Culture and Consciousness.* New Delhi.

———. 1990b. "Thought as Technology, Progress and Civilization". In *New Technological Civilization and Indian Society.* Simla: IIAS.

———. 1990c. "In Search of Quality of Life in Anthropology: Beyond Fragmentation". In *Quality of Life,* Simla: IIAS.

———. 1990d. "Holism and Life Style Studies — the Civilization Context". *Eastern Anthropologist.* Lucknow.

———. 1990e. "Alternative Futures: Towards an Integral Universe". *NMML Occasional Papers.* New Delhi (mimeo).

——. 1993b. "A Question of Consciousness". (Future of the Mind — Mind of the Future Seminar). New Delhi (mimeo).

——. 1995a. "Matter is Consciousness" (The Nature of Matter Seminar). New Delhi: IGNCA.

——. 1995b. "Holistic Science and Consciousness". (Nature and Man — An Integral Vision Seminar). New Delhi: IGNCA.

MARRIOT, MCKIM(ed.), 1963. *Village India: Studies in the Little Community*. Chicago.

——. 1974. "Caste System". *Encyclopaedia Britannica*. London.

——. and R. Inden. 1974. "Towards an Ethnosociology of South Asian Caste System". IXth International Congress of Anthropology-Ethnology. Chicago (mimeo).

MATHUR, K.S. and S.C. Varma(eds.). 1975. *Man and Society*. Lucknow.

MAYR, ERNST. 1991. *Towards a New Philosophy of Biology: Observations of an Evolutionist*. Harvard.

MISRA, VIDYA NIWAS. 1971. "Indian Concept of Civilization", in Malik(ed.).

MURTY, M.L.K. and G.D. SONTHEIMER. 1980. "Prehistoric Background to Pastoralism in the Southern Deccan in the Light of Oral Traditions, and Cults of Some Pastoral Communities". *Anthropos* (Germany).

MYERS, NORMAN (ed.). 1985. *The Gaia Atlas of Planet Management*. London.

PAULI,W. and C.G. Jung(ed.) 1955. *The Interpretation of Nature and the Psyche"*. New york.

PEARSON, KARL. 1892. *The Grammar of Science*. London.

PRIGOGINE, I. and Stengers. 1980. *From Being to Becoming*. San Francisco.

——. 1984. *Order out of Chaos*. New York.

REDFIELD, ROBERT. 1956. *Peasant Society and Culture*. Chicago.

——. 1961. *The Little Community and Peasant Society and Cultures.* Chicago.

SARASWATI B.N. 1973. *Contributions to the Study of Indian Civilization.* Dharwar.

——. 1977. "Notes on Kabir: A non-literate Intellectual", in Malik(ed.).

——. S.C.MALIK, and MADHU Khanna(ed.). 1994. *Art: The Integral Vision.* New Delhi: Nirmal Bose Foundation and D.K. Printworld.

SCHROEDINGER, E. 1948. *What is Life.* Cambridge University Press.

SHELDRAKE, R. 1980. *A New Science of Life.* London.

SINGER, MILTON(ed.). 1959. *Traditional India: Structure and Change.* Philadelphia.

—— and Bernard S. Cohn(ed.). 1968. *Structure and Change in Indian Society.* Chicago.

SOROKIN, PITRIM A. 1962. *Social and Cultural Dynamics* (four volumes). New Jersey.

STISKIN, NAHUN. 1972. *The Looking Glass God.* Canada.

TOYNBEE, ARNOLD J. 1947. *A Study of History* (six volumes). London.

TULKU, TARTHANG. 1977. *Time, Space and Knowledge.* California.

WEBER, RENEE. 1986. *Dialogue with Sages and Scientists.* New York.

INDEX